Producing

VEGETABLE CROPS

George W. Ware

U.S. Department of Agriculture;
Formerly, in Charge,
Fruit and Truck Branch Experiment Station,
University of Arkansas

Producing

J. P. McCollum

Professor of Plant Physiology,
College of Agriculture,
University of Illinois

VEGETABLE CROPS ———————

**The Interstate
Printers & Publishers, Inc.**

Danville, Illinois

FOREWORD

The people of the United States have a greater supply and wider choice of food than those of any other nation. Vegetable production for the tables of America is of tremendous economic importance to the nation and to the dietary requirements of the people. The phenomenal population increase in the United States necessitates at least a corresponding expansion in the production of vegetables which are so necessary to the national diet and the health of the people. Consequently, it is safe to predict that vegetable crops will continue to comprise a major segment of the agricultural economy.

This book deals with the fundamental principles, economics, and production practices of vegetable growing. The book has special appeal to those enrolled in vocational agriculture classes and students of agricultural colleges. It is useful equally as a manual for professional agriculturists, growers, and others involved in the trade. The text will be especially helpful to growers seeking factual information and guidance in developing and conducting profitable vegetable growing enterprises on their respective farms.

In developing the contents of this book, the authors have made use of the information developed through studies and research carried on by agricultural colleges and experiment stations, processors, merchants, and the practices followed by successful growers. The presentation is made by combining the text with supporting charts, maps, tables, and illustrations in a unique and interesting fashion. As a result, the book contains reliable, current information which has general application to all vegetable growing regions of the United States.

The authors of *Producing Vegetable Crops* are well qualified through years of extensive studies, research, and production experience to write on the subject. They are also familiar with the "action" method of teaching and have presented the contents in a manner which will have the greatest impact upon those who use the book.

George W. Ware, an agricultural graduate of the University of Arkansas, has spent his professional years in agricultural teaching, extension, research, and administration. For sixteen years he was in charge of the University of Arkansas Fruit and Truck Branch Experiment Station, specializing in fruit and vegetable research. With a master's degree in vegetable crops from Cornell University, he wrote the popular textbook, *Southern Vegetable Crops*, which was used extensively. Mr. Ware has also served the U.S. Government in Europe, South America, and the Far East as an agriculturist in several important posts. With these experiences, he has had an unusual opportunity to study and observe the domestic and international importance of vegetables.

J. P. McCollum is one of the nation's recognized authorities in the field of vegetable crops. He has had extensive experience and training in this field. Professor McCollum holds a B.S. degree in Horticulture from the Oklahoma State University and a Ph.D. degree with a major in vegetable crops from Cornell University. For many years he has been engaged in teaching and research in the Division of Vegetable Crops at the University of Illinois. In addition, he has worked with vegetables in some of the intensive truck-growing regions of New York, Florida, and Illinois. His research experience includes investigations of factors affecting fruit development, ascorbic acid, carotenoids, and other constituents of quality. He has also conducted research on seed problems, asparagus production, and soil fertility. Professor McCollum is indeed well qualified to play an important role in the production of this book.

Contacts with students, colleges and experiment stations, professional workers, seed breeders, growers, food processors, and handlers of fresh produce throughout the country reveal the need for a convenient up-to-date vegetable manual on the production, handling, and marketing of vegetable crops. It is believed that this book, *Producing Vegetable Crops*, will fill that need.

M. D. Mobley
Former Executive Secretary
American Vocational Association
Washington, D.C.

Joseph S. Vandemark
Professor of Vegetable Crops
University of Illinois
Urbana, Illinois

PREFACE

The basic principles of vegetable growing are universal, but production practices vary materially in different sections of the country, depending upon economic and environmental factors. Without neglecting fundamentals, discussions on both principles and practices have been adapted to conditions which prevail in most of the United States.

Section One, containing Chapters 1 through 13, deals with basic information and fundamental "principles." The information presented is generally applicable to all sections of the country. Section Two, embracing Chapters 14 through 33, discusses special crop production "practices" in the regions where the respective crops are grown.

The job-analysis plan, arranging production practices in order of seasonal sequence, has been employed in the vegetable chapters. The action idea prevails in spirit, arrangement, and content. The latest results of the agricultural experiment stations are incorporated and interpreted in the light of experience. The student or grower may adapt the general information to his own needs.

The purpose of this book is to give reliable, complete, coordinated, up-to-date information on the various phases of vegetable growing in the most systematic and convenient manner. It is designed as a text or reference book for vocational schools, junior colleges, and agricultural colleges; and as a handy manual for professional agricultural workers, growers, seedsmen, merchants, and others engaged in the industry.

The chapters are complete in themselves, but cross references are made to avoid repetition and to supply additional information. A brief glossary, including the most difficult words, precedes the index.

It is suggested that the reader, when using this book, study the chapters dealing with principles in connection with each production job as it is discussed. Teachers will find it helpful to assign pertinent parts of the general chapters on principles along with corresponding production practices in the crop chapters. Questions and problems have been omitted, as no set list will satisfy a large number of instructors or students under the existing widely different conditions.

The authors wish to express their appreciation to the many research workers, teachers, students, growers, and handlers for their valuable information and suggestions which were used generously in the contents and arrangement of this book.

Credit is due the U.S. Department of Agriculture, State Experiment Stations, and private establishments for photographs, charts, and related materials. Data on the shipping seasons, acreage, yields, unit price, and farm value of the principal vegetable crops were taken from official reports of the Statistical Reporting Service of the U.S. Department of Agriculture, and these are gratefully acknowledged.

The authors are especially indebted to Dr. A. E. Thompson for his contributions to Chapters, 4, 5, 20, 21, 23, 27, 28, and 32, to Dr. George W. Ware, Jr., for contributing Chapter 11, and to Mrs. George W. Ware for proofreading and editing.

George W. Ware   *John P. McCollum*

CONTENTS

SECTION TWO: PRACTICES

Section One

PRINCIPLES

INTRODUCTION TO SECTION ONE

The first thirteen chapters in Section One deal with the "principles" of plant growth and general information on vegetable production, handling, and marketing. The object of this section is to provide scientific information as a foundation for studying subsequent Chapters 14 through 33 of Section Two, which discuss the various production "practices" required in growing individual vegetable crops.

Some of the chapters, such as "Vegetable Breeding and Improvement," "Classification of Vegetables," and "Plant Growth and Development," may not appeal to the practical person, but they give a more thorough understanding of vegetables, and help one to see and meet production problems in the most scientific manner.

Chapters 5 through 13 discuss general principles of the various operations involved in vegetable production, are arranged in seasonal sequence, and correspond with the job analysis treatment of crop chapters in Section Two. The purpose of these discussions is not to give specific instructions, in the production of any particular vegetable, but to present general information which will help one to understand and carry out the specific practices contained in the crop chapters, 14 through 33, of Section Two.

A list of "Selected References" appears at the end of each chapter for the convenience of the reader in obtaining additional information on specific subjects.

CHAPTER 1

The Vegetable Industry

The dynamic multi-billion dollar vegetable industry has contributed greatly to the economy of the nation and the general welfare of its consumers. The people of the United States are supplied with more varieties of good quality vegetables throughout the year than the people of any other nation. Credit is due the producers, handlers, processors, distributors, and retailers for providing this abundance of wholesome food at equitable prices.

Historical

The growing of vegetables is an old art which has been practiced for centuries in most civilized countries. The number of kinds of vegetables and their uses were rather limited, however, until comparatively recent times.

The American colonial families were largely self-supporting, growing vegetables for a part of their food supply. With the industrial expansion which began about 1865, a marked change in vegetable growing took place. Concentrated populations became largely dependent upon special producers for their food supply, and as a result, commercial production of vegetables developed near population centers. This practice persisted from Civil War days until about 1910. Since then, vegetables have been produced commercially to a large extent in distant, specially adapted areas having favorable climate and the advantages of labor supply and season.

For a period following 1920, vegetable production increased more rapidly than any other type of crop production. This was due to improved facilities for production, processing, and distribution; educational and promotional programs dealing with the importance of vegetables in the

diet; and rising purchasing power and changing food habits. In response
to consumer demand, a large variety of fresh vegetables became available
throughout the year. In recent years, vegetable production has increased
at about the same rate as population expansion. This trend may be expected to continue in the future.

Types of Vegetable Growing

The several types of vegetable growing, some of which have been
developed as a result of changing economic and social conditions, are
briefly discussed here.

HOME GARDENING. In colonial days, the home garden was the principal
source of the fresh food supply for a large part of the population. Today,
the importance of the city, suburban, and farm home gardens as a factor
in the total production of vegetables cannot be overemphasized. This type
of vegetable production is discussed fully in Chapter 33.

MARKET GARDENING. As the cities became larger and more congested,
residents of the outskirts increased their production and peddled the surplus to those living in the more fully occupied areas. This gave rise to the
market-gardening industry, which has for its objective the production of
an assortment of vegetables for home market. Most markets, particularly
the large ones, are no longer local. The market gardeners, who originally
grew a large variety of vegetables under intensive and very expensive conditions, have been forced to change their types of farming to meet competition from specially adapted distant areas. These gardeners no longer
grow many kinds of vegetables, but are necessarily confined to producing
those which can be most profitably grown to supply or supplement the
demand in their respective localities.

COMMERCIAL PRODUCTION. Increased demand for vegetables throughout the year, rapid transportation, and uniform refrigeration facilities led
to the production of special crops in relatively large quantities for distant
markets. In general, truck farming is more extensive and specialized than
market gardening, and the location of truck-growing regions is determined
primarily by climatic factors and soils favoring the culture of special
crops. Since 1910, large areas for vegetable production in the South, West,
and Southwest have been developed.

PRODUCTION FOR PROCESSING. Although the northern states and California lead in the production of canned and frozen vegetables, this industry is scattered over a large part of the United States. Vegetables for processing are usually produced on a more extensive scale than those grown for market, and are frequently grown in rotation with farm crops. Because of the necessity of low-cost production, the industry has sought areas of favorable climate and lower costs. As a rule, processors contract for tonnage, with certain limitations on quality, at a figure lower than the market price for fresh vegetables. Primarily because of the convenience and economy of processed vegetables, the market demand for them has increased much faster than the demand for fresh vegetables.

VEGETABLE FORCING. Vegetable forcing, the production of vegetables out of their normal season, is accomplished by heat or protection from cold. Greenhouses are largely employed in the North, while cold frames are used to a considerable extent in the South.

VEGETABLE SEED PRODUCTION. The production of vegetable seed is a rather specialized industry carried on in regions where climatic conditions are favorable to seed production and curing. While most vegetable growers should not attempt to grow seed, they should know something of the problems involved in seed production and handling. These subjects are discussed in Chapters 4 and 5.

PHYSICAL FACTORS AND REQUIREMENTS

Climatic Requirements

Climate is the most important limiting factor in the commercial production of vegetables at long distances from the market. The principal truck-growing regions of the country have developed as a result of climatic conditions favorable to certain crops during the season in which they are grown. Now that transportation is generally available to all regions of the country, it is possible to grow any particular vegetable in any area which is best suited to it.

Of the climatic factors, temperature is generally the most important in determining the localization of truck-growing areas. Atmospheric humidity is also very important for some crops. For example, muskmelons are grown extensively in those areas where temperatures are high and humidity low. Rainfall is very important for the production of all vegetable crops except where irrigation is used.

Thompson and Kelley, in *Vegetable Crops*, state as follows: "Nearly all the important vegetable-growing regions of the South and parts of California, and the Southwest are important because the climate of those regions permits production during winter and spring when other regions cannot produce vegetables. In fact, these regions have become important in spite of transportation handicaps in the form of long hauls and high cost of transportation. While good refrigerator car service and good railroads make it possible for the Imperial Valley of California to be an important lettuce and muskmelon center, no one would produce these crops there because of these factors alone, for regions nearer the important markets have as good transportation facilities with shorter hauls and lower costs. All vegetable regions located at long distances from market are important primarily because of suitable climatic conditions for the production of the crop or crops at the time they are grown. For example, the Imperial Valley produces lettuce during the winter when the climate is satisfactory for the crop, and muskmelons in the spring and summer when the hot, dry weather is favorable for the growth and ripening of this crop. The area around Salinas, California, is the most important summer lettuce-producing region of the United States primarily because of the relatively low summer temperatures. In spite of high transportation costs, these regions and a few others in the West now control the lettuce market in the large cities of the Middlewest and East."

Soil Requirements

While climate largely determines the truck-growing regions, soil character is an important factor in selecting specific locations. Since soil requirements vary somewhat for different kinds of vegetables, the selection of the type of soil which is best suited to the crop or crops is important. Soil preference for different crops is discussed generally in Chapter 6, and in the chapters on specific crops.

Transportation Requirements

The earliest development of commercial vegetable production in the South and some other areas was confined to places which provided waterways for boat transportation to the major markets. This naturally restricted the kinds of vegetables and the flexibility of supply. Railroads have delivered the bulk of the produce for many years. With the introduction of commercial refrigeration in 1886 and the subsequent development of the refrigerator car, vegetable production spread to distant areas providing the most suitable climatic conditions.

Improved farm-to-market roads and the subsequent development of superhighways introduced the motor truck as a major means of transportation. With the improvement of the size, speed, and refrigeration of trucks, this means of transporting vegetables to market has continued to increase with resulting economy and promptness of delivery. Further im-

Fig. 1.1—Fresh sweet corn shipped in refrigerator truck.

USDA Photograph

provement of roads, fast refrigerator trucks, improved rail transportation, refrigerated boats, and the development of more economical air transportation will continue to stimulate vegetable growing in the areas with the most favorable growing conditions. The transportation of vegetables is discussed fully in Chapter 13.

OTHER FACTORS AND REQUIREMENTS

The Personal Factor

Successful vegetable farming depends to a considerable extent on the aptitude of the individual producer. Some farmers adapt themselves easily to truck growing, while others are slow to adjust themselves to such a type of farming. For example, many farmers do not like to produce vegetables, and they have little patience with the exacting requirements of intensive vegetable production, preferring to grow a crop that has a wider planting and harvesting range. Where the farms are large enough, many growers prefer to raise crops that can be handled entirely by machinery instead of growing vegetables which give higher returns per acre but require more hand labor.

Economic Difference Between Vegetable and Fruit Growing

Observers generally appreciate the fact that the requirements of horticultural crops are considerably different from those of field crops or livestock farming. There are also several essential differences between the vegetable and fruit industries which should be called to the attention of the reader.

1. Truck farming does not ordinarily involve a long-time investment as does an orchard, and the truck grower is not bound to grow the same crop each year.
2. Many trucking areas, particularly those in the process of development and exploitation, lack the stability of the orchard district which was methodically developed over a period of years. Getting into fruit growing is a slow process, and getting out may be even slower.
3. Since the problem of financing a truck crop is largely an annual one, tenants can be used, whereas few orchardists are willing to turn over their growing or bearing trees to temporary operators.

4. Co-operative effort and organization are somewhat more difficult among truck growers than fruit growers. Orchardists have years for making permanent plans and perfecting an organization, whereas vegetable "deals" come and go, and growers are often disappointed.

5. Truck farming is often promoted and financed by the dealers or commission men, and production is determined accordingly. Fruit growers are usually more independent and are more able to secure long-term credit.

6. The acreage and resulting production of truck crops are very flexible, responding easily to promotion, enthusiasm, or price outlook, whereas the fruit industry is slowly adjustable.

7. Truck crops are often grown by farmers with little or no experience, and as a result, frequent failures occur. If the fruit grower develops his own orchard, he is likely to be generally acquainted with the industry by the time his trees start bearing.

From the contrasts mentioned, one may infer that the vegetable industry is generally unstable and comparatively undesirable. This is not, necessarily the case, as many permanent , well organized, vegetable-producing areas have been established throughout the country.

SCOPE AND IMPORTANCE

An Extensive Major Industry

The vegetable industry contributes heavily to the national economy. In addition to the farmer's role, many businesses and millions of people are involved in processing, transporting, and marketing; and in manufacturing and supplying machines, seeds, fertilizers, pesticides, herbicides, packages, and related materials. Extensive educational, supply, and maintenance services are necessarily associated with the physical requirements of this dynamic industry.

The present outlook indicates that the vegetable industry should continue to be an important and comparatively profitable branch of agriculture. With increasing competition, the industry will profit by reducing the cost of production and marketing. This can be accomplished by growing improved varieties, using fertilizers judiciously, practicing effective pest control, supplementing cultivation with herbicides, managing labor more efficiently, utilizing mechanical harvesters and other labor-saving devices where possible, and by adopting improved marketing methods.

Acreage and Value

Vegetables as a group constitute an important segment of American agriculture, accounting for approximately 10 percent in value of all crops in 1965. The annual farm value of the principal vegetable crops, including potatoes and sweet potatoes, has averaged above $1.5 billion since 1945 and attained a level of $2.2 billion in 1965. Table 1.1 shows the relative acreage and value of vegetables in comparison with the other principal crops. The commercial values presented in this table do not include the products from gardens and the minor vegetable crops, the value of which probably exceeds $500,000,000.

Table 1.1—Harvested Acreage and Farm Value of Principal Crops Grown in the United States, 1945, 1954, and 1965.

Major Crops	1945		1954		1965	
	Acreage, 1,000	Value, $ Million	Acreage, 1,000	Value, $ Million	Acreage, 1,000	Value, $ Million
Total vegetables	7,295	1,584	5,529	1,518	4,961	2,162
Misc. vegetables	3,985	872	3,783	967	3,356	1,419
Potatoes	2,664	588	1,412	475	1,403	667
Sweet potatoes	646	124	332	76	202	76
Fruits and nuts	3,855	1,263	3,033	1,121	2,900	1,524
Corn	87,625	3,652	80,186	4,378	57,049	4,553
Wheat	65,157	1,661	54,356	2,082	44,313	1,770
Soybeans	10,740	402	17,047	841	34,551	2,002
Cotton	17,029	1,015	19,251	2,301	13,621	2,196
Tobacco	1,821	848	1,668	1,147	978	1,228
Rice	1,499	122	2,550	293	1,793	377
Total all crops	345,546	14,637	338,184	18,890	294,121	21,810

Tables showing the acreage, production, yield, unit price, and value of the principal vegetable crops by states are provided in the individual vegetable chapters in Section Two.

Data for 1945 and 1954 from the annual "Agricultural Statistics;" and 1965 data from "Annual Summary" and "Crop Values" reports of the Crop Reporting Board, USDA, December 20, 1965.

Principal Areas of Production;
Values and Trends

Due primarily to the increase in out-of-season vegetables, production has shifted to and expanded particularly in the West, South, and Southwest. Figures 1.2 and 1.3 show the approximate acreage distribution and corresponding farm value of commercial vegetables, excluding potatoes and sweet potatoes. Figure 1.5 shows the production trends of fresh and processed vegetables between 1954 and 1965.

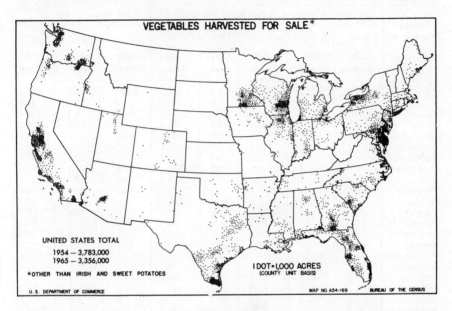

Fig. 1.2—Approximate acreage and distribution of commercial vegetables.

Table 1.2 ranks the relative importance of the leading states by acreages of the principal fresh and processed vegetables in 1965, and shows the corresponding farm value of each crop.

It is notable that California accounted for 34 percent of the estimated $1,422,600,000 total value of these vegetables, which exclude potatoes and sweet potatoes. Florida ranked second with 13 percent of the total value, followed by Texas and New York with 6.4 and 5.5 percent respectively. Because of the relatively high or low unit values of different vegetables, some states have large acreages and comparatively low farm values as shown in Table 1.2.

Relative Importance of Commercial Vegetables

The acreage and value of vegetable crops change primarily according to the increasing population, changing food habits, and corresponding de-

**Table 1.2—Principal Vegetables for Fresh Market and Processing:
Estimated Commercial Acreage, Production and Value by
Leading States, 1965.* (Ranked according to total
acreage by states.)**

States (Ranked by Total Acreage)	Harvested Acreage, 1,000 Acres			Production		Farm Value, $1,000,000		
	Fresh Market	Processed	Total	Fresh Market, Million Cwt.	Processed 1,000 Tons	Fresh Market	Processed	Total
California	386.9	205.8	592.7	69.1	2,680.5	359.1	133.4	492.5
Wisconsin	10.5	276.4	286.9	2.9	782.5	7.7	35.2	42.9
Florida	275.5	17.4	292.9	32.9	76.9	180.4	3.5	183.9
Texas	244.3	24.0	268.3	22.1	111.4	87.0	4.2	91.2
New York	75.4	91.2	166.6	13.1	480.7	42.6	16.6	59.2
Minnesota	3.2	156.6	159.8	0.8	437.4	1.7	16.3	18.0
Washington	15.0	139.8	154.8	2.6	370.5	11.4	26.7	38.1
New Jersey	73.4	60.0	133.4	7.2	393.1	39.1	22.2	61.3
Illinois	18.0	111.1	129.1	1.6	414.5	4.6	17.1	21.7
Oregon	16.5	110.6	127.1	4.2	403.8	10.9	25.7	36.6
Michigan	49.8	52.8	102.6	7.6	223.7	28.1	15.0	43.1
Maryland	18.3	69.0	87.3	1.8	261.3	5.5	12.4	17.9
Arizona	83.4	0.1	83.5	14.2	0.3	78.0	0.0	78.0
N. Carolina	53.0	24.9	77.9	3.8	72.3	15.6	5.3	20.9
Georgia	64.1	5.7	69.8	4.5	11.2	11.1	1.0	12.1
Pennsylvania	31.7	33.8	65.5	2.3	176.5	10.2	7.1	17.3
S. Carolina	59.0	4.5	63.5	3.7	10.5	14.8	0.6	15.4
Ohio	30.6	30.9	61.5	3.4	583.1	16.8	16.9	33.7
Indiana	14.3	32.5	46.8	2.2	351.0	6.6	9.6	16.2
Delaware	3.5	42.1	45.6	0.4	80.4	0.9	6.8	7.7
Virginia	28.2	15.5	43.7	2.1	86.2	10.8	3.6	14.4
Idaho	3.3	31.2	34.5	1.8	113.1	3.9	4.5	8.4
Alabama	27.0	5.5	32.5	1.9	11.5	6.3	0.7	7.0
Colorado	25.4	5.8	31.2	4.4	21.7	17.2	1.3	18.5
Arkansas	11.3	10.9	22.2	0.9	29.0	3.9	1.9	5.8
Oklahoma	11.5	5.2	16.7	0.8	15.9	1.4	1.0	2.4
All states	1,725.3	1,630.7	3,356.0	222.0	8,338.8	1,021.8	400.8	1,422.6

*Excludes potatoes, sweet potatoes and some of the less important vegetables.

Data from the "Annual Summary of Acreage, Production and Value of Principal Commercial Crops", Crop Reporting Board, USDA, December 20, 1965.

Detailed data on acreage, yield, production, unit price and farm value of the principal vegetable crops are presented by states in the vegetable chapters of Section Two.

mand. Table 1.3 shows some of these fluctuations and trends since 1945. The 22 principal vegetables, nine of which are also processed in large quantities, are ranked in descending order by total acreage in the 1965 column while comparative values are shown in the right-hand column of the table.

Table 1.3—Principal Commercial Vegetables for Fresh Market and Processing: Estimated Harvested Acreage and with Farm Value for 1945, 1954, and 1965. (Ranked according to total acreage in 1965.)

Principal Crops	Harvested Acreage in 1,000 Acres			Farm Value, $1,000		
	1945	1954	1965	1945	1954	1965
Potatoes	2,664.0	1,413.0	1,403.4	588.3	474.7	667.0
Corn, sweet	76.0	209.7	203.2	11.9	44.3	57.9
Corn, sweet*	487.3	453.2	376.9	22.0	30.8	36.0*
Total corn	563.3	662.9	580.1	33.9	75.1	93.9
Peas, green	69.7	13.7	4.6	14.1	3.4	1.8
Peas, green*	453.8	427.0	441.9	41.4	36.9	60.2*
Total peas	523.4	440.7	446.5	55.5	40.3	62.0
Tomatoes	283.1	236.4	158.5	112.9	129.2	191.5
Tomatoes*	515.4	262.9	244.3	70.4	65.6	159.7*
Total tomatoes	798.5	499.4	402.8	183.3	194.8	351.2
Watermelons	348.1	444.0	317.5	37.5	35.1	46.6
Beans, green	198.8	152.8	103.0	45.9	42.8	39.8
Beans, green*	129.2	153.9	229.3	22.4	41.4	51.8*
Total beans	328.0	306.7	332.3	68.3	84.2	91.7
Lettuce	173.9	206.4	216.2	88.8	125.2	189.8
Sweet potatoes	646.0	332.0	202.2	124.3	76.3	76.5
Cucumbers	44.1	52.8	57.4	13.6	18.8	28.0
Cucumbers*	101.2	138.3	109.3	9.4	17.8	32.6*
Total cucumbers	145.4	191.1	166.8	23.0	36.6	60.6
Asparagus	122.5	143.7	134.1	33.6	36.9	49.4
Cabbage	199.2	148.0	119.5	40.7	31.8	54.1
Cabbage*	22.7	15.8	12.4	3.1	2.5	3.1*
Total cabbage	221.8	163.9	131.9	43.8	34.3	57.1
Muskmelons	119.8	139.4	119.0	34.6	52.8	65.1
Onions	143.8	116.0	97.8	63.3	47.2	85.3
Carrots	97.3	79.8	79.8	43.6	48.9	61.2
Lima beans	23.5	16.5	13.1	6.4	3.4	3.5
Lima beans*	59.9	113.4	82.9	4.3	15.6	16.7*
Total limas	83.4	129.9	96.0	10.7	19.0	20.2
Spinach	67.1	32.3	20.4	13.9	9.8	9.2
Spinach*	44.8	25.2	21.4	6.8	4.0	5.0*
Total spinach	114.0	57.5	41.8	20.6	13.7	14.2
Peppers, green	29.2	48.0	47.6	13.7	21.2	37.2
Broccoli	13.7	35.7	37.7	7.2	13.8	18.5
Celery	42.8	35.8	31.4	62.9	48.8	61.4
Cauliflower	34.8	27.7	25.0	19.2	13.4	20.1
Beets	12.1	6.2	3.3	2.2	1.7	2.1
Beets*	18.1	16.1	14.4	3.7	3.1	3.3*
Total beets	30.2	22.3	17.7	5.9	4.8	5.4
Eggplants	6.0	4.7	4.0	2.9	2.2	3.3
All vegetables**	7,295.0	5,528.9	4,961.0	1,584.6	1,518.5	2,162.0

*Crops for processing.

**Includes 22 principal fresh vegetables, listed above, potatoes and sweet potatoes, artichokes, escarole, Brussels sprouts, garlic, kale, and shallots. Small quantities from Alaska and Hawaii are also included in the years reported.

Data from "Agricultural Statistics 1965," and the "Annual Summary of Acreage, Production and Value of Principal Commercial Crops," Crop Reporting Board, USDA, December 20, 1965.

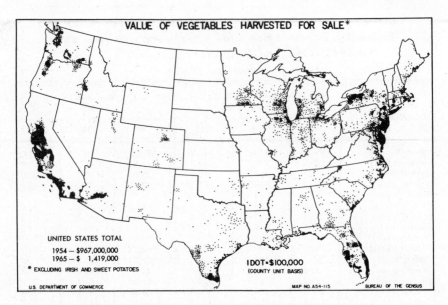

Fig. 1.3—Approximate farm value and distribution of commercial vegetables.

Potatoes continue to be the leading vegetable in acreage and value, accounting for about 31 percent of the total farm value of all commercial vegetables in 1965. Tomatoes ranked second in value, accounting for 16.3 percent, followed by peas 8.9, lettuce 8.8, and green beans and onions which represented 4.2 and 4.0 percent respectively. Consumer preference will no doubt continue to change the relative importance of vegetables and vegetable products.

Trends in Vegetable Consumption

The average per capita consumption of fresh and processed vegetables has remained fairly constant in recent years. A slight increase from 224 to 230 pounds per person occurred between 1950 and 1963 as shown in Figure 1.4.

During the 13-year period, the per capita consumption of fresh market vegetables declined consistently from 140 to 126 pounds. Canned vegetables increased from 77 to 86 pounds, and frozen items rose from 7 to 18 pounds per capita annually during the 1950-1962 period (Fig. 1.4). Figure 1.5 shows a rather constant production of vegetables for fresh market but an increase in those for processing. This has resulted primarily from a demand by the consumer for vegetables already prepared for use.

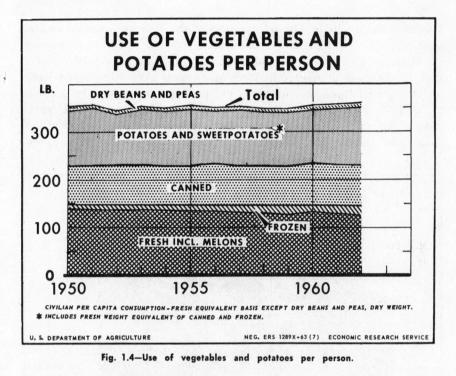

Fig. 1.4—Use of vegetables and potatoes per person.

THE CHANGING VEGETABLE INDUSTRY ✗

Vegetable production is a dynamic, ever-changing major segment of the American economy. In spite of the great competition among food items and the whims of consumers, the present per capita consumption of vegetables is expected to be maintained at approximately the current level.

Trends in Labor Efficiency

From the standpoint of labor, vegetable production is perhaps the most unstable and critical of all farm industries in the United States. The seasonality of growing and harvesting precludes the year-round employment of workers for vegetables only, and critical periods of growing and harvesting tax the ingenuity of vegetable growers and others involved in this important industry.

Mexican nationals, commonly known as Braceros, have been used to supplement the domestic work force. Under Public Law 78, as many as 445,197 Mexican workers were permitted to do seasonal farm work in the

United States in 1956. The termination of the Bracero program in December, 1964, required many commercial vegetable growers to replace the Braceros with domestics, machines, or both. As a result, there was a slight contraction of acreage in 1965. Many more domestic workers were recruited, mechanization increased, and production returned to normal.

A 1964 report by the Economic Research Service of the U.S. Department of Agriculture states that areas of production are scattered from the Gulf Coast and Mexican border northward to Canada. Seasonal progres-

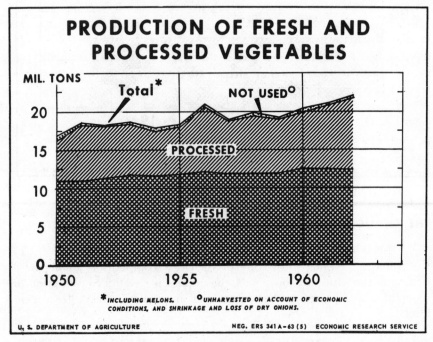

Fig. 1.5—Production of fresh and processed vegetables.

sion of production has these areas overlapping in need for workers, and the demand for labor in an area frequently exceeds supply. Unlike most of the field crops, many vegetables ripen unevenly and require frequent repetitive pickings. For some of these crops, mechanization of harvesting appears remote if at all possible, and labor used per acre is extremely high. In most vegetable areas, there are too few local workers to meet the demand. Producers depend upon the migration of great numbers of workers from one area to another to take care of peak labor requirements during critical production and harvest periods. These are only some of the reasons why vegetable production presents a baffling picture to farmers, economists, labor-placement officials, and others interested in terminating stoop-labor and eliminating the necessity for farm workers to leave home and migrate from one area to another in quest of work.

The task of producing vegetables for a growing population with changing food habits is not small. Within this dynamic industry which has experienced increases in acreage and yields of most vegetables and expanded overall production considerably, what has happened to labor requirements? Has the stoop-labor involved in thinning, weeding, and harvesting continued at the comparatively high level of man-hours required for such operations? Are vegetable crops still produced by hand predominantly; and with increasing yields, are these crops using more labor per acre? The information provided by the Economic Research Service, as presented in Table 1.4, shows that most vegetables have enjoyed a remarkable increase in output per man-hour between 1939 and 1959.

Comparison of Labor Requirements, by Crops and Years

The overall average labor requirements of growing and harvesting an acre of commercial vegetable crops dropped from approximately 119 man-hours (53 preharvest and 66 harvest) in 1939 to 90 man-hours (31 preharvest and 59 harvest) in 1959. During this 20-year period, labor requirements for fresh market vegetables declined from 147 man-hours (66 preharvest and 81 harvest) in 1939 to 112 man-hours (43 preharvest and 69 harvest) in 1959. Vegetables grown for processing required an average of 73 man-hours per acre (31 preharvest and 42 harvest) in 1939, and this figure decreased to 63 man-hours (16 preharvest and 47 harvest) in 1959.

Table 1.4 shows the relative changes in acreage yields, man-hour requirements, and the unit output per man-hour for the principal vegetables for fresh market and processing. Similar data for potatoes and sweet potatoes are provided at the bottom of the table.

In summarizing, the Economic Research Service of the U.S. Department of Agriculture reported in 1964 that the fresh market vegetables registering the greatest gains in efficiency of labor were spinach, carrots, onions, beets, and garlic. For each of these crops, output per man-hour more than doubled from 1939 to 1959. Spinach experienced the greatest increase in labor efficiency. Operations performed in growing this crop

Table 1.4—Estimated Yield and Output per Man-hour of Vegetables Produced Commercially for Fresh Market and for Processing,* 1939 Compared with 1959.

Crops	Yield per Acre, Cwt.		Man-hours per Acre		Output per Man-hour, Cwt.		Percent Change in Output per Man-hour
	1939	1959	1939	1959	1939	1959	1939 over 1959
Asparagus	22	23	190	173	.12	.13	8%
Asparagus*	21	22	94	130	.22	.18	—18*
Beans, lima	22	22	102	120	.22	.18	—18
Beans, lima*	12	21	64	34	.20	.62	210*
Beans, snap	29	36	132	133	.22	.27	23
Beans, snap*	36	45	131	91	.28	.50	79*
Beets	93	119	201	94	.46	1.27	176
Beets*	108	207	146	58	.74	3.56	381*
Broccoli	58	50	184	129	.32	.39	22
Cabbage	124	167	108	104	1.15	1.61	40
Cabbage*	149	275	94	56	1.58	4.90	210*
Cantaloups (Melons)	61	104	115	109	.53	.95	79
Carrots	154	190	284	105	.54	1.81	235
Cauliflower	127	79	268	106	.47	.75	60
Celery	251	415	371	335	.68	1.24	82
Corn, sweet	32	60	49	48	.65	1.25	92
Corn, sweet*	53	76	46	12	1.16	6.20	434*
Cucumbers	54	77	127	114	.43	.68	58
Cucumbers*	29	67	95	155	.30	.44	47*
Eggplants	74	101	185	328	.40	.31	—22
Escarole	162	126	288	124	.56	1.02	82
Garlic	42	85	188	162	.22	.52	136
Kale	67	70	147	145	.46	.48	4
Lettuce	101	159	141	115	.72	1.38	92
Onions	135	226	271	139	.50	1.63	226
Peas, green	28	37	144	128	.19	.29	53
Peas, green*	16	27	25	11	.64	2.40	275*
Peppers, green	62	71	180	200	.34	.36	6
Spinach	46	58	124	32	.37	1.81	389
Spinach*	54	91	83	22	.64	4.22	559*
Tomatoes	66	102	189	186	.35	.55	57
Tomatoes*	111	238	106	137	1.04	1.74	67*
Watermelons	59	82	60	44	.98	1.86	90
Average— Fresh Market Crops	75	111	147	112	.51	.99	94
Average— Processed Crops	59	88	73	63	.82	1.40	71
Potatoes and Sweet Potatoes							
Potatoes	73	184	69	50	1.05	3.67	250
Sweet potatoes	47	74	118	96	.39	.76	95

*Crops for processing.
Data from "Labor Used to Produce Vegetables," USDA Statistical Bull. No. 341, March, 1964.

have changed materially in the past twenty years. Preharvest labor has dropped nearly two-thirds, largely as a result of precision planting and the application of selective herbicides. The former has eliminated the need for hand thinning and the latter hand hoeing and weeding. Harvest labor has dropped 83 percent, while yields have increased substantially. Spinach harvesting in 1939 was performed entirely by hand with workers cutting and packing leaves into baskets. Virtually the entire fresh market crop was mechanically harvested in 1959.

Carrots, onions, and beets experienced tremendous declines in preharvest labor per acre. For these crops, selective herbicides have been developed, providing effective weed control and eliminating the costly, repetitive hand weeding and hoeing operations which were commonly performed in 1939. Precision planters have been especially helpful in reducing the labor required in thinning carrots and onions; most growers no longer thin these crops.

Considerable mechanization is employed in the production and harvesting of vegetables for processing, but the productivity of labor has not increased as fast in this area of production as it has with fresh market crops. The output per man-hour of vegetables for processing increased 71 percent from 1939 to 1959, while that for fresh market crops increased 94 percent during the same period. Largest increases in the productivity of labor on some of the crops for processing are shown by spinach with an increased output per man-hour of 559 percent and sweet corn, beets, and green peas, with increases of 434, 381, and 275 percents, respectively. All these crops have experienced revolutionary changes in production since 1939.

Factors Responsible for Increased Labor Efficiency

Motor power and several other factors are responsible for increasing output per man-hour. Prior to 1939, the shift from horse to tractor power had not been so rapid in vegetable production as in other crop enterprises because many truck crop operations were too small to justify the purchase of a tractor. Also, a small row-crop tractor having good maneuverability and good operator visibility was not available to vegetable growers until about 1940. Thus, the 1939 man-hours reflect, to a considerable extent, horse-powered operations—particularly in the preharvest operations. Since that time, the shift from horse to tractor power has been rapid. While some horses are still used in the production of vegetables in a few areas, they have all but disappeared.

Besides tractor power, crop dusting, spraying, and fertilizing operations are now being performed by airplane in many areas. This source of power and the improvement of machinery in general have further reduced labor input per acre. Additional factors contributing to labor efficiency include the shifting of vegetable crops, particularly those for processing, to more suitable areas of production; the increase in size of vegetable farms; and improved farm and market transportation.

Vegetable yields per acre have been increasing as a result of many factors. Plant breeders have developed new and better producing varieties; more fertilizers and better methods of placement are used; chemical controls for weeds, insects, and diseases have been developed and adopted; improved machines and equipment have been developed which enable growers to perform tasks at the optimum time with a minimum of plant damage; and irrigation of vegetable acreage has increased even in the humid areas of the East. These are some of the factors responsible for the 45 percent increase in yield per acre of all vegetables from 1939 to 1959.

The cost of producing vegetables and the trends in labor efficiency are discussed under the "Trends in Production Efficiency" sections of the respective vegetable chapters of Section Two.

Increasing Importance of Processed Vegetables

In addition to the rising population and per capita income, the development of new and improved products by recent technologies should increase the demand for processed vegetables. The increased number of employed women; a growing aversion of the average housewife to products which have to be peeled, shucked, scraped, chopped, or washed; and the general desire of the average American to spend more time in activities outside of the home will have a continuing impact on the demand for "convenience foods," including vegetables.

The big increase in frozen vegetables has been due in part to technological improvements in freezing and packaging, but also due to the development of refrigerated facilities in retail stores for handling the products. The difficulty in maintaining quality in very perishable vegetables is greatly reduced by freezing. It is easy to understand why a vegetable like peas, frozen and attractively packaged, has replaced the more expensive fresh product that has to be shelled before use.

The range and versatility of vegetable products are also increasing due to new methods of processing. Dehydrofreezing of vegetables by which some of the water is removed before freezing reduces bulk and weight. The process is expensive but the cost of packaging and handling is reduced. Freeze-drying, a process whereby moisture is removed from a product in the frozen state, produces a lightweight, dried product that can be shipped and stored without refrigeration. New products suitable for special uses and improvements in quality due to methods of processing will increase the demand for processed vegetables.

Trends in the Size and Number of Farms

The 1961 U.S. Census of Agriculture reported that the 3,500,000 acres of vegetables, excluding potatoes and sweet potatoes, harvested for sale represented 1.1 percent of the acreage of land from which crops were harvested in 1959. Of all types of farms, 5 percent were classified as vegetable farms.

From 1929 to 1959 (Table 1.5), harvested vegetable acreage increased about 24 percent overall, but substantial declines were registered in the Northeast and East South Central regions. The greatest increases in acreage developed in the Pacific, West South Central, and Mountain regions and some parts of the East North Central and West North Central areas. Concurrently, the number of vegetable farms decreased 71 percent during the 30-year period. The average size of these farms rose from 4.5 acres in 1929 to 6.2 acres in 1939, then to 11 and 19 acres in 1949 and 1959 respectively. The size and type of vegetable farms and the shifting of production varied considerably on a regional, state, and local basis.

The 1964 Census of Agriculture showed that the number of farms growing vegetables declined from 183,000 in 1959 to 132,000 in 1964. However, the acreage remained substantially the same during this period, indicating an increase in average size of farm.

Shifting Marketing Requirements

A knowledge of supply and consumption is essential to an understanding of the changes in marketing in the vegetable industry. Supply, consumption, and markets interact constantly in our dynamic economy. The introduction of a technological change such as quick-freezing started a chain of events in the vegetable industry which affected almost every part of it. New areas increased production, while others stood still or declined. New marketing channels, embodying new firms with different buying, selling, and handling practices, took a share of the market from established firms handling fresh and canned vegetables.

When consumers increase their demand for one product, or for one form of a product at the expense of the other products, the market structure is influenced, and the demand for the services of some firms increases while the demand for others decreases. Such a change in consumer demand for the products of different areas, affects not only the growers in those areas, but marketing firms and transportation agencies as well.

The tendency for more vegetables to be merchandised by large retailers has increased the demand for large supplies of vegetables, graded and packed uniformly. This has placed the small grower at a disadvantage as compared to the large grower in a specialized region of production.

Table 1.5—Number of Farms Reporting Vegetable Sales and Total Acreage of Vegetables (Other Than Potatoes and Sweet Potatoes) by Geographical Divisions.

Geographical Divisions	Number of Farms, 1,000				Percent of All Farms in 1959	Harvested Acreage, 1,000				Percent of Cropland Harvested in 1959
	1929	1939	1949	1959		1929	1939	1949	1959	
North East	27	16	11	5	8.8	80	64	63	50	2.3
Middle Atlantic	80	54	37	20	10.0	389	420	452	374	3.5
East North Central	119	89	73	36	5.5	552	529	639	616	1.1
West North Central	48	28	19	12	1.5	188	167	195	197	0.2
South Atlantic	146	118	93	45	7.7	617	698	835	671	3.4
East South Central	78	45	35	23	4.1	143	127	161	123	0.8
West South Central	80	73	51	22	4.5	297	408	614	402	1.0
Mountain	23	18	12	6	4.4	148	139	187	177	0.8
Pacific	28	22	18	14	7.0	400	504	723	881	5.6
U.S. Total	629	463	349	183		2,814	3,056	3,869	3,491	

Data from Censuses of Agriculture.

CONTRACT PRODUCTION OF COMMERCIAL VEGETABLES

Truck farming is often financed by dealers and processors. A U.S. Department of Agriculture report, involving 2,500 vegetable growers in 12 major commercial areas of the United States for the 1958-1959 season, revealed that approximately one-third of the growers and one-fifth of the total area surveyed was under contract. An additional 5 percent of the growers were dealers or processors who grew another one-fifth of the total. Contracting (between vegetable growers and processors or dealers) is more prevalent in the production of vegetables for processing than in the growing of vegetables for fresh market. About two-thirds of the acreage of vegetables for processing was under contract, compared with less than a tenth of the acreage for fresh market.

By contrast, vertical integration (when processors or dealers are also growers) in production is more common in vegetables grown for fresh market than in vegetables produced for processing. Growers handled the dealer and processor services for about one-fourth of the acreage for fresh market, while they handled them for only 5 percent of the acreage for processing.

The percentage of growers with contracts varies greatly by areas and commodities. Variations are due partly to custom, but more often to differences in the need for control of quality or production techniques. For example, nearly all green peas for processing were under contract because close supervision of factors controlling quality and timing appeared to be essential.

Specifications set forth in contracts varied widely between crops and areas, but differences were greater between areas. Price arrangements were indicated in a large proportion of the contracts, either in terms of specific price commitments, or in terms of how the price was figured. Many different specifications for variety, grade, seed, fertilizers, and cultural practices were found in contracts. Most contracts provided at least some labor, equipment, materials, or financing for these items. Three-fourths of the contracts specified a fieldman for advice, counsel, and inspection, as the fieldman is a key link in the decision-making process.

SOURCES OF INFORMATION

During the formative period of the truck-growing industry, producers relied largely on commercial agencies for information on varieties and production methods. As truck growing became more stabilized in specially adapted areas, trial and error resulted in improved varieties and cultural practices. Truck growers, seed companies, and handling agencies have been alert to make improvements as problems and competition increased. As the industry expanded, more complex problems of production and marketing arose. Producers did not have the time, money, patience, facilities, or training to solve many of them.

The experiment stations and commercial organizations have worked out many of the vegetable growers' problems of pest control, nutrition, processing, marketing, and other economic factors. With restricted resources, it has been impossible for the experiment stations to answer specific questions as they arose in a fast-developing, ever-changing industry. Realizing that production problems vary considerably from section to section, most of the states and the U.S. Department of Agriculture have established branch stations and outlying test fields in the areas of production. With the improvement of research personnel and working facilities during recent years, the experiment stations have made many valuable findings on varieties, fertilizers, pest control, and general cultural and marketing practices for the different crops.

Producers, processors, distributors, and consumers of agricultural products need a great deal of information on changes in production and on markets. The U.S. Department of Agriculture publishes a vast array of information on many aspects of the production, marketing, and consumption of foods. Likewise, the state experiment stations (a list of which is provided in the Appendix) and many commercial industries and organizations have published general and specific information on practically all aspects of producing, handling, and marketing vegetables. Most of these publications are free upon request.

SELECTED REFERENCES

Anonymous, "Consumers All," USDA Yearbook, 1961.

Anonymous, "Outlook of the Vegetable Situation," USDA, ERS, (Quarterly).

Anonymous, "The World Food Deficit," USDA, FAS, Reprint 1961.

Burk, Marguerite C., "Trends and Patterns in U. S. Food Consumption," USDA, *Agriculture Handbook 214*, 1961.

Gavett, E. E., "Labor Used to Produce Vegetables—Estimates by Years," USDA Statistical Bull. 341, 1964.

Gavett, E. E., "Truck Crop Practices, Marion County, Oregon," USDA, ERS-169, 1964.

Gavett, E. E., "Truck Crop Production Practices, Erie County, New York," USDA, ERS-207, 1965.

Gavett, E. E., "Truck Crop Production Practices, San Joaquin County, California," USDA, ERS, 1964.

Gavett, E. E., "Truck Crop Production Practices, Yakima County, Washington," USDA, ERS-172, 1964.

Manchester, A. C. and Podany, J. C., "Shifts in Supply Areas and Consumption Rates for Vegetables, 1931 to 1955," USDA Marketing Research Report 221, 1958.

McElroy, R. C. and Gavett, E. E., "Termination of the Bracero Program," USDA, Agr. Ec. Rep. No. 77, 1965.

Mighell, R. L., Jones, L. A., and Gavett, E. E., "Contract Production of Truck Crops in Twelve Selected Areas," USDA, ERS-152, 1964.

CHAPTER 2

Classifying Vegetables

The relationship of vegetable crops is important to know. Growth habits and susceptibility to injury by insects and diseases are likely to be similar for members of the same species and genus—sometimes even of the same family. The reader of this book should learn the relation of the crops to one another at this time because, in later chapters, the crops are discussed individually rather than as groups of closely related crops.

All vegetables belong to the division of plants known as *Angiospermae*, having ovules in a carpel or ovary. They may be grouped into either Class I, *Monocotyledonae* or Class II, *Dicotyledonae*, having one or two seed leaves, respectively. The plants may be further classified into family, genus, species, and sometimes botanical variety.

A botanical classification alone, however, does not completely satisfy the needs of the student interested in the production of vegetables. He needs to have some orderly arrangement in mind which will help him relate one crop to another in respect to their cultural requirements and uses as human food.

The members of the same botanical family may be grown for different plant parts. For example, some members of the *Umbelliferae* are grown for their foliage, others for their fruits, and still others for their fleshy root parts. The following classification is based upon the use made of the vegetable. By comparing the three lists, the student may see at a glance which crops belong to the same botanical family. Even though some of the vegetable crops in these lists are uncommon, they have been included in order to acquaint the student with the general relationships and the uses for which these little-known vegetables may be grown.

BOTANICAL FAMILIES AND CROP USE

1. Vegetables of which the leaves, flower parts, or stems are used.

Liliaceae. Lily family.
  Asparagus, *Asparagus officinalis* var. *altilis.*
  Chive, chives, *Allium schoenoprasum.*
Chenopodiaceae. Goosefoot family.
  Beet, *Beta vulgaris.*
  Chard, *Beta vulgaris* var. *cicla.*
  Orach, *Atriplex hortensis.*
  Spinach (prickly-seeded), *Spinacia oleracea.*
  Spinach (round-seeded), *Spinacia oleracea* var. *inermis.*
Umbelliferae. Parsley family.
  Celery, *Apium graveolens* var. *dulce.*
  Chervil, *Anthriscus cerefolium.*
  Fennel, *Foeniculum vulgare.*
  Parsley, *Petroselinum crispum.*
Valerianaceae. Valerian family.
  Corn salad, fetticus, *Valerianella oliteria.*
Compositae. Composite or Sunflower family.
  Artichoke, *Cynara scolymus.*
  Cardoon, *Cynara cardunculus.*
  Chicory, witloof, *Cichorium intybus.*
  Dandelion, *Taraxacum officinale.*
  Endive, *Cichorium endivia.*
  Lettuce, *Lactuca sativa.*
Polygonaceae. Buckwheat family.
  Rhubarb, *Rheum rhaponticum.*
  Sorrel, *Rumex acetosa.*
  Spinach dock, *Rumex patientia.*

Aizoaceae. Carpetweed family.
  New Zealand spinach, *Tetragonia expansa.*
Araliaceae. Ginseng family.
  Udo, *Aralia cordata.*
Cruciferae. Mustard family.
  Brussels sprouts, *Brassica oleracea* var. *gemmifera.*
  Cabbage, *Brassica oleracea* var. *capitata.*
  Cauliflower, *Brassica oleracea* var. *botrytis.*
  Collard, *Brassica oleracea* var. *viridis.*
  Cress, *Lepidium sativum.*
  Kale, Borecole, *Brassical oleracea* var. *viridis.*
  Kohlrabi, *Brassica oleraceae* var. *gongylodes.*
  Mustard, leaf, *Brassica juncea.*
  Mustard, Southern Curled, *Brassica juncea* var. *crispifolia.*
  Pak-choe. Chinese cabbage, *Brassica chinensis.*
  Pe-tsai, Chinese cabbage, *Brassica pekinensis.*
  Seakale, *Crambe maritima.*
  Sprouting broccoli, *Brassica oleracea* var. *italica.*
  Turnip, Seven Top, *Brassica rapa* var. *septiceps.*
  Upland cress, *Barbarea verna (praecox).*
  Watercress, *Nasturtium officinale.*

2. Vegetables of which the underground parts are used.

Liliaceae. Lily family.
  Garlic, *Allium sativum.*
  Leek, *Allium porrum.*
  Onion, *Allium cepa.*
  Shallot, *Allium ascalonicum.*
  Welsh onion, *Allium fistulosum.*
Dioscoreaceae. Yam family.
  Yam (true), *Dioscorea batatas.*
Chenopodiaceae. Goosefoot family.
  Beet, *Beta vulguris.*
Cruciferae. Mustard family.
  Horseradish, *Armoracia rusticana.*

Umbelliferae. Parsley family.
  Carrot, *Daucus carota* var. *sativa.*
  Celeriac, *Apium graveolens* var. *rapaceum.*
  Hamburg parsley, *Petroselinum crispum* var. *radicosum.*
  Parsnip, *Pastinaca sativa.*
Solanaceae. Nightshade family.
  Potato, *Solanum tuberosum.*
Compositae. Composite or Sunflower family.
  Black salsify, *Scorzonera hispanica.*

Radish, *Raphanus sativus.*
Rutabaga, *Brassica campestris* var. *napobrassica.*
Turnip, *Brassica rapa.*
Convolvulaceae. Morning-glory family.
Sweet potato, *Ipomoea batatas.*

Chicory, *Cichorium intybus.*
Jerusalem artichoke, *Helianthus tuberosus.*
Salsify, *Tragopogon porrifolius.*
Spanish salsify, *Scolymus hispanicus.*

3. Vegetables of which the fruits or seeds are used.

Gramineae. Grass family.
 Sweet corn, *Zea mays* var. *saccharata.*
Malvaceae. Mallow family.
 Okra (gumbo), *Hibiscus esculentus.*
Leguminosae. Pulse or Pea family.
 Asparagus or Yardlong bean, *Vigna sesquipedalis.*
 Broad bean, *Vicia faba.*
 Bush bean, *Phaseolus vulgaris* var. *humilis.*
 Bush Lima bean, *Phaseolus limensis* var. *limenanus.*
 Cowpea, *Vigna sinensis.*
 Edible podded pea, *Pisum sativum* var. *macrocarpon.*
 Kidney bean, *Phaseolus vulgaris.*
 Lima bean, *Phaseolus limensis.*
 Pea (English pea), *Pisum sativum.*
 Peanut (underground fruits), *Arachis hypogaea.*
 Scarlet runner bean, *Phaseolus coccineus.*
 Sieva bean, *Phaseolus lunatus.*
 Soybean, *Glycine max.*
 White Dutch runner bean, *Phaseolus coccineus* var. *albus.*

Umbelliferae. Parsley family.
 Caraway, *Carum carvi.*
 Dill, *Anethum graveolens.*
Martyniaceae. Martynia family.
 Martynia, *Proboscidea louisiana.*
Solanaceae. Nightshade family.
 Eggplant, *Solanum melongena.*
 Groundcherry (huck tomato), *Physalis pubescens.*
 Pepper (bell or sweet), *Capsicum frutescens* var. *grossum.*
 Tomato, *Lycopersicon esculentum.*
Cucurbitaceae. Gourd or Melon family
 Bush pumpkin, (summer squash), *Cucurbita pepo* var. *melopepo.*
 Chayote, *Sechium edule.*
 Cucumber, *Cucumis sativus.*
 Cushaw, *Cucurbita moschata.*
 Gherkin, *Cucumis anguria.*
 Muskmelon (cantaloup), *Cucumis melo.*
 Pumpkin, *Cucurbita pepo.*
 Squash, *Cucurbita maxima.*
 Watermelon, *Citrullus vulgaris.*
 Winter melon (cassaba), *Cucumis melo* var. *inodorus.*

All plants in the families given in the above classification are dicotyledonous, having two seed leaves, except for those of the Grass and Lily families, which are monocotyledonous, with one seed leaf.

ADAPTATION TO HEAT AND COLD

Vegetables differ materially in their adaptation to high and low temperatures. They fall naturally into two groups. The first group includes those vegetables which grow best under relatively cool conditions, and the second group includes those which require relatively high temperatures.

The cool-season crops can withstand light frosts. Some of them can even endure winter freezing, notably asparagus and rhubarb. Thus, it is this group of crops that one plants earliest in the spring and late in the season for fall and winter harvest. These are the hardy and half-hardy vegetables listed in Table 2.1. The separation into hardy and half-hardy crops is based primarily on the ability of the seed to germinate at low soil temperatures and of the young plants to withstand frosts. This grouping does not necessarily apply to the full-grown plants. Carrot, beet, parsnip, and salsify can remain in the ground late in the fall because of the protection given the root by the soil. In this sense they are more hardy than some of the so-called hardy crops.

Table 2.1—General Classification by Resistance to Spring Frosts.

Cool-Season Crops		Warm-Season Crops	
Hardy	Half Hardy	Tender	Very Tender
Asparagus	Beet	Cowpea	Cucumber
Broccoli	Carrot	New Zealand	Eggplant
Brussels sprouts	Cauliflower	spinach	Lima bean
Cabbage	Celery	Snap bean	Muskmelon
Chives	Chard	Soybean	Okra
Collards	Chinese cabbage	Sweet corn	Pepper
Dasheen	Globe artichoke	Tomato	Pumpkin
Garlic	Endive		Squash
Horseradish	Lettuce		Sweet potato
Kale	Parsnip		Watermelon
Kohlrabi	Potato		
Leek	Salsify		
Mustard			
Onion			
Parsley			
Peas			
Radish			
Rhubarb			
Rutabaga			
Spinach			
Turnip			

The plants that will grow successfully in warm weather are so tender that their growth is checked when the air is cool and death results quickly if they are frosted. The tender crops are a little less susceptible to injury from cool weather than are the very tender crops. There is considerable variation in the soil temperature necessary for seed germination within the tender and very tender groups.

While the cool-season crops are unable to withstand the high summer temperatures of the South, some of them are affected also by prolonged exposure to relatively cool temperatures. The biennials—celery, beet, cabbage, and carrot—may produce seedstalks instead of edible growth the first year if, during the winter months, growing plants are subjected to an average temperature of 50° F. or lower for several weeks. The spring and fall planting dates of different vegetables are given by zones in Tables 8.2 and 8.3 respectively.

SEASON OF GROWTH OF VEGETABLES

The season of the year in which a vegetable may be grown most successfully depends upon the region of production. In southern Florida and in the lower Rio Grande Valley some of the warm-season crops can be grown during winter. In the spring, plantings must be made progressively later from south to north, with every hundred miles making about a week's difference in planting time. This rule-of-thumb may be modified, however, where climate is affected by large bodies of water.

A system of listing vegetables according to the time of year in which they may be grown is an advantage in planning rotations and making cropping plans. The following classification is based on season of growth and use.

Cool-Season Crops

1. Crops quickly reaching edible maturity (spring and fall):
   Leaf lettuce, spinach, mustard, radishes, turnips, kohlrabi, and peas.
2. Crops usually transplanted:
   a. Spring crops
      Head lettuce, Cos lettuce, cabbage, cauliflower, broccoli, and celery.
   b. Fall crops
      Cabbage, cauliflower, broccoli, Brussels sprouts, and celery.
3. Crops that endure summer heat:
   Swiss chard, kale, collards, New Zealand spinach, parsley, endive, onions, leeks, garlic, shallots, chives, potatoes, beets, carrots, parsnips, salsify, and horseradish (the last three withstand winter freezing).
4. Perennial crops:
   Asparagus, rhubarb, and globe artichoke.

Warm-Season Crops

1. Crops usually not transplanted:
   Snap beans, Lima beans, southern peas, sweet corn, popcorn, okra, muskmelon, watermelon, cucumber, squashes, and pumpkin.
2. Crops usually transplanted:
   Tomatoes, eggplants, peppers, and sweet potatoes.

SELECTED REFERENCE

Bailey, L. H., *Manual of Cultivated Plants*, New York: The Macmillan Company, 1949.

CHAPTER 3

Plant Growth and Development

Before discussing the principles and practices involved in vegetable production, a brief review of plant growth and development is desirable. The plant consists of groups of cells which are considered the structural units of a plant in much the same way that bricks are considered the structural units of a building. In mature plants, cells vary in size, shape, and arrangement. Under microscopic examination, the cells at the root and shoot tips are found to be small and box-shaped with dense contents. These cells are dividing, adding new cells to the plant, and increasing its length. If the region just back of the dividing cells is examined, the cells are found to be larger than those at the tip. This region is called the zone of enlargement, and the increase in size also adds length to the plant.

Examination of the region back of the zone of enlargement shows that marked changes have taken place. Some cells, known as the water-conducting cells, have lost their cross walls and have formed a series of pipes. Secondary thickenings have formed in the walls of other cells, forming a series of strands throughout the plant body and serving as framework for the plant in much the same way as steel girders serve as framework for a building. The epidermal cells have become toothed and flanged and have deposited a coat of wax on the outside.

Students of plant life have found that the growth and development of plants consist essentially of three phases: (1) the making of cells, (2) the enlargement of cells, and (3) the maturation of cells. A separate discussion on each of these follows.

MAKING OF CELLS

Where Cells Divide

As stated, cell division occurs at the root and shoot tips (Fig. 3.1). Essentially, cell division has to do with the making of new cell walls and new protoplasm. The cell walls consist of cellulose and pectin, a sticky substance which binds the cellulose fibers together. Protoplasm is the living substance of plants and consists largely of water, sugars, fats, and proteins. Cell division depends primarily on (1) the manufacture of

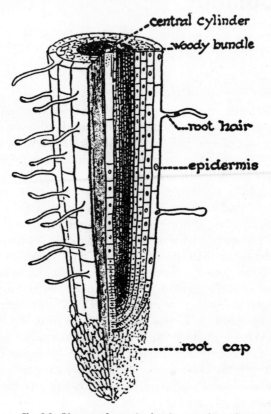

Fig. 3.1—Diagram of root tip showing growing point.

sugars and proteins, (2) the translocation of the sugars and proteins to the growing points, and (3) the liberation of energy.

How and Where the Sugars Are Made

Sugars are manufactured in the green cells of plants. Carbon dioxide from the air and water from the soil combine with the aid of sunlight and chlorophyll (the green pigment of plants) to make the sugars. They may remain unchanged or they may be changed into a great variety of more complex compounds such as starch and cellulose. The simple sugars supply living cells with energy. The cellulose is used to make all cell walls, while starch is stored and later changed back to sugar and used by the plant. Certain plants store large quantities of starch and are used for food, notable examples being Irish and sweet potatoes.

Factors Affecting Sugar Manufacture

The manufacture of sugar depends on a large number of factors. Most important are (1) leaf area, (2) amount of chlorophyll per unit area of leaf surface, (3) certain minerals in the soil solution, (4) activity of the stomata (small pores in green tissue which allow carbon dioxide, oxygen, and water vapor to pass through), and (5) sunlight.

Generally, the greater the leaf area, the greater is the opportunity for the manufacture of sugar. In other words a plant with a large leaf area will make more sugar in a given time than a plant with a small leaf area. Since the root tips require sugars for making new cells, plants with a larger leaf area will have a larger root system than those with a small leaf area. Hence the growth of the roots and the stems and the yield are dependent on the health and abundance of the leaves.

Although chlorophyll is an essential ingredient for photosynthesis its abundance exerts a surprisingly weak quantitative influence on photosynthesis. Since the normal carbon dioxide content of the air is only about three parts in ten thousand, it is generally the limiting factor for photosynthesis. Only where light intensity is low does the concentration of chlorophyll exert a significant effect on photosynthesis.

Minerals Necessary for Sugar Manufacture

Certain minerals—potassium, magnesium, manganese, and iron—are necessary for the making of sugars. When these minerals are absent from the soil solution, the leaves become yellow and chlorotic and do not make sugars. For example, it has been found that snap beans growing in soil lacking in available magnesium, manganese, and iron, contain less sugars and produce lower yields than those growing in soil which contains these minerals.

Influence of the Stomata

The stomata are small openings or pores in the leaves and stems which allow carbon dioxide and oxygen to enter and leave the plant (Fig. 3.2). Since carbon dioxide is essential for the manufacture of sugar, this process is curtailed when the stomata are completely closed. Under certain conditions, the stomata are closed; while under other conditions, they are open. Light and the water supply are the most important factors affecting the opening of the stomata. With most plants, the stomata are open in the day and closed at night provided the plant receives adequate amounts of water. When the water supply within the plants begin to diminish, the stomata close.

How and Where Proteins Are Made

Proteins are made in the leaves and roots. Their manufacture depends on sugar manufacture and on the absorption of minerals from the soil. Sugars and nitrogen are used in the manufacture of all proteins, and some also require phosphorus, potash, and sulfur. Since nitrogen is necessary for the manufacture of all proteins and since protoplasm is largely made up of proteins, the nitrogen supply in the soil is particularly important.

How the Nitrogen Supply Is Maintained

The nitrogen may be present in the soil in the form of organic matter, ammonia, and nitrates. The latter two forms are available to plants but nitrates are free to move in the soil and are thus more readily absorbed. They are also readily leached, especially from sandy soils. Organic matter is decomposed, forming ammonia which is further oxidized to nitrates by soil micro-organisms. The most important factors affecting nitrate formation are: (1) the amount of readily decomposable organic matter in the soil, (2) the temperature, (3) the water supply, (4) the supply of oxygen, and (5) the acidity of the soil.

As a rule, the higher the temperature (between 32° F. and 86° F.) the greater is the activity of soil micro-organisms. Obviously, bacterial activity will be greater in summer than in winter. Because bacterial activity is low during cold weather, growers of truck crops in winter and early spring often apply readily available forms of nitrogen as side dressings.

Nitrifying organisms require plenty of fresh air, which supplies the necessary oxygen for the vital process of respiration. If the soil is poorly drained or water-logged, the air is displaced and the bacteria are affected

accordingly. The acidity of the soil is also important. Investigations have
shown that nitrifying bacteria work best when the soil is slightly acid.

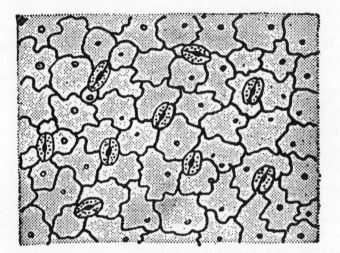

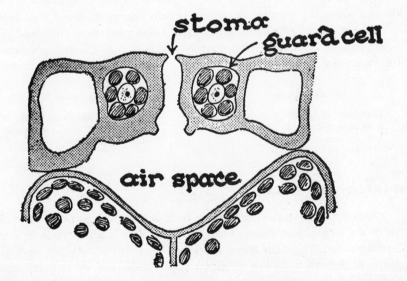

Fig. 3.2—Stomatal apparatus of the leaf. Note that the guard cells contain chloroplasts.

How the Foods Are Translocated

In order for cells to divide, the food substances must be transported from the place where they are made to the place where they are used. Translocation of the foods depends on the water supply; in fact, the water stream within the plant is important in the upward movement of minerals. Two rather distinct conducting systems exist in plants. One carries sugars and other foods, always in solution, to various growing points in the stem and roots and to the storage regions. The other carries water and minerals obtained from the soil solution.

Relationship Between Energy, Work, and Growth

Growth is an expression of work. When plant cells are growing, they are dividing and hence a growing plant is working against the pressure of the atmosphere. In order to grow, the cells must have a source of energy. This energy is derived from simple sugars, and is obtained through the process of respiration. This is exactly the same way that animals obtain energy. Respiration is exactly the opposite of sugar manufacture or photosynthesis. In respiration, the simple sugars decompose to carbon dioxide and water with the liberation of energy. In photosynthesis, energy from absorbed light is used by green cells to produce sugars from carbon dioxide and water. By respiration, plants obtain energy for their vital needs.

The processes of photosynthesis and respiration from the standpoint of (1) time of occurrence, (2) seat of operation, and (3) energy relations are contrasted below:

Photosynthesis	*Respiration*
1. Occurs in green cells only	1. Occurs in all living cells
2. Occurs during day only	2. Occurs both day and night
3. Fixes energy	3. Liberates energy

ENLARGING OF CELLS

As stated before, the regions just back of the growing point have cells which are larger than those at the tips (Fig. 3.3). This increase in size is dependent largely on the water supply in the plant and on the stretching ability of the cell wall. For example, if the amount of water going into a single cell is the same as the amount going out for a given length of time, the cell does not materially change in size. However, if the amount going in is somewhat greater than the amount going out, the cell increases in

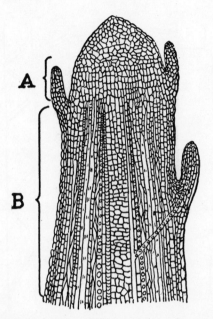

Fig. 3.3—Diagram of a longitudinal section of the growing tip of a stem showing (a) region of cell maturation and (b) region of cell enlargement.

size. Consequently, abundant supplies of water are necessary for cell enlargement. In other words, the stretching of the cell walls by absorption of water increases cell size and growth.

The amount of water going into a plant cell depends on the concentration of sugars and minerals in the cell sap and on the elasticity or resistance of the cell wall. The amount of water going out of a plant depends on the forces of evaporation. As a rule, the greater the evaporation the greater will be the outgo, provided abundant water is available. The effect of evaporation on plant growth will be discussed later.

MATURING OF CELLS

Examination of the plant body back of the region of elongation reveals that the cells have greatly changed in form and structure (Fig. 3.4). The cells which have lost their cross walls have become a series of pipes, and are known as the water-conducting cells. A mature stem shows long fiberlike cells, which have thick walls and small cavities, and appear in the form of strands. The epidermal or skin cells are toothed and flanged and have a deposit of waxy material on the outside. Examination of the

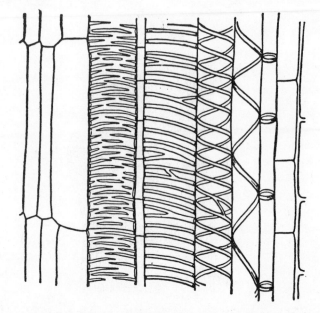

Fig. 3.4—Detailed section of area of mature cells in stem.

cortex or pitch of most plants shows that the cells are filled with starch (Fig. 3.5).

All of these changes are manifestations of cell maturation or cell differentiation. Most important of these changes are (1) the thickening of the cell wall, (2) the formation of fibers, (3) the storage of starch, and

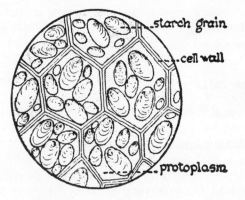

Fig. 3.5—Cells of a bean seed filled with starch grains.

(4) the accumulation of sugars. These changes are dependent on a supply of sugars, which must be available, in order that cells may mature or differentiate.

Vegetative-Reproductive Phases of Plant Growth

As previously stated, sugars are needed for the formation of protoplasm and for the making of new cell walls. When new cells are formed, the plant is actually developing its stems, leaves, and roots. Since sugars are needed for the making of new cells, they are also necessary for the development of stems, leaves, and roots. When the plant is developing its stems and leaves, sugars are being used, and this development is called the vegetative phase of plant growth.

Sugars are also used for the thickening of the cell wall, for the storage of starch, and for the formation and development of flowers and fruit. These changes result in the storage of carbohydrates, which takes place when all the sugar is not used in respiration and the development of stems and leaves.

Although a plant may be developing vegetative parts while producing flowers and fruits, one or the other phase of development is usually dominant. In some plants the growth of vegetative buds is arrested by developing fruits. In others, such as corn, the axes of plants terminate in a flower.

Environmental Influence on the Type of Plant Growth

Environment is the sum total of our surroundings and it markedly influences our behavior. The same is true with plants, since their growth and development are materially influenced by the various factors of their surroundings or environment. Since these factors affect the manufacture and utilization of sugars in a general way, they influence the growth and behavior of plants. The principal environmental factors which influence growth and behavior of vegetable crops are (1) the water supply, (2) light, (3) temperature, and (4) the nutrient supply.

WATER INFLUENCE ON THE VEGETATIVE-REPRODUCTIVE PHASES OF GROWTH

To understand the factors of the environment which affect the water supply within the plant, the student must have a working knowledge of the factors which influence the intake and the outgo of water.

As stated before, water is necessary for cell division, for cell enlargement, and for maintaining turgor. Cells are in a state of turgor when they are fully stretched. In general, the amount of water going into a plant must equal that going out. When the intake is much less than the outgo, the cells lose their turgor and the plant wilts. Cell division is reduced when the intake of water is less than the outgo, even though wilting does not occur. When cell division is reduced, sugars accumulate; and when cell division stops or is retarded, the sugars which accumulate change into starch, cellulose, or lignin (the woody matter of plants), cell walls thicken, certain cells become woody, and others store carbohydrates in the form of starch. When abundant water is available, other factors of the environment being favorable, plants are able to make and enlarge new cells. Hence, an abundant water supply favors the vegetative phase of growth. When moderate supplies are available, and other factors of the environment are favorable, the rates of cell division and plant growth decrease, carbohydrates accumulate, and the reproductive phase of growth may be favored. These effects of water explain why an abundant supply is necessary to promote the rapid growth of lettuce, spinach, and other leafy vegetables, and how crops become woody when the weather is dry.

Factors Influencing the Intake of Water

Principal factors influencing the intake of water are (1) the area of absorbing surface, namely, the area and number of root hairs, (2) concentration of the soil solution, (3) amount of available water in the soil, (4) soil temperature, and (5) the soil's oxygen supply.

A primary function of the root system is the absorption of water. However, not all the roots of vegetable crops absorb water. Water absorption is confined largely to the root hairs and the areas just back of the growing points in the region where the cells enlarge. The root hairs are simply tubular expansions of epidermal or skin cells (Fig. 3.6). These expansions greatly increase the water-absorbing surface of the plant.

Inside the root hair, sugars and other materials are in a solution which is normally more concentrated than the solution in the soil. Consequently, there is a diffusion of water, called osmosis, from the soil solution into the root hairs and into the plant. If the soil is cold, the movement of water in the soil will be slower than when it is warm. In addition, root hairs require moderately warm temperature for growth. The oxygen supply in the soil also influences water absorption. Root hairs need oxygen for respiration, and they do their best work when the soil is plentifully supplied with air.

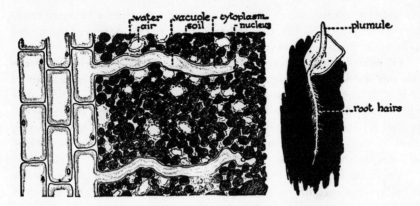

Fig. 3.6—Root hairs of corn. Note attached soil particles.

Factors Influencing the Outgo of Water

The principal factors influencing the outgo of water are (1) air temperature, (2) relative humidity, (3) light intensity, (4) air movement, (5) area of evaporating surface, and (6) the number and size of the stomata.

Air temperature, light intensity, air movement, the area of evaporating surface, and stomatal diameter affect the outgo of water directly, while relative humidity affects the outgo of water indirectly. In other words, the higher the air temperature and light intensity, or the greater the evaporating surface (the stem and leaf surface), the air movement, or the diameter of the stomata, the greater is the outgo. Conversely, the higher the relative humidity, the lesser is the outgo.

An important gardening practice which affects the water supply within the plant is transplanting. Transplanting always destroys roots, hence it always decreases the water supply within the plant and the plant's capacity to absorb water. Generally, vegetable crops transplanted in cloudy or drizzly weather recover more quickly from the check in growth incident to transplanting than those transplanted in sunny weather. Transplanting is discussed fully in Chapter 7.

LIGHT INFLUENCE ON THE VEGETATIVE-REPRODUCTIVE PHASES OF GROWTH

The effect of light on plants is dependent upon: (1) light intensity,

(2) light duration, and (3) light quality. Light intensity varies with the season, being greater in summer than in winter. In general, investigations have shown, within limits, that the manufacture of sugars is proportional to the light intensity, provided other factors are not limiting.

Of primary importance is the duration of light, which also varies with the season, as the daily light period is shorter in winter than in summer. Generally, more sugars are made in long days than in short ones. Experiments show that the length of day markedly influences the vegetative and reproductive phases of plant growth. Some plants flower during short days only, others during long days only, while still others flower during short, medium, and long days.

Vegetable crops which flower or develop their storage organs during short days are certain varieties of potatoes, Lima beans, and soybeans. Those which flower during the long days are spinach, spring radishes, and lettuce.

Light quality refers to the spectral distribution. Visible light consists of red, orange, yellow, green, blue, indigo, and violet rays. The red and violet rays of sunlight influence sugar manufacture more than the green rays.

TEMPERATURE INFLUENCE ON GROWTH

Within rather narrow limits, generally between 40° and 85° F., the rate of cell division and growth is proportional to the temperature, provided other factors are not limiting. When the temperature is low, the rate of cell division and growth is slow. When growth is slow, sugars are used less rapidly than when the rate of growth is high; hence in cool weather, other factors being favorable, sugars accumulate. At relatively high temperatures, growth is rapid and sugars do not accumulate, but are used in respiration and growth. Low temperatures stimulate some plants to change from the vegetative to the reproductive phase. Among these are the biennials and some perennials.

Vegetable crops differ in their temperature requirements. Some crops, such as melons, cucumbers, and eggplants, thrive best under a relatively high temperature, while others, such as lettuce and celery, grow best under a relatively cool temperature. However, the best temperature is not necessarily the one at which the plant makes the most rapid growth. The different vegetables are grouped according to seasonal preference in Chapter 2.

SELECTED REFERENCES

Galston, A. W., *The Life of the Green Plant*, Englewood Cliffs, N. J.: Prentice-Hall, 1964.

Leopold, A. C., *Auxins and Plant Growth*, Univ. of California Press, 1955.

Leopold, A. C., *Plant Growth and Development*, New York: McGraw-Hill, 1964.

Loewy, A. G. and Siekevitz, P., *Cell Structure and Function*, New York: Holt, Rinehart and Winston, 1963.

McElroy, W. D., *Cell Physiology and Biochemistry*, Englewood Cliffs, N. J.: Prentice-Hall, Inc., 1965.

Meyer, B. S., Anderson, D. B., and Bohning, R. H., *Introduction to Plant Physiology*, Princeton, N. J.: Van Nostrand, 1960.

Rosenberg, J. L., *Photosynthesis*, New York: Holt, Rinehart and Winston, 1965.

CHAPTER 4

Breeding and Improving Vegetables

The vegetable industry is looking more and more to the plant breeder for help with its problems. The breeder must solve the problems of each area by developing varieties suited to it. Already, though the work has scarcely begun, results have been spectacular. Rust-resistant asparagus, mosaic-resistant spinach, yellows-resistant cabbage, wilt-resistant peas, watermelons, and tomatoes, mildew-resistant muskmelons, and brown blight-resistant lettuce are among the contributions that have helped to save the industry in different districts.

Improvement is relatively easy if plants with the desired characters can be secured by selection; but where hybridization must be used, the procedure may become somewhat complicated. Controlled hybridization to produce first-generation hybrids is currently in practice with such crops as sweet corn, onions, tomatoes, cucumbers, cabbage, eggplant, spinach, and summer squash. Others undoubtedly will be added to the list as new methods are devised for economical production of the hybrid seed. Before planning a vegetable-breeding program, one must know something about the chromosomes and genes, so important in heredity, and about their behavior in growth and reproduction.

CELLS, CHROMOSOMES, AND GENES

A plant or a portion thereof is shown by the microscope to consist of innumerable small cells. Many of these, especially the rapidly growing root and stem tips, contain a small round or elliptical body called the nucleus embedded in a mass of more transparent material, the cytoplasm. Within the nucleus are small rod-shaped bodies, the chromosomes, distinguishable only when the cells are undergoing division. All cells of the same species have the same number of chromosomes, occurring in pairs. In other words, every chromosome within a cell has its exact duplicate in size, shape, and composition. Each body cell of the onion (*Allium cepa*) contains 8 pairs of chromosomes, one set of 8 having been derived from the male parent and the other set of 8 from the female parent. At each cell division, during growth of the plant, these 16 chromosomes divide longitudinally, each daughter cell receiving chromosomes of the same number and composition as the mother cell. These chromosomes carry the factors or "genes" that determine whether a fertilized egg will develop into an animal or plant and whether the individual will possess desirable or undesirable characters. Each character is the expression of one or more genes as modified by the environment. Characters are the attributes which identify an individual.

The genes are distributed along the chromosome like beads on a string, each in its definite location. During cell division, when the chromosomes divide lengthwise, all genes also divide, so that the two daughter cells have the same genic complex as the parent cell.

In most chromosomes there are probably several hundred genes, all tending to remain together as a unit. Genes belonging in the same chromosome are said to be linked; collectively they are known as a linkage group. A plant has as many linkage groups as it has pairs of chromosomes. When certain genes are linked, the characters they express will also be linked. In other words, linked characters tend to remain together more often than to be separated.

Not only are the chromosomes in pairs, but the genes on them are also in pairs, arranged in the same linear order. The two members of a pair of genes are called *allelomorphs*. If both members of a pair of genes are alike, the plant is homozygous (pure) at that point; that is, it will breed true for the character that depends upon this pair of genes for its expression.

SEGREGATION AND RECOMBINATION

In plant growth, when the body cells divide, the daughter cells receive the same number of chromosomes that were in the mother cell. In the flower, however, another type of division known as reduction division occurs in cells preceding the formation of the sperms and eggs. Instead of each chromosome dividing, the pairs meet at the middle of the cell; then the members of each pair move to opposite ends, and two cells are formed in which the number of chromosomes is reduced to one-half that of the body cells (Fig. 4.1).

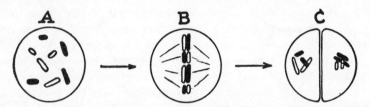

Fig. 4.1—The mother cell (A) contains four pairs of chromosomes. Those colored black have been derived from the male parent, the white from the female parent. Preparatory to reduction division (B) members of a pair meet at the center of the cell. And (C), members of a pair have moved away from each other, and a wall has formed between. Note that the chromosomes derived from the male or female parent do not remain together.

The set of chromosomes derived from the one parent or the other do not remain together; they segregate in all possible combinations. For example, two varieties of tomatoes differ in the color of the mature fruit, one being red and the other yellow. This difference is determined by a single pair of genes. The genes for red color are represented by the symbols $R\ R;$ the genes for yellow by $r\ r$. In the formation of the germ cells the red-fruited tomato will produce sperms and eggs with the gene for red, and the yellow-fruited tomato, sperms and eggs with the gene for yellow (Fig. 4.2). When a cross is made, the chromosome number is doubled, and the pair of chromosomes containing R and r are present in the fertilized egg and in all the body cells of the hybrid. This hybrid will produce eggs and sperms of which one-half will have the chromosome with the gene for red (R) and the other half will have the chromosome with the gene for yellow (r).

When this hybrid (F_1) is self-fertilized, there will be three possible combinations between eggs and sperm—RR, Rr, and rr, as shown in the checkerboard (Fig. 4.4). Fertilized eggs will be produced in the ratio of one RR pure for red, two Rr hybrid for red, and one rr pure for yellow. The Rr plant will have red fruit because in this instance red is dominant to yellow. The yellow gene, though present, does not express itself and is therefore said to be recessive. The fertilized egg containing rr will produce a plant that will breed true for yellow, and the RR plant will breed true for red. The Rr plant, however, is hybrid for fruit color, and when self-fertilized will produce a progeny that will segregate again in the ratio

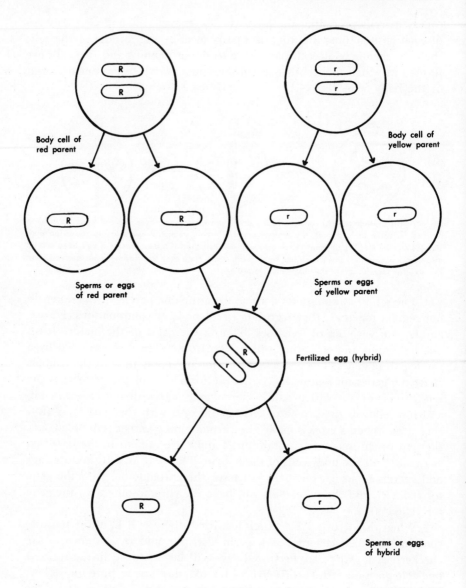

Body cell of
red parent

Body cell of
yellow parent

Sperms or eggs
of red parent

Sperms or eggs
of yellow parent

Fertilized egg (hybrid)

Sperms or eggs
of hybrid

Fig. 4.2—This diagram shows only the pair of chromosomes carrying the genes "R" and "r."

of one *RR:* two *Rr:* one *rr.* From external appearances the fruits can be classified into two color groups, red and yellow, known as phenotypes. From the standpoint of genic composition, however, they can be placed in three groups called genotypes.

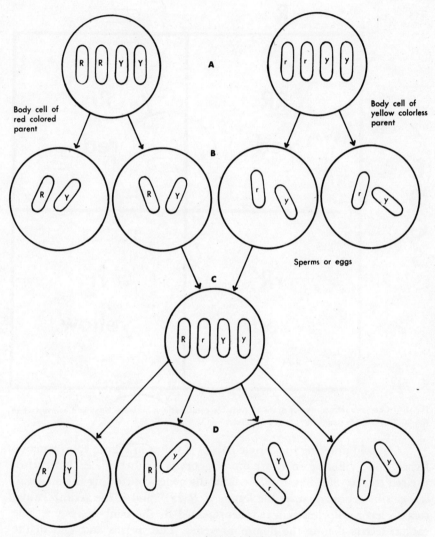

Fig. 4.3—A: Genic composition of two tomato plants, one being pure for red fruit and yellow skin, and the other for yellow fruit and colorless skin. B: Sperms or eggs, only one member of each pair present. C: Fertilized egg (hybrid). D: Four kinds of sperms and eggs formed. Only those chromosomes and genes are represented with which we are concerned here.

SPERMS

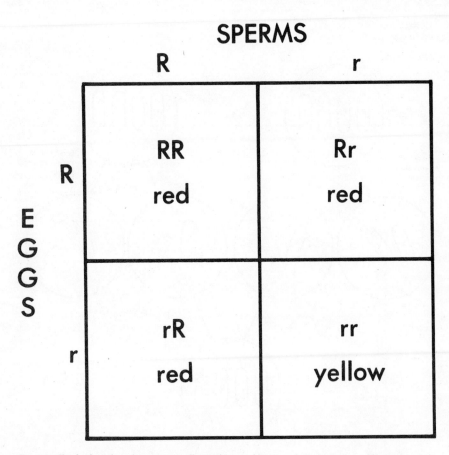

Fig. 4.4—Checkerboard to demonstrate all possible combinations between eggs and sperms when the "F₁" hybrid for genes "Rr" is self-fertilized.

A hybrid differing in a single pair of genes as in Figure 4.2 is a monohybrid; one differing in two pairs of genes is a dihybrid. If the fruit of the red tomato also has a yellow skin, the genes controlling these characters can be represented by the letters $R\ R\ Y\ Y$; and if the yellow-fruited tomato has a colorless skin it is represented by the symbols $r\ r\ y\ y$. The capital letters denote the dominant genes. The sperms and eggs of the red, yellow-skinned tomato will all contain genes $R\ Y$, and those of the yellow, colorless-skinned tomato, genes $r\ y$ (Fig. 4.3). The fertilized egg and all body cells of the hybrid (F_1) will contain $Rr\ Yy$; and will have red fruit with yellow skins. At reduction division four kinds of eggs and sperms will be formed: RY, Ry, rY, and ry. When this hybrid plant is self-fertilized, eggs and sperms will unite in all possible combinations, best illustrated with a checkerboard (Fig. 4.5).

In the resulting progeny (F_2) there are four phenotypic classes in the following ratio: nine of the plants will have red fruit with yellow skin;

SPERMS

		RY	Ry	rY	ry
E G G S	**RY**	RRYY red colored	RRYy red colored	RrYY red colored	RrYy red colored
	Ry	RRyY red colored	RRyy red colorless	RryY red colored	Rryy red colorless
	rY	rRYY red colored	rRYy red colored	rrYY yellow colored	rrYy yellow colored
	ry	rRyY red colored	rRyy red colorless	rryY yellow colored	rryy yellow colorless

Fig. 4.5—Checkerboard to demonstrate all possible combinations between eggs and sperms when the "F₁" hybrid for the genes "RrYy" is self-fertilized.

three will have red fruit with colorless skin and will be pink in appearance because of the lack of yellow pigment in the skin; three will have yellow fruit with yellow skin; and one will have yellow fruit with colorless skin, appearing pale yellow. Of the two new combinations—red fruit-colorless skin and yellow fruit-colored skin—one plant out of three will breed true for the new combination. Phenotypic dihybrid ratios other than the 9:3:3:1 occur frequently, but lack of space prevents their consideration.

If, in a certain case, the genes *A* and *B* occurred in the same chromosome and their allelomorphs *a* and *b* in the other member of the pair (Fig. 4.6), then, more of the eggs and sperms would contain the *AB* and *ab*

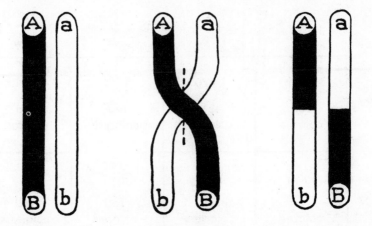

Fig. 4.6—In this figure, on the left, are shown two genes, "A" and "B," and their allelomorphs in opposite ends of a pair of chromosomes. A break causing an exchange in similar parts of a pair of chromosomes would have "A" and "b" in one member and "aB" in the other member of the pair. This phenomenon is known as crossing-over.

combination than *Ab* and *aB*, and segregation in the F_2 would not correspond to the 9:3:3:1 ratio. Fortunately for the breeder, even two genes in the same chromosome do not always remain together. At some stage in the early reduction division, when the members of a pair of chromosomes lie close together, a break occasionally occurs, and there is an exchange of homologous parts, known as crossing-over. More breaks occur between two genes located far apart on a chromosome than between two that are close together. Where genes are closely linked, one must usually grow a large number of plants in order to secure the desired crossover.

FLOWERS, POLLINATION, AND FERTILIZATION

People do not, as a rule, think of plants in terms of sex, mainly because the two sexes are not always separated as they usually are in animals. In only a few vegetables (spinach and asparagus, for example) are the sexes in different plants. Sex is expressed primarily in the flower parts; and when making crosses one must distinguish male from female whether they be in the same flower (perfect), in different flowers of the same plant (monoecious), or in different plants (dioecious).

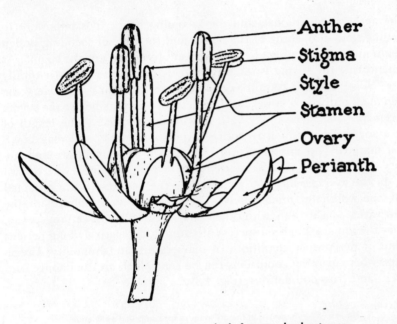

Anther
Stigma
Style
Stamen
Ovary
Perianth

Fig. 4.7—Onion flower. Inner whorl of stamens has burst open.

Truck-Crop Plants, McGraw-Hill Book Co.

Most species of vegetables have four whorls of floral organs—sepals, petals, stamens, and pistils; some lack one or more whorls. From the standpoint of reproduction only the stamens and pistils are important. The stamen, or male part of the flower, contains within its mature anther a yellowish powder called pollen that produces the sperms. The pistil, or female part, has within its ovary one or more small, white, kidney-shaped objects, the ovules, which contain the eggs.

The transfer of pollen from the anther to the stigma of the pistil is called pollination. Self-pollination occurs when pollen is transferred from the anther to the stigma of the same flower or from one flower to another of the same plant; cross-pollination, when the transfer is from one plant to another. Plants that depend upon insects and wind are mainly cross-pollinated. Asparagus, onions, and cabbage are pollinated chiefly by insects; spinach, beets, and corn by the wind. In peas, beans, lettuce, and tomatoes, self-pollination is the rule.

The technique one uses to make a pollination will vary with the structure and the normal mode of pollination of the flower and whether self- or cross-pollinations are being made. To develop a technique the flower structure must be studied to determine the size, shape, and position of the anthers and stigmas, and the blooming habit. It is important to know the time of opening of the flower and the time of shedding pollen in relation to the opening of the flower and receptivity of the stigma. As a general rule the stigma is receptive shortly before the flower naturally opens. However, with certain vegetables such as onions and celery the pollen of an individual flower may shed two to four days before the stigma is receptive. The reverse may be true with other species. The length of time a stigma may remain receptive varies considerably and may be affected markedly by environmental factors such as temperature and humidity. The stigmas of most species remain receptive from one to two days on the average, but as a general rule the best results are obtained when one pollinates immediately. The longevity and viability of the pollen varies considerably with different species. Pollen of certain species, such as the tomato, has been successfully stored for relatively long periods of time under proper conditions of temperature and humidity. Greenhouses, where growing conditions can be controlled, are commonly used for self- and cross-pollinations (Fig. 4.8).

Fig. 4.8—Carrots grown in the greenhouse for controlled pollination.

USDA Photograph

VARIATION

It is rare that two plants are exactly alike, no matter how uniform the variety to which they belong appears en masse. The variations between plants may be of two types: those caused by the environment and those caused by the difference in genic make-up of the chromosomes. Variations caused by a difference in environmental factors such as moisture, temperature, and light are not inherited. The principal effect of these factors is upon the size of the plant or its parts.

Variations originating in the genic material of the chromosomes are heritable. They may arise in several ways—as a recombination of characters; change of a single gene; change of several genes; or a loss or gain of a portion of a chromosome, an entire chromosome, or whole sets of chromosomes.

Methods have been recently devised to increase variability within plants. One method is to change the number of chromosomes. A chemical called colchicine has been found that will double the number of chromosomes. Besides colchicine, other chemicals, applications of heat, and wounding the stems have also done the same. Plants with more sets of chromosomes than the two normally found are called polyploids. Tomato plants which normally have 12 pairs or 24 chromosomes before treatment with colchicine have been shown to have 48 chromosomes after treatments. These plants with four sets of chromosomes are called tetraploids. The normal tomatoes are called diploids. Plants with three sets of chromosomes, called triploids, have been obtained by crossing a tetraploid with a diploid. The hybrid seedless watermelon, which is a triploid, is obtained in this way. The triploid is highly sterile and seedless, and is grown commercially by interplanting it with a normal diploid line that serves as a pollinator necessary for fruit set.

Polyploids can sometimes be recognized by their increased size and more luxuriant growth, but this is not always true. Artificially induced tetraploids generally are less fertile than their diploid parents. As a general rule tetraploids have not proved directly useful for most vegetable crops. They have, however, proved directly useful in some flowers such as snapdragons and marigolds where the increased size of the flower is of importance.

Changes in genes and sections of chromosomes have been induced by various means. Mutations can be brought about by the use of X rays, gamma rays, thermal neutrons, ultraviolet rays, and certain chemicals such as the nitrogen mustards. Many of the mutations or changes that result are detrimental to the plant, but sources of disease resistance and higher yields have been found recently with these methods.

Crop improvement is possible because plants do differ in their heritable characteristics. However, it is often impossible to tell by looking at a superior-appearing plant whether the desirable characters are heritable or nonheritable. The plant breeder has to spend much of his time distinguishing between these two kinds of variation. The real proof of a selection's superiority is to grow progenies from the plant. If the characteristic is passed down from parent to progeny then we know it is inherited and can be successfully selected.

METHODS OF IMPROVEMENT

Crop improvement through plant breeding is chiefly accomplished by selection and hybridization and the combination of the two. Selection is effective only when differences are heritable. Variation is not created by selection, but existing, desirable variation may be collected and concentrated by selection. Hybridization or crossing two or more sources may result in new and superior combinations of characters.

Hybrids are valuable for a number of reasons. A combination of uniformity and vigor can be obtained that is difficult to get in any other way; early and total yields can be increased. Certain characteristics such as the seedless condition in watermelons are possible only in hybrids. However, indiscriminate crossing of plants should be avoided. One should always have a definite reason or clear-cut objective in mind before starting to make crosses between plants. If not, much effort can be lost and no worthwhile results obtained.

The natural sources of variation should be adequately explored before hybridizing. When progress is no longer possible or economical through continued use of natural variation, then it is time to resort to controlled hybridization. On the other hand, hybridization may be needed early in a breeding program if the varieties in use do not contain a specific character which is needed. Early hybridization may be necessary, for example, to obtain disease resistance, since many otherwise good varieties are limited in production because they are susceptible to one disease or another.

Selection usually follows hybridization to isolate the superior combinations that may arise. Frequently selections may be back-crossed to one of the parents for several generations. This is done to incorporate some desirable feature such as disease resistance into an otherwise desirable variety lacking only in this one character.

Commercial use may sometimes be made of F_1 hybrids, or the first generation following a cross. Many combinations are usually made and tested to find the one that is best suited to the conditions under which it is to be used.

Certain situations make the production of hybrid seed economical. Any condition which aids in the separation of the male and female elements of a flower or plant will help provide a method for making economical crosses between plants. The monoecious flowering habit in corn separates the female ear from the male tassel. An inbred line can be made essentially female by removing the tassel before it has shed its pollen. Allowing another line to shed pollen in the presence of the detasseled line will make the desired cross, provided the two lines are isolated from other corn plantings. Another means is provided by conditions of male sterility. Certain inherited factors bring about sterility within the male parts of the flowers that effectively make the flower and plant female. If some means are provided to transfer fertile pollen from another line, hybrid seed can be easily and economically produced. Male sterility has been found in nearly every kind of vegetable. The production of hybrid seed in onions is entirely based upon the use of male sterility. Methods of using male sterility are being worked out to produce hybrids with such crops as beets, carrots, squash, sweet corn, tomatoes, eggplant, and peppers.

The actual method of breeding used depends upon the crop and the objectives sought. For our purposes here, we divide crops into four groups: (1) those naturally self-pollinated, (2) those naturally cross-pollinated, (3) those often or partially cross-pollinated, and (4) those vegetatively propagated. Space does not permit an extensive discussion of breeding methods and objectives for all the crops in each group.

PLANTS NATURALLY SELF-POLLINATED

Important vegetable crops that are naturally self-pollinated include peas, snap and field beans, tomatoes, and lettuce. Self-pollination is not absolute, as some crossing usually occurs in all. Within this group of plants little if any loss in vigor is caused by inbreeding that results from self-pollination. Essentially homozygous or pure lines are developed in a few generations because self-pollination is the most intensive form of inbreeding. Selection within a pure line is therefore likely to be ineffective. In old or unselected varieties an opportunity exists for increased variability arising from mixtures, mutations, and natural crossing. Therefore, the chances for obtaining improvement by selection are much greater from old than from new varieties.

The two general methods of selection are mass selection and pedigree selection. With mass selection a fairly large number of desirable plants with relatively similar characteristics are selected and the seed is bulked and planted. The selected lot is usually compared with the original variety. Mass selection is most useful in dealing with characters that are not modified greatly by environment. Under certain conditions it is possible to obtain quicker results from mass selection than from pedigree selection since uniformity for one character may be obtained with less danger of altering other varietal characteristics. Rapid changes in varietal type are not usually made with mass selection. Mass selection is less useful than pedigree selection for characters which are modified greatly by environment because the effects of heredity and environment are not separated. A form of mass selection is commonly used by seedsmen to maintain a stock or variety by eliminating undesirable or inferior plants. This practice is commonly called roguing. As a general rule, seed stocks of self-pollinated crops are relatively easy to maintain true to type by isolation and selection.

The pedigree system of selection may be superior to mass selection as more rapid progress may usually be expected. It is, however, more expensive to operate and requires more record-taking. In practice, the single plant selections are kept separate and the progenies are grown out for evaluation. The original selections from a variable population will isolate many pure lines, within which further selection is not likely to be effective. The main problem is to find out which of the pure lines are the best. Further selection of lines is usually based upon the performance of the whole row. Many of the lines are discarded for one reason or another, leaving a relatively small number to be tested in the following years. Final selection should be based on tests in several seasons and in different locations throughout the area in which the variety is expected to be used.

When controlled hybridizations are made between plants to produce new sources of variation and obtain new combinations, some form of selection is begun as soon as segregation of the characters occurs. Pedigree selection is most commonly used and mass selection is seldom used following hybridization.

Within self-pollinated crops, hybrid vigor is commonly found when different pure lines are crossed. Since self-pollination is the general rule, inbreeding is unnecessary to obtain pure lines in this group of plants.

Whether or not it is economically feasible to use hybrid vigor depends upon the cost of producing the hybrid seed in relation to the value of the increased yields. Since most self-pollinated crops produce a relatively small amount of pollen, which is not transferred by the wind or by insects to any significant degree, hand-pollination is most likely necessary to bring about a transfer of pollen between plants. If many seeds are produced by each hand-pollination and if few seeds are needed per acre, it may be feasible to use hybrids. With tomatoes, for example, a relatively large number of seeds may be obtained in each fruit by each hand-pollination, and the increased yields justify hybridization for greenhouse and early-market use. With crops like peas and beans, it is very unlikely that hybrids will ever be used because of the difficulty in making hand pollinations and the small number of seeds per pollination.

PLANTS NATURALLY CROSS-POLLINATED

Important vegetable crops that are naturally cross-pollinated include plants of the cabbage family such as cabbage, cauliflower, rutabagas, turnips, and radishes; root crops including carrots, beets, parsnips; and other crops such as onions, sweet corn, asparagus, spinach, and rhubarb. Most of these crops have perfect flowers (both sexes in the same flower). The pollen of the perfect-flowered species is largely transferred by the wind or insects. Sweet corn is monoecious (male and female flowers separate but on the same plant), and asparagus and spinach are dioecious (separate male and female plants). The monoecious and dioecious conditions are responsible for a very high degree of cross-pollination. Most crops that are highly cross-pollinated lose vigor with inbreeding.

The development of true breeding varieties may be accomplished by selecting naturally occurring plants with desirable characteristics. Mass selection is usually preferable to pedigree selection because varieties can be obtained that are relatively uniform for observable characters but still retain vigor. The Danish type of cabbage used in New York and other Eastern states was originally developed by this method. If pedigree selection is used with controlled pollination, these crops ordinarily lose so much vigor by inbreeding that the strains developed are seldom directly useful. Pedigree selection is occasionally practiced without control of the pollen parent and is commonly referred to as ear-to-row breeding in corn. The results from this method have not been completely satisfactory. It has proved successful in changing specific characters, but the yield is often reduced at the same time because of the close breeding.

Combinations of pedigree and mass selection are sometimes used. This method is useful in dealing with characters that are modified greatly by environment. After a generation or two of pedigree selection, a fairly large number of selected lines should be massed to regain vigor. This method has been used successfully with both onions and carrots.

Variation may be produced by controlled hybridization in much the same manner as with self-pollinated crops. Frequently natural crossing will provide abundant recombinations of characters within existing varieties. If specific characters are missing in a variety they may be incorporated by making appropriate controlled crosses.

It is with cross-pollinated crops that the commercial use of first-generation F_1 hybrids has gained the most favor. F_1 hybrids make up a very high percentage of the sweet corn grown both for market and processing. Hybrids of cabbage and spinach are in commercial production. Experimental hybrids of asparagus, carrots, and beets have been produced and should soon join the commercial ranks. Hybrid vigor is commonly found when two inbred lines are crossed.

Yields of hybrid onions were compared with that of the leading variety, Early Yellow Globe. In summarizing the data recorded for three years at four locations in New York State the following was found: 12 percent of the hybrids yielded significantly more and 14 percent significantly less, while 74 percent were not significantly different from Early Yellow Globe. The hybrids that outyielded this variety produced an average yield of 213 fifty-pound bushels per acre more than the check variety. Some of the hybrids that yielded the most were not acceptable commercially because of such things as poor storage quality, poor color, and thin skins. Some of the hybrids which yielded no more than Early Yellow Globe were actually superior because of earlier maturity, better color, and the ability to keep longer in storage (Fig. 4.9).

Breeding methods for improvement of dioecious crops have not received much study. Mass selection has been the most common method. Since the sexes are separated into separate plants they cannot be closely inbred. Brother-sister or sib mating is the closest form of inbreeding. Dioecious plants usually lose vigor on sibbing. Occasionally plants can be found in crops such as spinach and asparagus that have both sexes on the same plant. These plants can then be inbred. As already mentioned, F_1 hybrids are now in use with spinach and have been experimentally produced in asparagus. Increased yields of from 20 to 50 percent have been reported for spinach hybrids over that obtained by commercial varieties.

Fig. 4.9—Comparative yields of the hybrid Granex (center) and parents, TEG 951, left and YB 936, right.

USDA Photograph

PLANTS PARTIALLY CROSS-POLLINATED

Lima beans, eggplants, peppers, celery, potatoes, and those in the cucurbit family such as cucumbers, squash, pumpkins, muskmelons, and watermelons are usually classified as being partially cross-pollinated. The amount of crossing will vary for these crops depending upon the environment. The breeding methods employed will vary depending upon the amount of crossing and the loss in vigor resulting from self-pollination.

In general most of these crops do not lose as much vigor with inbreeding as one might expect. Care must be taken in producing seed of these plants in order to maintain purity of stocks and varieties. Hybrids of summer squash, winter squash, cucumbers, muskmelons, watermelons, and eggplants are in production. Pepper hybrids should soon be on the market. Male sterility has been found and is the basis for the economical production of hybrid seed within most of the vegetables in the group.

An experiment with eggplant in Pennsylvania illustrates the extent of hybrid vigor one may obtain in this group of plants. Seven varieties of eggplant representing a range of types were crossed in all possible combinations. Sixteen of the possible 21 hybrids were compared with the parents for yields. Table 4.1 shows the ranges in yield in tons per acre and the average yields of the parents and hybrids. The hybrids clearly outyielded the parent varieties in both early and total yield.

Table 4.1—A Comparison of Early and Total Yields of Parental Varieties of Eggplants and Their F₁ Hybrids.

	Parental Varieties		F_1 Hybrids	
	Range in Tons/Acre	Average Yield, Tons/Acre	Range in Tons/Acre	Average Yield, Tons/Acre
Early yield	1.5-6.6	4.1	3.6-11.8	8.0
Total yield	11.0-19.9	15.2	19.3-37.1	24.9

PLANTS VEGETATIVELY PROPAGATED

Vegetable crops propagated chiefly by vegetative means are: potatoes, sweet potatoes, globe artichokes, rhubarb, garlic, and horseradish. In breeding vegetatively propagated crops, if one plant is found with desirable characteristics, an indefinite number of plants can be obtained that are identical to the selected plant. Selection among plants produced by vegetative propagation will not be effective.

In some crops favorable mutations may occur quite frequently. These may accumulate in old or unselected varieties. Some mutations or changes are easily recognized, such as red skins on white potato tubers.

Much of the improvement in the sweet potato has been made by the selection of favorable mutations. In the Puerto Rican variety of sweet potato, the mutation rate is fairly high, one in about every 7,000 plants. Most varieties of sweet potatoes do not bloom readily in the United States, but in the West Indies, conditions are favorable for flowering of some varieties. The sweet potato flower closely resembles that of the morning glory, to which it is closely related. The nonflowering varieties of sweet potatoes have been induced to flower by grafting a small portion of the growing point on certain species of morning glory. It is now possible to make crosses among any of the varieties of sweet potatoes. As with the potato, desirable seedlings can be maintained indefinitely by vegetative propagation.

SELECTED REFERENCES

Butler, J. D., *et al.*, "Plant Breeding as a Hobby," Ill. Agr. Ext. Cir. 817, 1960.
Hays, H. K., Immer, F. R., and Smith, D. C., *Methods of Plant Breeding*, New York: McGraw-Hill Book Company, 1955.

CHAPTER 5

Seeds and Seed Growing

A seed is an undeveloped and dormant plant, usually with a reserve food supply and protected by a seed coat. It results from the union of the male nucleus from the pollen grain with the female or egg nucleus in the ovary of the flower. It carries a combination of the hereditary characteristics of the two parents. When air, warmth, and moisture are favorable, the little plant starts to grow.

The product as harvested by the planter may be much worse than the seed from which it has sprung, but it can be no better. The hereditary content of the little seed sets the upper limit of both performance and quality. We can do much with fertilizer, water, and care to get out of a plant the best that it has, but we can get no more than it has received from its parents.

The price of seed for most vegetable crops is a small fraction of the total cost, and merit in seed may greatly increase yield or selling value or both. Hence, the utmost care is called for in buying seed, and one may well afford to pay increased prices for seed, provided he is satisfied value is delivered.

THE CHARACTERS OF GOOD SEED

Good seed is (1) clean, (2) disease-free, (3) viable, (4) well developed, and (5) of good heritage.

To be clean, seed must be free of foreign matter, such as other kinds of seeds, dirt, or plant fragments. Vegetable seeds seldom cause serious trouble in this respect.

Freedom from Diseases

Seed should not carry disease to infect the new crop. To insure that it doesn't, the seed should be grown without contamination. This may be accomplished by its production in disease-free areas, and by the use of rigid control methods. Sometimes diseases on the outside of the seed can be destroyed by poison treatments. Corrosive sublimate, for example, can be used for damping-off fungi. In other cases, such as blackleg of cabbage, heat (hot-water treatment) will kill fungi within the seed. Great care must be used, however, not to injure the germinating seed.

Viability of Seed

Seed must have enough vitality to complete the process of germination. The little plant must be able to break the soil and bring its leaves above ground, so that it may grow independently of its stored food. Growth prior to that stage may be described merely as sprouting.

A correct stand of plants in the field is very important. It costs nearly as much to cultivate half a stand as a full stand, and over-seeding results either in costly thinning or harmful crowding. So the planter should know what his seed will do under his own conditions of soil, temperature, and moisture. Many varieties of seed, a year or more old, are usable, but one must know their viability to use them safely.

Most good seedsmen test their seeds and sell only seed of high viability (Fig. 5.1). Minimum germination requirements for most vegetables have been set by the Federal government. If germination is below

Fig. 5.1—Seed should not only germinate but also produce vigorous seedlings.

Associated Seed Growers, Inc.

these minimums for seed moving in interstate commerce, the package must be labeled "Below Standard" and the percentage of germination must be stated. Many states have similar laws applying to seed raised and sold within the state.

Probably the best test for casual use is to plant counted seeds in rows in a flat of the soil to be used or in a greenhouse bed, covering as usual. The temperature and moisture are kept constantly favorable, and the seedlings counted after they appear. From these data the percentage of germination can be calculated.

Another way is to count out the seeds, placing them between folds of blotters or cotton flannel in a dish with water enough to keep them moist but not enough to exclude air. The dish is kept at a temperature of about 70° F. and sprouts are counted. Weak or slow sprouts should not be counted, as they may not be able to get through the soil under field conditions. The "rag-doll" test is good for coarse seeds such as peas, beans, and sweet corn. Seeds are counted out on long strips of cotton flannel or other cloth and properly marked. The cloth is then rolled up, moistened, and kept at about 65° to 70° F. The sprouted seeds are later counted and the percentage calculated.

The viability of seed may be determined by a cold test. The seeds are usually planted in flats of unsterilized soil and held at a temperature of about 45° F. for one week. They are then germinated at normal temperatures. Weak and injured seeds become infected with micro-organisms and fail to germinate. This test simulates field conditions early in the season, but is difficult to standardize.

Seed testing has become a highly technical enterprise and good laboratories do not always agree perfectly. Nevertheless, both professional and home testing are of great value. Tests must be made carefully and, in case of doubt, they should be rechecked, checked with seedsmen, or with the state seed laboratories.

Different kinds of seed require different conditions of temperature, aeration, and even light. For example, spinach will not germinate well in very warm weather, even though there is moisture in the soil. Also, some seeds, such as lettuce, undergo a period of dormancy just after harvest when viability is very low. Light is effective in breaking this dormancy.

Longevity of Seed

A sample of celery seed 15 years old gave a 50 percent stand in a trial some years ago, and other kinds occasionally perform similarly. Onions, sweet corn, and parsnips, on the other hand, are known to be unreliable the second season and should be used only after satisfactory tests. When it is desirable to use old seed, a careful test should be made and the rate of sowing increased as necessary.

Changes in temperature alone seem to have little influence on the vitality of seed. If seed is dry, freezing is harmless, as is heating to any ordinary atmospheric temperature. Let the climate be humid or the seed moist and the seed is soon worthless. Onion seed stored eight months in Michigan lost nothing in vitality, while a similar lot in Alabama declined to zero. Tomatoes, watermelons, and radishes suffered less. Seeds generally keep well in cool northern climates and in the dry climate of the Southwest, but in the humid South and Southeast seeds lose their viability very rapidly. Conditions favoring longevity of seeds are low temperature, low humidity, and low seed moisture content.

Table 5.1 gives a general idea of the length of time seeds may be expected to retain their vitality under normal conditions. Information on the different kinds of seed appears in the special crop chapters.

Table 5.1—Length of Time Seeds May Be Expected to Retain Their Vitality.*

Kind of Vegetable	Years	Kind of Vegetable	Years
Asparagus	3	Onion	1
Beans	3	Parsley	2
Beet	4	Parsnip	1
Brussels sprouts	4	Peas	3
Cabbage	4	Pepper	3
Carrot	3	Pumpkin	4
Cauliflower	4	Radish	4
Celery	5	Rutabaga	4
Cucumber	5	Spinach	4
Eggplant	5	Squash	4
Endive	5	Sweet corn	1
Kale	4	Tomato	3
Lettuce	5	Turnip	4
Muskmelon	5	Watermelon	5
Okra	2		

*When stored under favorable conditions, seed of the age indicated (from harvest not from time of purchase) should be viable. Seed is often good much longer, but specific lots may not survive so long.

Size of Seed

If one sifts the seed and plants the larger ones, will he harvest a better crop? Much study has been focused on this problem with considerable confusion of results, but it seems to resolve itself into the following: larger seeds give a slightly earlier and more uniform maturity.

Medium-sized seeds will also mature evenly. Sizing the seed makes it possible to sow more accurately with seeders or drills and get more uniform stands. These advantages make it profitable in some cases to separate into three sizes, planting the two larger sizes separately, but discarding the small seeds, many of which are weak or improperly matured.

Trueness to a Good Name

After all, the important point about seed is what kind of plant and product it will bring forth, and how it will perform. So far as the seed is concerned, this is mainly a matter of heredity. The seed must truly represent a good variety and a strain suitable for the conditions and markets contemplated. These matters are not so easily measured as count per ounce or percentage of viability, but they are just as important.

CLASSIFICATION OF VEGETABLES

To buy seed satisfactorily, one needs to understand the classification of the various forms of vegetable plants. The different vegetables are classified botanically in Chapter 2.

A horticultural classification of the vegetables includes the following gradations: (1) the kind, (2) the variety, (3) the strain, and (4) the stock.

Kind

A kind includes all the plants which, in general usage, are accepted as a single vegetable, as, for example, tomato, cabbage, bean. This is not the same as the genus or the species of botanical classification. The species *Brassica oleracea* includes several kinds (cabbage, cauliflower, and others). The beans come from more than one species (*Phaseolus vulgaris*, *P. lunatus*, etc.).

Variety

A variety includes those plants of a given kind which are practically alike in important characteristics. Each variety should be distinct from all others in one or more prominent and significant features. Named varieties that are not distinct should be classified as strains of a recognized variety or as mere synonyms.

The line between varieties is not always sharply drawn and is at present a matter of informal consensus, which results in great confusion. The only prospect for making varieties definite lies in the establishment of some generally accepted authority, such as the U.S. Department of Agriculture or a national board of vegetable nomenclature. Well-conducted studies of variety characters have much weight in establishing types and should be conducted on a continuing basis from year to year at representative locations throughout the country.

Strain

A strain includes those plants of a given variety which possess its general characteristics but which differ from others of the variety in one important respect, or two or three minor respects, the differences not being great enough to justify a new variety name. Thus Cherokee is a standard variety of bean and Resistant Cherokee is a mosaic-resistant strain of this variety. Golden Self-Blanching is a standard celery, while Tall Golden Self-Blanching is a strain that is more vigorous, earlier, and more spreading, and has broader and thinner leafstalks. The distinction between variety and strain is based simply on degrees of difference.

Stock

A stock represents all plants of the same parentage or pedigree. Differences between various stocks of a variety or strain should be very slight. A seed grower may maintain more than one stock of a strain, each representing a single pedigree line. Two seed growers may have stocks so nearly alike as to be indistinguishable, but as long as they are separately maintained, they are distinct stocks.

The distinctions of the definitions of strain and stock are not hard and fast; in fact, the seed trade is anything but consistent in its use of terms. The idea of a stock as distinct from a strain is based on the concept of parentage or pedigree lines. While some seed houses practically ignore the pedigree idea, many keep careful records and are able to trace parentage through several generations. At the same time, stocks of presumably nearly equal excellence are often used interchangeably.

As the buying public becomes more discriminating and willing to pay for greater care in seed production, the pedigree idea is finding fuller application in trade practice.

VEGETABLE TRIALS

The term "trial" usually refers to growing, observing, and recording the characteristics of plant and product of a given sample of seed, while the term "testing" is usually used in connection with purity and germination. Trials are the means of knowing the character of the stocks which are planted. They may be very simple, mere observations of a planted sample in comparison with another, or only in comparison with a memory-picture or an idea of what is wanted. Trials may be elaborate and exhaustive involving great care in procuring samples, in repeating the plantings, in seeing that growing conditions are uniform, and in making careful observations dealing with these many characters. Such elaborate trials are carried on by the U.S. Department of Agriculture, the state experiment stations, and by many progressive breeders and seedsmen. Results appear in public bulletins, in catalogues, and in a variety of manuals for seedsmen.

The grower may well depend on other observers for the main points about a new offering, but he must himself make the final selection for his own situation. This means simple but careful trials and comparisons on a small scale before large plantings are made. Novelties are often alluring and every advance comes first as a novelty. While one is not wise to ignore the new things, neither should he make sudden shifts from the old to the new.

Anyone interested in the careful trial of samples of vegetable seeds may make his own list of points to be observed. He may find schedules of points in many variety bulletins, and he may write for suggestions to experienced workers, who are usually glad to help. The tabular system of recording observations enters characters across the top of the sheet and names or numbers of samples at the side, or vice versa. Thus, one character may be studied at a time in all samples, and notations may be made in harmony with one another. Otherwise, if all characters of small, early sorts are described first and the characters of large, late sorts are taken up later, a "drift" of one's impressions is bound to occur. Measurements by the tabular system are accurate, easily read, easily compared, and easily handled statistically. Brevity and ease of reading are served by using numerical ratings instead of words, one representing a very low degree of a character, five medium, and nine high. Intermediate steps may be used as needed. Mechanical methods should not, however, crowd out the general estimate of merit and informal comparisons that may be less scientific but none the less enlightening.

The grower may learn much from his own short trial rows, but the final verdict will depend upon field performance. Matters of evenness of maturity, small differences in earliness (often important in marketing), yield, ease of harvesting and handling, holding up in marketing, and table quality may be revealed only in very elaborate, formal trials, with many replications and carefully measured observations. After all, a crop or perhaps several crops must be grown to tell the whole story.

THE SEED BUSINESS

Most planters buy their seed in preference to saving it or growing it themselves. The seed trade has become a specialized and highly technical business, having many different branches and offering services of many degrees of merit. In general, breeding and service about keep up to what planters demand and are willing to pay for. Seed houses have constantly advanced in breeding, production, and service. There are enough good houses that one need not take undue risk in buying from unreliable sources. This is especially important, as the merit or demerit of a sample of seed is not evident on inspection. Like insurance or banking, the seed business represents a trust relationship and is dependent upon the character of men, their ideals, integrity, and practices. Even good seed from an unreliable house is of only temporary value, for the buyer does not know that he can get the same value again.

Seed houses may engage in any or all of the following services: (1) breeding, (2) growing, (3) wholesale dealing, (4) importing, and (5) distributing (serving commercial or home planters or both). They may handle but one kind of seed or they may handle all kinds and other merchandise besides. There is some confusion in use of the term "wholesale," as it may be applied to transactions between seed growers and merchants, or between seed growers and planters who grow vegetables to sell.

Improving and Maintaining Stocks

New varieties and strains arise by discovery of a plant of distinct type among others, by mass selection for better type, or by crossing and selection. For a general understanding of breeding vegetable plants, refer to Chapter 4. In recent years, an increasing number of improvements have come through definite efforts toward a preconceived type, crossing and selecting until the desired result is attained, and fixing the type through pure-line breeding. Many experiment stations and seed houses employ highly trained scientists for this work (Fig. 5.2).

Intensive breeding work yields stock seed in small quantities. A good house treasures its stock seed, reproducing it with great care under selection (choosing the best plants) and roguing (discarding off-type plants)

Fig. 5.2—Isolation cages used in a commercial plant breeding operation by the Crookham company, Caldwell, Idaho.

USDA Photograph

from year to year. Good market seed is faithfully rogued, but if stock seed has been well bred, only a few plants need to be discarded. From this stock seed, market seed is grown in especially suitable regions. Cheap seed may represent simple crop growing with little attention to keeping the stock true, to say nothing of improving it.

Seed producers must not only improve their stocks, but also be thoroughly acquainted with the merit of these stocks. Dealers also should know the qualities of the stocks they handle. To this end, special trial grounds are often maintained. Some houses depend upon observation in the fields of their customers. A combination of both methods is best, each making its own contributions.

Some seedsmen buy certain kinds of seed a year in advance and carefully test a sample from the actual lot before selling for planting. Such seed is properly called proved or proven seed, and the term should not be applied to seed that has merely been tested for germination or to seed supposed to be of the same stock as a tested sample.

Non-warranty Clause

The non-warranty clause as adopted by the American Seed Trade Association, is as follows: "We give no warranty, expressed or implied, as to description, purity, productiveness, or any other matter of any seeds or bulbs we send out, and we will not be in any way responsible for the crop. If the purchaser does not accept the goods on these terms, they are at once to be returned."

Most seedsmen use this clause, or words to the same effect. While this seems harsh toward the buyer, a moment's thought reveals the fact that a crop failure may be due to many causes other than poor seed, and that it is usually impossible to tell what cause is responsible. If the seedsman were to assume all these risks in addition to the risks of error on his own part or on the part of those upon whom he depends, the cost would be excessive. Furthermore, the clause protects the seedsman against imposition. At the same time, the seedsman should not take advantage of the clause to dodge responsibility that is rightfully his. Good seed houses are careful, and when they are at fault often make substantial adjustments. There are plenty of such houses, where the buyer can obtain good seed and good service on the usual non-warranty terms.

Where Seed Comes From

Vegetable seed may be bred in many climates. Market crops produced by multiplying well-bred stock seeds are grown where soil, climate, and economic conditions are favorable. Pea- and bean-seed production moved from East to West largely because of disease and poor conditions for curing in the East. A large part of the muskmelon and cucumber seed comes from Colorado and California, while production of hybrid sweet-corn seed is centered in Idaho. Before World War II a large amount of seed was imported from such countries as Denmark and the Netherlands. During the war this supply was cut off and seed was produced in the United States and Canada. Since the war, increasing amounts of seed have been received from Europe, but domestic production for many kinds is much greater than it was before the war. Seed growers in the United States and Canada have learned to do a good job of producing seed. The skill and care of the seedsmen are far more important for quality of seed than is the place of production. Much of the hybrid seed of vegetables requiring hand pollination is produced in Japan where cost of labor is low. The use of male-sterile plants eliminates expensive hand pollination (Fig. 5.3).

BUYING SEED

Judicious buying of seed calls for utmost care, and emphasis should be placed on the ultimate value of the crop rather than on the initial cost

Fig. 5.3—Roguing male-sterile seed rows in hybrid onion seed production.

of the seed. In general, one should buy from seedsmen of established reputation who cater to commercial planters; that is, from houses accustomed to serving critical trade. One may well inquire among neighbors and at meetings to learn what houses hold reputations for quality of seed, dependability, and good service. Then one's own experience becomes a valuable guide.

Catalogues

The seed catalogue is a fascinating book, and none would care for a drab and colorless offering of goods. A good merchant is enthusiastic after he has expended cash and care to get the best. We need, however, to learn which houses are given to extravagant claims and which keep praise and merit fairly abreast. One may readily distinguish between statements of opinion, "The best we have ever seen," and statements of fact, "A week earlier than Rutgers." Catalogues of the more dependable houses are nowadays giving a larger measure of actual facts, telling what a variety is like. Pictures are less extravagant and more informing, though it is the cataloguers' business to show fine specimens of true type. Unfortunately, there are too many catalogues that are less than candid in their statements.

Known Origin

The planter has as much right to assurance about his seed as to know the name of the car he buys. Many seedsmen are not yet ready to tell where they get their seed, but, even in these cases, the buyer should insist on definite stock numbers and assurance that will enable him to buy seed of the same parentage next year or be told it is not available. In the meantime, wholesale producers and breeders are advertising more widely, retailers are realizing it is well to feature the name of a good seed grower, and the idea of known origin is gradually spreading. Some houses now stamp stock numbers on all packages and most good houses keep records of stock numbers of lots delivered.

The planter may profitably learn who are breeders and producers of good seed and ask for their products. If the salesman mentions some other source, find out if it ranks with the best. Thus knowledge of buying is built up.

Buying in Advance

Many growers buy seed a year ahead and plant a sample for careful trial. Even though the lot proves bad and is discarded, the loss is but a fraction of the value of a crop. This practice is feasible only with suitable climate and storage facilities and only for certain kinds of seed. Onions, parsnips, and sweet corn are likely to decline in germination too rapidly for this plan, and the cost of bean and pea seeds is too great. Growers of celery and cabbage follow the scheme with great satisfaction. As better knowledge of seed storage is developed, the practice may be more widely adopted in areas where it is normally difficult to store seed.

Cost of Good Seed

As already pointed out, the cost of seed for an acre of most crops is but a small fraction of expected returns. Cheap seed, if poor, may cost many dollars per acre. At the same time, a high price does not necessarily mean good seed and often very good seed is to be had at moderate, though seldom at very low, prices. Buying on bids alone and seeking the cheapest are to be utterly condemned, unless the bidder meets definite specifications regarding purity, vitality, and trueness to the desired type.

GROWING SEED

Growing seed to sell is an alluring business and offers satisfying rewards to the man who likes it and can give it the exacting care it requires.

The man who grows his own seed is assured of its origin and parentage. He can select his own ideal, to suit his own lands and markets, and he comes to understand and enjoy his crop and to profit in its management as few are able to do. His sacrifices are serious. He must establish his ideal and not waver in selection, and must be the soul of patience. Much work must be done at the right time, whether it is convenient or not, and the rush of selection or curing may coincide with the rush of marketing. Careful study of the crop in hand and of breeding in general is required.

Success, however, may bring others to the door to buy, and some very satisfactory seed businesses have been started in this way.

Casual seed saving as a matter of cutting production cost is likely to be disappointing.

SELECTED REFERENCES

Anonymous, "The Preservation of Viability and Vigor in Vegetable Seeds," Associated Seed Growers, Inc., Asgrow Monograph No. 2, 1954.

Anonymous, Seeds, The Yearbook of Agriculture, USDA, 1961.

Hawthorne, L. R. and Pollard, L. H., Vegetable and Flower Seed Production, New York: The Blackiston Company, 1954.

Huelsen, W. A. and Brown, W. M., "Physical Damage to Sweet Corn Seed," Ill. Agr. Exp. Sta. Bull. 561, 1962.

Schudel, H. L., "Vegetable Seed Production in Oregon," Ore. Agr. Exp. Sta. Bull. 512, 1952.

Toole, E. H., et al., "Physiology of Seed Germination," Ann. Rev. Plant Physiology 7: 299–324, 1956.

Toole, E. H., "Storage of Vegetable Seed," USDA Leaflet 220, 1958.

Toole, E. H., Toole, V. K., and Gorman, E. A., "Vegetable-Seed Storage as Affected by Temperature and Relative Humidity," USDA Tech. Bull. 972, 1948.

CHAPTER 6

Managing Soils and Fertilizing

Vegetables are generally grown most successfully on soils with a continuous supply of nutrients and moisture. These conditions are necessary for tender, succulent growth, which is often a requisite for quality. Many of the vegetable crops have limited root systems and mature in a short season. Others must grow rapidly before the time of fruit set or before the time of unfavorable weather in order to make good yields. Any of these crops require a high level of fertility.

CHOOSING SOILS FOR VEGETABLES

Physical Requirements

When earliness is of more importance than total yield, sandy soils and sandy loams are best. These soils are well aerated, drying out and warming up rapidly in the spring. They are often low in nutrients and moisture retention, but moisture is usually excessive in the spring anyway.

When large yields are more important than earliness and moisture is likely to become limited, silt loams, clay loams, and muck soils are best. They usually contain considerable reserve food material and retain moisture well. By proper soil management, the food reserves may be made available. If not worked while wet, these soils are fairly loose and friable, qualities necessary for vegetable crops. Clays and heavy soils are not usually well adapted to vegetable crops, because of poor aeration and consequent poor nutrient liberation and root growth. They may, however, be used advantageously for late crops started during warm, dry weather.

Chemical Requirements

Soils must contain large amounts of the bulk nutrients, nitrogen and phosphorus, in readily available form and in the right proportion for the various types of vegetables. Each vegetable requires nutrients in certain ratios for best results, as will be discussed later. Moderate amounts of the nutrients which are largely catalytic and corrective, including potassium, magnesium, calcium, sulfur, and iron, must be present in available form. Traces of several other elements are essential, but as a rule, are present in sufficient amounts in normal soils.

The reaction of the soil should be such that favorable amounts of nutrients are kept available to the plant, and at the same time, the reaction should not cause toxic amounts of any element to be brought into solution.

CONSERVING SOIL AND MOISTURE

Soils with only a slight grade are desired for growing vegetables. When soils of moderate to steep grades are used, measures should be adopted to conserve soil and moisture. These include terracing, contour cultivation, and strip cropping.

Flat land may have no erosion problem, but it does have drainage and leaching problems. If the subsoil is loose and permits ready drainage, no provision for drainage need be made, but, if the subsoil is tight and water tends to stand on the land, a drainage system pays big dividends. Tile properly installed is best because it permits free use of the land, although open ditch drainage is better than none. Care must be taken to prevent overdrainage because excessive leaching and lack of moisture may result.

Leaching is greatest during periods when the land is not in use, especially in the winter, and during these periods some sort of cover crop may be used to absorb nutrients as they are liberated, and to hold them for use by the next crop.

PREPARING THE SOIL

Breaking

Land should be loosened 6 to 8 inches for vegetables. If the soil has never been plowed more than 6 inches, care should be taken to bring up only about an inch of subsoil at a time, especially if the subsoil is heavy.

Fall plowing has advantages in regions of winter freezing, but in the South its value is questionable, because of leaching and erosion of sloping soils, which do not freeze much in the winter. However, if level, heavy soils are plowed deeply, and especially if a covering of coarse organic matter is turned under, the losses from leaching and erosion are not so great, and probably will be more than offset by the following advantages: (1) improved physical conditions, resulting from alternate wetting and drying and light freezing; (2) reduction in insects, because of exposure to the weather; (3) rotting of organic materials in contact with the soil, thereby increasing the humus and liberating nutrients; and (4) relieving the pressure of spring work by making it possible to work the soil earlier in the spring.

Spring plowing should not be done too far in advance of planting unless heavy cover crops are turned under. Special care must be used to avoid working the soil when it is too wet. If the soil crumbles readily after being pressed in the hand, it is dry enough to plow; but if it retains its form, the land is too wet for breaking. Cultipackers and rollers also break up clods and smooth the surface for planting.

Finishing

Plowed land must be disked well, usually in both directions, before planting, as it is very essential to have a fine seedbed for most vegetables. A plank drag and Meeker harrow are commonly used to follow the diskings.

CHOOSING THE SOIL REACTION

Adjusting Soil Reaction

The proper soil reaction depends more on the nature of the soil than it does on the peculiar reaction requirements of the crop to be grown. If the proper amounts and ratios of nutrients for the crop are maintained and no compounds are allowed to be present in toxic concentrations, it makes little difference to the crop what the reaction is as long as it is in the growth range of pH 5 to pH 8 (Table 6.1). The reaction, however, greatly varies the nutrient balance and toxic conditions in each soil type, and it is very difficult to maintain the balance in an alkaline soil.

When the average of many soil types is taken, vegetable crops seem to fall into certain classes as to the pH preference, because of certain nutrient preferences and toxic tolerances. The vegetable crops vary in their

Table 6.1—pH and Corresponding Soil Reaction.*

pH	Soil Reaction	pH	Soil Reaction
4.5	Very acid	7.0	Neutral
5.0	Acid	7.25	Slightly alkaline**
5.5	Medium acid	7.5	Medium alkaline
6.0	Slightly acid	7.75	Strongly alkaline
6.5	Very slightly acid	8.0	Very strongly alkaline

*pH represents the degree of active acidity and alkalinity (not total acidity and alkalinity) in a soil. The scale used to indicate the degree sets the value 7.07 as the neutral point, or the pH of pure water (the active acidity or alkalinity of water). With this as the starting point, the value for alkalinity is anything greater—up to 14.14. The reason for this scale and these limits requires an understanding of logarithms, normal solutions, and ionization.

**Graduation is less on the alkaline side than on the acid side as there are 2.5 units on the acid side and only one unit on the alkaline side, which are within the limits of plant growth.

responses to soil reaction (pH), some growing best on acid soils while others require soils of neutral reaction. The vegetable crops are grouped according to pH requirements (Fig. 6.1). As may be seen, all thrive at a pH range of 6.0 to 6.5. Sometimes potatoes may be grown in soil with a pH of about 5.0 to avoid serious damage from scab. Also, cabbage may be grown in a slightly alkaline soil to reduce damage from club root.

CONTROLLING SOIL REACTION

Determining the Need for Lime

Use should be made of soil reaction kits which indicate the approximate pH of soils. Too much confidence, however, should not be placed in the various lime-requirement tests, as they are usually adapted to legume crop rotations in general farming, and may not be indicative of vegetable crop needs.

If reaction tests indicate rather strong acidity, it is advisable to apply several rates of lime on a few small sections of land before liming the entire farm, as liming is not universally beneficial to vegetables, even on acid soils. If lime is found to pay on the particular crops which are to be grown on these sections, it may be used more freely.

Applying Lime

If lime is needed for quick action, a finely ground agricultural limestone is recommended. Lime should be mixed well in the top 3 to 4 inches of soil. A commercial lime spreader is best for making application, although a shovel may be used for small areas. A grain drill can be used, when light applications are to be made.   .

The rate of application depends on the type of soil, degree of reaction present, reaction desired, and the form of lime. Less lime is needed to cause change at high acidity than at low acidity.

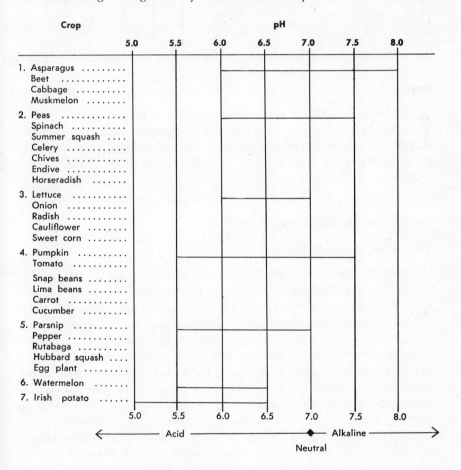

Fig. 6.1—Optimum pH range for vegetable crops.

Table 6.2—Agricultural Ground Limestone Requirement.

pH Test	Tons per Acre			
	Sandy Soils	Silt Loam Soils	Clay Loam Soils	Muck Soils
6.5 and above	0	0	0	0
6.2-6.4	1	2	2	0
5.8-6.1	2	3	3	0
5.4-5.7	3	4	5	0
4.8-5.3	4	6	7	2
4.2-4.7	5	8	–	3

Sources

Dolomitic limestone contains magnesium as well as calcium, and it is usually best to use limestone that has some magnesium; but too much magnesium is much more likely to cause harmful effects than too much calcium. Marls are a good source of limestone in areas where they are available.

MAINTAINING ORGANIC MATTER

Values of Organic Matter

Organic matter increases the porosity of heavy soils, which, in turn, increases water absorption and lessens water run-off, leaching, and erosion. The increased porosity also causes greater aeration, which favors the right kind of bacteria for nutrient liberation and direct chemical oxidation processes. On the other hand, organic matter will help to keep sandy soils from becoming too porous. The black color imparted by organic matter causes heat absorption, aiding the soil to warm up quickly, provided that the amount of water present is not excessive. The use of fresh organic matter too close to planting time of vegetables may cause (1) burning from rapid decomposition; (2) formation of excessively aerated layers and pockets, which interfere in water movement; (3) locking of available nitrogen by decomposition bacteria; (4) mechanical interference to plowing and cultivation; and (5) formation of toxic organic compounds, under certain anaerobic and non-colloidal conditions. If air and moisture are favorable and sufficient time is allowed, these difficulties will be overcome. Addition of lime, if needed, and nitrate will aid in cases of nitrogen deficiency.

Maintaining Organic Matter by Animal Manures

If animal manure can be secured cheaply, it is the best material for maintaining the organic content of the soil as well as a good source of nitrogen. When used, however, it is necessary to watch and maintain the phosphorous supply, since animal manure is usually low in phosphorus. Although fresh and strawy manures may cause damage if used too near planting time, they have the following advantage over rotted manure if applied far enough in advance of the crop: (1) less nutrients are lost through decomposition and leaching; (2) more bacteria are added to the soil; (3) more energy is provided for bacteria, resulting in a much greater liberation of nutrients through solvent action; and (4) buffer effects are greater. Decomposed manure which has been well cared for, however, is very valuable because it (1) can be applied just ahead of the crop; (2) is higher in percentage of total nutrients, if excessive leaching has been stopped; (3) is much higher in readily available nutrients; (4) has no burning effects; (5) produces more uniform action throughout the soil mass; (6) usually contains more phosphorus in relation to the nitrogen, thus furnishing a more balanced nutrient supply; (7) destroys or reduces weed seed germination; and (8) offers less mechanical interference. Usually, it is advantageous to use fresh manure in the fall and well-rotted manure in the spring.

In many cases, natural manures are rather expensive and difficult to secure, especially for a market gardener who keeps no livestock. However, with tractors replacing animals on the farm, more crop residues are available for maintaining soil organic matter.

The rate of manurial application varies greatly with the land, the crop, the cost of manure, and the kind of manure. Often 30 to 40 tons, especially of the strawy type of cow manure, are not excessive. Many experiment stations have shown that light applications supplemented by commercial fertilizers, especially phosphate, are more economical than manure alone. Chicken manure should be put on very lightly, and far enough from the plants to avoid burning. Broadcasting of manure is best, except in the case of widely spaced hills of cucurbits or melons.

Maintaining Organic Matter by Green Manures

For the vegetable gardener with plenty of relatively cheap land, one of the cheapest and most efficient ways to secure nitrogen and organic matter is through the use of legumes. However, for a gardener located on a limited area of expensive land, the use of legumes may not be advisable, and he would likely profit by the use of manure, winter cover crops, and commercial fertilizers.

Green vegetation incorporated into the soil rots much more quickly than dry material. When vegetation is allowed to dry out before it is turned under, the nutrients are transformed to less available forms. Long exposure to oxidation in the weather may result in a loss of nitrogen.

Besides increasing the organic content and adding air nitrogen to the soil, legumes (1) conserve soluble nutrients, (2) improve the subsoil by penetrating it and incorporating organic materials into it, (3) make mineral nutrients available, (4) transfer them to the topsoil, (5) favor bacterial growth, and (6) reduce erosion.

The first consideration in choosing a legume is its adaptation to soil and climate. After this, the amount of readily incorporated vegetation produced in the time available should determine the choice.

If the legume is to be grown on land that does not contain inoculating organisms, the seed must be inoculated. This may be done naturally, using soil known to contain the organism, or artificially, with material purchased from a seed firm or other source.

Nonlegumes have all the values of legumes with the exception that they do not actually add atmospheric nitrogen to the soil. The grasses are used as cover crops because they are easily started and form a nonerosive surface which quickly prevents leaching. Rye is almost universally used as a winter cover by general farmers, but there is some question as to its value for the southern vegetable gardener, because it is difficult to kill and hinders early gardening. In many cases in the southern states, vegetables are grown in the late fall and early spring, and cool-season crops are grown during January and February so that rye would be of little value. Oats make a good cover if sown in the fall, but this crop is subject to winter injury.

Various methods are employed in planting cover crops. A seed drill has the advantage of planting at uniform depth and rate, and saves unnecessary operations. The hand-broadcast method is uncertain and requires more seed for satisfactory coverage.

USING COMMERCIAL FERTILIZERS

Importance of Commercial Fertilizers

Commercial fertilizers are added to a soil with the particular purpose of directly increasing the amounts of nutrients available to plants. They are not added to improve physical conditions nor to make soil reserves available. Manures and lime do more than simply add nutrients and, for this reason, often produce better results than commercial fertilizers alone. However, stable manure, organic matter, or lime cannot be depended on to produce enough available nutrients in many soils with low reserves; and even in fertile soils, organic materials and lime may cause improper nutrient ratios. No soil, no matter how fertile, can provide adequate soil

Fig. 6.2—Celery grown on sandy soil in Florida. Plants on the left received well balanced fertilizer, while those on the right were unfertilized.

fertility for all types of vegetables. Commercial fertilizers are necessary to furnish limiting elements in the most economical manner and to maintain proper ratios of the nutrients for the particular crop being grown (Fig. 6.2).

Chemical Elements Essential to Growth

Of the several essential elements, nitrogen, phosphorus, and potassium are the ones most generally lacking. The different elements are discussed here, and the composition of fertilizers is given in Table 6.3.

Table 6.3—The Composition of Fertilizers.

Fertilizer	Nitrogen (N) Percent	Phosphorus (P) Percent	Potassium (K) Percent
Organic Fertilizers			
Bat guano	10.0	1.8	1.7
Blood	13.0	0.9	0.8
Blood and bone	6.5	3.1	. . .
Bone black	1.3	6.6	. . .
Bone meal, raw	3.0	6.6	. . .
Steamed	2.0	6.6	. . .
Castor bean meal	5.5	0.9	0.8
Cottonseed meal	6.0	1.3	0.8
Fish meal	10.0	1.8	. . .
Garbage tankage	1.5	0.9	0.6
Horn and hoof meal	12.0	0.9	. . .
Sewerage sludge	1.5	0.6	0.3
Activated	6.0	1.3	0.1
Tankage	9.0	2.6	. . .
Inorganic Fertilizers			
Ammoniated superphosphate	3.0	7.0	. . .
Ammonium nitrate	33.0 to 33.5	. . .	. . .
Ammonium nitrate—lime (A-N-L, Cal-Nitro)	20.5	. . .	. . .
Ammonium phosphate	11.0	21.0	. . .
Ammonium phosphate— sulfate	16.0	8.8	. . .
Ammonium sulfate	20.5	. . .	. . .
Anhydrous ammonia	82.0	. . .	. . .
Aqua ammonium phosphate	8.0	10.3	. . .
Aqueous ammonia	20.0	. . .	. . .
Calcium cyanamide	21.0	. . .	. . .
Calcium nitrate	15.5	. . .	. . .
Calurea	34.0	. . .	. . .
Diammonium phosphate	21.0	23.3	. . .
Nitrate of potash	13.0	. . .	36.5
Nitrate of soda	16.0	. . .	. . .
Nitrate of soda—potash	15.0	. . .	11.6
Nitrogen solutions	18.0 to 41.0	. . .	. . .
Urea	42.0 to 46.0	. . .	. . .
Ureaform	35.0 to 38.0	. . .	. . .
Basic phosphate slag	. . .	4.4	. . .
Calcium metaphosphate	. . .	27.7	. . .
Phosphoric acid solution	. . .	22.3	. . .
Potassium metaphosphate	. . .	24.2	31.5
Rock phosphate*	. . .	14.51	. . .
Superphosphate	. . .	7.0 to 8.8	. . .
Treble (double) superphosphate	. . .	18.5 to 20.7	. . .
Kainit	. . .	. . .	10.0 to 13.3
Manure salts	. . .	. . .	16.6 to 24.9
Muriate of potash	. . .	. . .	39.8 to 51.5
Potassium ammonium nitrate	16.0	. . .	27.0
Sulfate of potash	. . .	. . .	39.8 to 43.2
Sulfate of potash— magnesia	. . .	. . .	17.4 to 18.3

*Total phosphorus, not the available.

NITROGEN. Nitrogen builds up the vegetative portions of the plant, producing large green leaves, and is also necessary for filling out fruits. If it is present in large amounts in relation to other elements, it will cause excessive vegetative growth and succulence.

Nitrogen fertilizers that leave an acid residue are ammonium sulfate, ammonium nitrate, and ammonium phosphate. Nitrogen fertilizers that leave an alkaline residue are sodium nitrate, calcium nitrate, potassium nitrate, and cyanamide.

Cottonseed meal, linseed meal, castor-oil meal, blood, tankage, fish tankage, guano, and urea are all organic and are neutral in their effect on soil reaction. The high cost of organic carriers of nitrogen and their slow availability (except urea) would make them impractical, in most circumstances.

Nitrogen fertilizers should be used cautiously since there is danger of burning the seeds or plants. The acid fertilizers should be used on nearly neutral to alkaline soils; the alkaline fertilizers, on nearly neutral to acid soils. The neutral organic fertilizers can be used on either acid or alkaline soils, but only when slow availability is desired. Nitrates are immediately available and the ammonia salts are fairly rapidly available.

PHOSPHORUS. Phosphorus is necessary for cellular metabolism and is especially essential in fruit and seed production. The plant will be stunted and the fruit will fail to set if phosphate is inadequate, especially if nitrogen is high. Phosphate also stimulates root production and seed development.

Natural phosphate rocks and animal bones are the chief source of phosphorus fertilizers. Both have to be treated with acid (usually sulfuric) to make the phosphorus available. Superphosphate fertilizers have been standardized to contain 8.8 percent phosphorus. Phosphatic fertilizers with higher analyses (20.7 percent treble superphosphate) are now in general use.

Phosphorus is known as an immobile element. Soon after application it becomes adsorbed on the clay particles and does not remain in solution. The roots of the plant must come in contact with these particles to get phosphorus and for this reason a crop can absorb only a small amount of the phosphorus available in the soil. In contrast with nitrogen, phosphorus must be present in the soil in large amounts. Phosphorus is often applied in bands at the time of planting to provide a high concentration near the roots of the young plants.

POTASSIUM. Potassium is important in the formation and translocation of carbohydrates and, hence, is important to root and tuber crops and in the formation of large rigid stems as in celery and rhubarb. It is also important in disease resistance, protein formation, and cell division. It does not, however, form part of the cell tissue and is not a bulk nutrient as are nitrogen and phosphorus.

Muriate and sulfate of potash, and wood ashes are the main sources of potassium. Some mineral soils contain enough potassium for all crops except those mentioned above, although most muck and sandy soils are deficient. Excess does little harm unless it becomes concentrated enough to cause exosmosis, but the cost of the excess results in financial loss to the grower.

CALCIUM. The main function of calcium seems to be corrective in nature. It combines with toxic acids developed in the life processes of the plant, and helps overcome the effects of too large amounts of other elements, such as magnesium. Calcium seems to be necessary in the normal absorption of all nutrients. It is rarely limiting for plant use, but it is needed in soil reaction control. Rather large amounts do no direct injury to the plant, but indirectly the hydroxide or carbonate in the soil may be injurious by making certain elements unavailable.

OTHER ELEMENTS. Space will not permit discussion of other elements and therefore a few of the more important ones with their main function are merely listed as follows: (1) magnesium, link in chlorophyll-molecule, fat, and oil formation; (2) sulfur, essential to certain proteins in crucifers and onions; (3) iron, catalytic agent in chlorophyll action; and (4) manganese, needed for oxidation and reduction reactions. Boron, copper, and zinc have also been found to be essential, although their exact functions are unknown.

DETERMINING FERTILIZER ANALYSIS, FORMULA, AND RATIO

Analysis

Commercial fertilizers should always bear a tag which gives the analysis, such as 3-8-6. The first figure means 3 percent nitrogen; the second, 8 percent available phosphorus; and the third, 6 percent water-soluble potassium.

This example is a low-analysis fertilizer, but there are now available high-analysis fertilizers, such as 6-16-12, which contain exactly twice the quantity of nutrients as 3-8-6. In buying fertilizer, attention should be paid to the price per fertilizer unit[1] instead of the price per ton. Thirty-three percent ammonium nitrate at $80 per ton makes each pound of nitrogen cost about 12 cents; 20.2 percent treble superphosphate at $82 per ton makes each pound of phosphorus cost 20 cents; and 41.5 percent muriate of potash at $50 per ton makes each pound of potassium cost six cents. This would mean that a 3-5-6 should cost $34.40 per ton. One could then afford to pay $68.80 per ton for a 6-10-12 fertilizer, or $103.20 for a 9-20-18. In fact, somewhat more than this could be paid because transportation and application costs are less per unit of nutrients in high-analysis fertilizers. The high-analysis fertilizers are a little more difficult to distribute evenly, and are more likely to burn on contact with seeds or plants; but, other than this, they are as good as the low-analysis fertilizers. Laws in some of the states require that at least 20 units of fertilizer be present; hence a 3-8-6 could no longer be sold in such a state, since it totals only 17 units. The use of highly concentrated chemicals may not be desirable because mineral impurities in low-analysis fertilizers may be of value in supplying minor elements, especially on sandy and muck soils.

Formula

The formula tells what kind of materials are used to make the units of available fertilizers. For example, a standard vegetable fertilizer may have an analysis of 5-10-5. This tells how much of each element is available, but does not give the source of the elements. The formula should be given, reading as follows: 2½ percent nitrogen as 20 percent ammonium sulfate; 2½ percent nitrogen as 15 percent sodium nitrate; 10 percent phosphorus as 20 percent treble superphosphate; and 5 percent potassium as 40 percent potassium chloride. A buyer of fertilizers should demand the formula and note the rate of availability of the nitrogen, and the effect the compounds may have on soil reaction. Such physical factors as freedom from caking and ease of drilling are also important.

---

[1] A fertilizer unit equals 1 pound of the actual element. For example, 100 pounds of 15 percent nitrate of soda contains 15 units of nitrogen (N), 100 pounds of 20 percent treble superphosphate contains 20 units of phosphorus (P), and 100 pounds of 41 percent muriate of potash contains 41 units of potassium (K).

Ratio

Fertilizer ratio differs from analysis in that it expresses the fertilizer in the ratio of one element to another, usually in terms of nitrogen. For instance, 5-10-5 is the analysis, but 1-2-1 is the ratio. Therefore, ratio does not tell how much of each element there is but, in this case, it simply says there is twice as much phosphorus as nitrogen and the same amount of potassium as nitrogen. The proportion which the elements bear to each other in a fertilizer is very important. A desirable ratio depends on the time of application, the soil nutrients available to the plant, and the particular demands of the crop being grown.

Table 6.4—Guide to the Nitrogen Fertilizer Requirements of Vegetable Crops.

Crop	Estimated Total Nitrogen Requirement	
	Dark-colored Soils Lbs. per A.	Light-colored Soils Lbs. per A.
Asparagus	80	100
Beans	30	45
Beet	50	65
Cabbage, late	60	75
Carrot	60	75
Cauliflower	65	80
Corn, late	40	55
Cucumber	20	45
Eggplant	30	45
Horseradish	45	60
Lettuce	45	60
Muskmelon	20	35
Onion	45	60
Parsnip	60	75
Peas	20	35
Pepper	30	45
Potato, late	60	75
Pumpkin and squash		
Summer squash	30	45
Winter pumpkin	60	75
Spinach	50	60
Sweet potato	30	40
Tomato	60	75
Turnip	50	50
Watermelon	20	35

DETERMINING FERTILIZER REQUIREMENTS

If other soil and climatic factors are favorable, it is desirable to fertilize vegetable crops so as to maintain a high level of production. Rapid

Table 6.5—Phosphorus (P) and Potassium (K) Recommended for the Vegetable Crops Grouped According to Requirements.*

Soil Test		Requirement per Group (in Pounds per Acre)			
		I	II	III	IV
P	Very low	132	105	62	26
	Low	105	62	26	9
	Medium	70	18	18	9
	High	35	9	18	9
	Very high	18	9	18	9
K	Very low	200	200	152	56
	Low	160	160	112	16
	Medium	112	112	96	16
	High	64	64	80	16
	Very high	64	16	80	16
Crops:		Tomato Potato Pepper Eggplant Cabbage Cauliflower Broccoli Cucumber Melon Squash Pumpkin	Asparagus Onion Sweet corn Spinach Lettuce Sweet potato	Carrot Parsnip Beet Radish Turnip Horseradish	Beans Peas

*Phosphorus and potassium are given as elements instead of oxides; 20 percent phosphorus (P) equals 45.5 percent phosphorus pentoxide (P_2O_5), and 40 percent potassium (K) equals 48 percent potassium oxide (K_2O).

soil tests may be used to determine requirements for phosphorus and potassium but due to the sudden changes in availability of nitrogen, frequent tests are necessary for this element. Plant tissue tests will reveal the nutrient needs of a plant, although a deficiency may be due to an impaired root system and not to the supply of nutrients in the soil. Information from tissue tests can be used for making applications of readily available nitrogen. Phosphorus and potassium should be applied in the soil before the root system of the plant is established and before tissue tests can be made.

A guide for nitrogen requirements is shown in Table 6.4. Previous cropping, the presence of decomposable residues, and leaching should be considered in determining the amounts of nitrogen to be applied.

The vegetable crops are divided into four groups according to their phosphorus and potassium requirements. These are shown in Table 6.5 along with amounts to apply for given soil tests. Some fertilizer is recommended even for soils giving very high tests, in order to maintain a high level of fertility. A home garden may be treated as if all crops were in Group I.

SELECTED REFERENCES

Courter, J. W., Vandemark, J. S., and Arnold, C. Y., "Fertilizing Greenhouse Vegetables," Ill. Agr. Ext. Cir. 922, 1966.

Davis, J. R. and Cook, R. L., "Fertilizing Through Irrigation Water," Mich. Agr. Ext. Bull. 324, 1954.

Graham, E. R., "Soil Testing," Mo. Agr. Exp. Sta. Bull. 734, 1959.

Karraker, P. E. and Kelley, J. B., "Use of Anhydrous Ammonia as a Nitrogen Fertilizer," Ky. Agr. Ext. Cir. 519, 1954.

Kellog, C. E., *Our Garden Soils*, New York: The Macmillan Company, 1952.

Minges, P. A., *et al.*, "Vegetable Production Recommendations for New York," N. Y. State Agr. Ext. Pub., 1964.

Sayre, C. B. and Vittum, M. T., "Effect of Different Sources of Fertilizer Nutrients and Different Rates of Fertilizer Applications on Yields of Vegetable Canning Crops," N. Y. Bull. 749, 1952.

CHAPTER 7

Growing Plants, Hardening, and Transplanting

Many vegetable-crop plants are commonly started in specially prepared beds and the young plants are later transplanted into the field or garden. Cabbage, cauliflower, Brussels sprouts, celery, tomatoes, eggplant, peppers, sweet potatoes, and others are generally started in special beds so that the grower can give them good care with a minimum of labor during the early stages of growth.

PLANT-GROWING STRUCTURES

There are many advantages in starting plants in greenhouses, hotbeds, or cold frames, including (1) lengthening of the growing season; (2) producing an earlier crop, thereby getting the advantage of early market; and (3) protecting the young plants against unfavorable weather conditions.

Greenhouses

Greenhouse construction and management are specialized subjects and are discussed here only from the standpoint of use by the market gardener and truck grower as an adjunct to outdoor gardening.

In the colder regions, greenhouses are superior to hotbeds or cold frames for starting plants. Some of the advantages of greenhouses over other forcing structures are (1) better temperature control, (2) better regulation of ventilation and less danger of chilling the plants, and (3) more convenient arrangement for work in caring for the plants.

When a greenhouse is to be used only for growing plants for transplanting, one cannot afford an expensive structure. For this reason there is demand for small, inexpensive houses. One of the new glazing films seems to be the answer to low-cost greenhouse construction, especially in the milder regions of the country. Such a greenhouse is shown in Figure 7.1.

Fig. 7.1—Inexpensive plant growing house covered with glazing film.

Photograph by E. C. Wittmeyer

Glazing films in use include polyethylene, polyvinyl chloride (PVC or vinyl), and polyester (Mylar). These are compared in Table 7.1. The cost of plastic-covered greenhouses in terms of square footage of ground covered may be roughly estimated by multiplying 2.4 or 2.0 times the film cost for a 1,000- or 4,000-square-foot house, respectively. Types of construction and comparative costs are discussed in University of Illinois Circular 857. More durable films are being developed, and these should become available for future use.

Many growers have built inexpensive frame structures and covered them with hotbed sash. Some of these are low with the eaves only a few inches above the ground level, while others have walls entirely above ground. In the low houses, the walks between the beds are excavated to the depth of 2 or 3 feet and the beds or benches are near the ground level. This type is more easily heated than the high type, but is less convenient.

Table 7.1—Light and Heat Transmission Characteristics of Some Plastic Films, Glass, and Water.

	Thick-ness	Trans-mission of Visible Light	Transparent to	
			Ultra-violet	Infrared
	mils	percent		
Polyethylene*	2	87	Yes	Yes
Polyvinyl chloride* ..	13	87	Slight	No
Polyvinyl chloride* ..	3	88	Yes	Slight
Polyester*	4	88	No	Slight
Fiberglass (clear)	125	80-90	Slight	Intermediate
Glass*	125	90	No	No
Water*	2	96	Yes	No

*Data taken from Trickett, E. S., and Goulden, J. D. S., "The Radiation Transmission and Heat Conserving Properties of Some Plastic Films," **Jour. Agr. Eng. Res.**, 3 (4): 281-287, 1958.

The low type of structure is not satisfactory on poorly drained soil.

The high type of sash house has walls extending 2 to 4 or more feet above the surface of the ground. The walls may be of concrete, hollow tile, or wood up to the eaves plate, or they may be part wood or concrete with glass above. The only advantage of a sash house is its low cost; therefore, where considerable labor and money are expended on walls, framework, and heating system, it would seem wise to build a standard greenhouse rather than a sash house.

Hotbeds

A hotbed is a specially prepared bed to which artificial heat is supplied by hot air, hot water, steam, or electricity.

The frame of the hotbed may be made of wood or other building materials. If it is made of wood, 2- by 4-inch lumber is used for posts at the corners and at intervals of 4 to 6 feet along the sides of the bed. Boards or planks are nailed to the posts on the inner side. When 16-inch boards are used, it is desirable to use a double layer. The frame usually extends to the bottom of the bed and it should extend 12 to 18 inches above the ground at the back and 6 to 12 inches at the front. The slope of the sash should be to the south or southeast, if possible. The standard hotbed sash is 3 by 6 feet. Every 3 feet there should be a crossbar or slide placed across the bed for the edges of the sash to rest upon. For these crossbars, 2- by 3-inch pieces are satisfactory and they should be mortised into the sides of the frames flush with the top of the sides. A ½-inch strip, nailed in the center of these bars to prevent binding of the sash, is an advantage. When this is used the crossbars need to be at least 3 feet and ½ inch apart. Durable wood, such as cedar, locust, or chestnut for posts and cypress for the frame, is desirable (Fig. 7.2).

Fig. 7.2—Sash removed from hotbed to show construction.

Hot water or steam may be used for heating the hotbed, but neither of these methods is practicable in a small bed, unless the system is used for other purposes. For either of these methods, the heating pipes may be placed in a pit beneath the floor of the bed, or the flow pipe may be placed in the bed above the soil. If placed above the soil, the flow pipe may be located under the center of the ridge in double-width beds or near the top of the high side of single-width beds. In either case the returns are placed on the sides at a lower level than the flow pipe. The temperature can be regulated better in steam- or hot-water-heated beds than in flue-heated beds.

Beds heated by hot air are known as flue-heated beds, since the heated air is conducted from a fire box through tile flues placed beneath the bed. These are cheaper to construct than hot-water or steam-heated beds, but they are not as satisfactory. The fire box is built in a pit at one end of the bed and the heated air and fumes are conducted through tile flues which slope gently upward to the farther end of the bed where they come to the surface. The fumes and air circulate under the floor of the bed and finally pass out through a chimney at one end.

The size of the tile to be used is determined by the size of the bed. A bed 12 by 60 feet should have two lines of 6-inch tiles, while one 12 by 30 feet may be heated satisfactorily with one line of 8-inch tiles.

Electric Hotbeds

Electric hotbeds have been used in recent years. A special heating cable is placed in a pit below the ground level. Some authorities recommend placing the cable on a layer of cinders to reduce loss of heat to the soil below. A layer of 4 to 6 inches of soil is placed over the cable. A thermostat is used to control the temperature of the bed. The initial cost of the construction is relatively high, but the cost of labor in caring for beds heated by electricity is less than for beds heated by steam or hot water.

Cold Frames

The main difference between hotbeds and cold frames is that hotbeds have some form of artificial heat while cold frames have not. Cold frames are used for (1) starting plants when some protection is needed; (2) hardening plants that have been started in greenhouses or hotbeds; and (3) growing crops such as lettuce, beets, parsley, and radishes, to maturity. If only a little protection is necessary, cold frames are satisfactory. In some sections of the South, as in the vicinity of Norfolk, Virginia, such crops as cucumbers, melons, beets, and others, are started in cold frames; then, when the weather permits, the frames are removed and the crops receive field culture.

Cold frames are constructed in very much the same way as hotbeds except that no provision for heat is necessary for the former (Fig. 7.3). Permanent cold frames commonly are made of concrete, while temporary ones are built of boards or plank.

Cold frames are covered with glass sash, with plastic film, with canvas, or with other kinds of cloth. In the colder regions, glass sash is desirable, but in mild regions, where the temperature permits removing the cover during most of the day, canvas or other cloth covering is satisfactory.

GROWING PLANTS

Good plants are essential for successful vegetable growing. In order to have good plants for setting in the field, the grower must use good seed of the stock and variety suited to the conditions under which the crop is

Fig. 7.3—Cold frames are quite similar to hotbeds in construction, but are usually less permanent. These frames are cheap and movable.

USDA Photograph

to be grown. He must use good soil for the plant bed, and use care and judgment in sowing the seed and managing the bed.

Preparing the Soil

A loose, friable soil should be used for the plant bed; a sandy loam, well supplied with humus, meets the requirements. It is desirable to prepare a compost pile at least a year before the soil is to be used. The best kind of compost is made by piling soil, containing a good sod, and manure in alternate layers, using one part of manure to two or three parts of soil according to need. If soil is heavy, some sand should be added to the compost pile at the time it is made or at the time the soil is to be used. The pile should be built up with nearly straight sides and should be flat on top so that water will not run off. The heap should be chopped down and turned at least once before being used in order to mix the ingredients. Before the soil is used for the seedbed, it should be sifted through a coarse screen or run through a soil shredder.

Sowing Seed

Moisture, oxygen, and some degree of heat are necessary for germination. In specially prepared seedbeds, moisture is provided artificially when needed, but to maintain uniform moisture, the soil must be of good texture. Heat is also supplied artificially when the plants are started in greenhouses or hotbeds.

The time of sowing seeds is determined largely by the time it is desired to set the plants in the field and the methods used in growing the plants. If plants are to be set directly from the seedbed to the field, sowing can be done later than if plants are transplanted prior to field setting. Many growers start plants too early and this results in stunted plants, or else they become too tall and "leggy."

Seeds are planted in flats or directly into the soil of the plant bed. Where greenhouses or hotbeds are used for starting plants, flats are fairly common. They are filled with a good friable soil and well firmed to prevent too much settling. The flat is usually filled and the soil is pressed

Fig. 7.4—A board with cleats is used in getting uniform depth and spacing of rows in seeding flats.

Univ. of Ill. Photograph

down with the hands along the edges and in the corners; then more soil is added and a straight edge is used to level off the surface with the top of the flat. A board is then used to compact the soil and to leave it level and slightly below the top of the flat. Cleats may be attached to the board to make the rows (Fig. 7.4).

Most seeds are sown in rows in the flat or in the soil of the bed. In flats, the rows are spaced about 2 inches apart; but when the seeds are sown in the soil of the hotbed, greenhouse bench, or in open beds, the space between the rows is greater, usually 3 to 6 inches.

A simple method of measuring the distance between the rows and making the groove to receive the seed is to use a stick about 2 inches wide, ¼ to ½ inch thick, and of a length to fit the flat. The edge of the stick is pressed into the soil to the depth desired. A similar method may also be used when the seed is to be planted in beds up to 6 feet wide, in which case the stick should be about 6 feet long and of the width desired. When this method is used in flats all of the rows are made before sowing any seed. The seed is sown thinly and is covered by sifting fine soil over the rows and firming it lightly (Fig. 7.5 and Fig. 7.6).

Fig. 7.5—Vibrator is used to get uniform rate of seeding.

Univ. of Ill. Photograph

Fig. 7.6—Seeds may be covered with soil, sand, or other materials to improve germination.

Univ. of Ill. Photograph

A rake-like marker frequently is used for making rows for seed sowing in hotbeds, cold frames, or outdoor beds. For sowing seed on a large scale, a seed drill may be used to advantage. Small seed, such as celery seed, are sometimes sown broadcast and covered very lightly with fine soil or merely covered with burlap.

The depth of covering is governed largely by the size of seed and the texture of the soil. Very small seed should be covered lightly, if at all. Cabbage seed and others of similar size are covered to the depth of about ¼ inch when sown under protection, while beet seed should be covered ½ inch under similar conditions. On heavy soil, the covering should be less than on light soil.

In the milder sections of the South, where winter production of vegetables is important, many plants must be started in the summer or early fall and some protection against high temperature and intense sunlight is needed. Some method of shading the seedbed usually is employed under these conditions. Lath, cloth of the type of cheesecloth or tobacco cloth, sacks, and straw mats are among the materials used for shading the young plants.

Caring for the Seedbed

Good, stocky plants are desired and to get them care must be given to watering and to regulating the temperature and ventilation in greenhouses or other structures.

As soon as the seeds are planted and covered, the seedbed should be carefully watered, preferably with a fine spray from a sprinkling can or with a fine rose on a garden hose. The seedbed should never be allowed to dry out and it should not be kept soaked. Until the plants are well established, the bed should be kept fairly moist but not wet. After the plants are well established, it is best to water thoroughly, preferably in the forenoon, and then to withhold water until the plants show the need of it. Ordinarily no water should be applied on cloudy, damp days. Before the plants are taken up for planting in the field, the bed should be given a thorough soaking, so that as much soil as possible will adhere to the roots.

The temperature that should be maintained in greenhouses or hotbeds depends on the crops grown. Tomatoes, peppers, eggplants, and melons thrive best at a relatively high temperature, 60° to 70° F., while cabbage, lettuce, cauliflower, celery, and other cool-season crops will make better growth, although not so rapid, at temperatures 10 degrees lower. Slow, steady growth is preferable to rapid growth.

Ventilation aids in the control of temperature and of the humidity of the air. In greenhouses, ventilation is obtained by opening the ventilators, while in hotbeds and sash-covered cold frames, the sashes may be raised at one end or pulled down a short distance. On warm days the sash may be removed entirely. In ventilating during cool weather, the wind should not be allowed to strike the plants.

Commercial Plant Growing

The production of vegetable plants for sale is of considerable importance in some regions of the South, especially in the Rio Grande Valley of Texas and in the Tifton-Valdosta section of Georgia. Other areas where plants are grown for sale on a fairly large scale include sections of northern Florida, and certain areas in South Carolina, Virginia, Louisiana, and Arkansas. These plants are shipped to northern states and to other sections of the South.

Certain sections of the Rio Grande Valley are devoted to direct field plantings of cabbage, onions, sweet potatoes, and tomatoes, while in eastern Texas, onions, cabbage, and tomatoes are started in hotbeds, transferred to cold frames, and then sold for field planting. Most of the plants are shipped out of Texas to northern markets in early spring. From approximately 15,000 acres in the state devoted to this use, the following number of plants are shipped annually: sweet potatoes, 750 million; tomatoes, 100 million; cabbage, 400 million; and onions, 900 million. Of those mentioned, onion plant production is by far the most intensive, and in no other section of the country does the business reach so high a state of specialization. Both the soils and climate seem especially favorable.

The Tifton-Valdosta plant-growing area of south Georgia comprises about five counties that have built up, largely within the past three decades, a production of more than 1,000 carloads of plants annually. Early warm springs are very favorable to field planting of seed in this area and the Norfolk and Tifton series of soils of this section are admirably adapted to the production of plants.

Georgia-grown tomato plants are shipped in carload lots to the leading vegetable districts of New Jersey, New York, Indiana, and other states. Many of them are grown under contract for canners. There is such a thorough understanding between the producers and consumers of the plants that there is less than 48 hours' lapse between the time the plants are pulled and the time they are being set in the fields of Indiana or elsewhere. No refrigeration is used in the shipping cars.

Cabbage, onion, and sweet potato plants are grown in part under contract, while a large percentage of them are placed on the open market or shipped by local express or trucks. Eggplants and cauliflower plants are grown under contract for regular customers and seldom do they appear on the open market. The yields per acre of plants grown in the field with no heat or irrigation are approximately as follows: tomato, 100 thousand; cabbage, 250 thousand; onion, 750 thousand; and pepper, 250 thousand.

TRANSPLANTING

Plants that are started in greenhouses, hotbeds, or cold frames frequently are transplanted or pricked out before they are set out. Some may be transplanted more than once before being set in the field.

Fig. 7.7—Transplanting pepper seedlings before they become crowded.

Univ. of III. Photograph

Methods Used

A common practice is to sow the seed rather thickly; then, when the first true leaves are fairly well developed, to transplant the seedlings into flats or into the soil of the plant bed. For best results, the soil must be moist but not sticky. After the soil has been compacted with a board, holes to receive the plants are made with the finger, with a small dibble, or with a spotting board. The spotting board saves time and insures that the plants will be evenly spaced in straight rows (Fig. 7.7).

The spacing of the seedlings in the transplanting bed varies with the kind of plant and the time they are to remain in the bed. For celery, spacing varies from 1 by 1 inch to 2 by 2 inches, while larger-growing plants are spaced from $1\frac{1}{2}$ by $1\frac{1}{2}$ to 4 by 4 inches, depending on the time they are to be grown before setting in the field. Some plants, such as tomatoes, peppers, and eggplants, are frequently transplanted more than once before field setting. At the first transplanting, they are spaced $1\frac{1}{2}$

Fig. 7.8—Well spaced tomato plants in flat.

Univ. of Ill. Photograph

by 1½ or 2 by 2 inches, and, as soon as the plants begin to crowd, they are transplanted again, giving them more space. Unless saving space is of importance, it is better to transplant seedlings only once and to give them the desired spacing at this time (Fig. 7.8).

In transplanting, the soil should be pressed down around the roots, taking care to fill the hole at the bottom. Pressure should not be exerted against the stems of soft, succulent plants, as this might injure or kill them. After each transplanting, the soil should be watered to settle it around the roots. Shading the plants for a day after transplanting usually is an advantage.

Plants are frequently grown in individual containers, such as clay, paper, or peat pots; paper or wood veneer bands; or tin cans. The seed may be sown in the soil in the container, or the seedlings may be grown in flats or beds and transplanted into the containers later. The main advantage in using pots and plant bands is that the roots are not disturbed when the plants are set in the field.

Clay pots are considered best, but are expensive. New clay pots absorb nitrates from the soil solution, and for this reason, old pots often give better results than new ones. However, new pots can be soaked in a solution of nitrate of soda to make up the deficiency.

Containers made of carbonaceous material, such as wood, paper, and raw peat, have sometimes given unsatisfactory results. These materials supply energy food for bacteria that cause the decomposition of the carbonaceous material. These bacteria consume nitrates and thus compete with the plants for the nitrate supply in the soil. The remedy is to supply enough nitrates for both the plants and the bacteria. The nitrates used by the bacteria are built up into complex compounds which, on the death and decomposition of the organisms, return the nitrogen to the soil.

Advantages and Disadvantages of Transplanting

The main advantages in transplanting plants before setting them in the field are (1) economy in the use of space in the greenhouse, hotbed, or cold frame; (2) saving of labor in the care of the plant bed; and (3) better spacing of the plants in the bed. When the plants are to be transplanted, much less space is needed for the seedbed than is the case when they are to remain there until field setting. If they are not to be transplanted, sufficient space must be given to allow the plants to grow for several weeks without serious crowding. This would require more labor in caring for the seedbed.

When the seedlings are removed from the seedbed, the ends of the roots are broken off and this results in greater root branching. Transplanted plants have a much greater number of short branch roots, and therefore a greater absorbing surface than do similar plants that have not been transplanted. When these plants are taken up for setting in the field, there is a larger mass of feeding roots in the block of soil around the roots than in a similar block of soil around the roots of nontransplanted plants.

Many growers believe that transplanting results in the development of a more stocky plant with a better root system and that these increase the yield and hasten maturity. Experimental evidence presented by Loomis, however, indicates that transplanting in itself does not increase yield or hasten maturity. The increase in space and better conditions usually given the transplanted plants do have these effects.

The main disadvantages of transplanting are the extra labor required and the check in growth that results from taking up and resetting the plants. The extra labor may be offset by the economy in the use of valuable greenhouse or hotbed space and in the saving of labor in caring for the plants. Although all plants are checked in growth by transplanting, some are checked less than others. With those that are checked but little, this may be offset by the increase in root branching. Transplanting when the plants are large usually results in delayed maturity and, in some cases, in reduced yield. Sweet corn, cucumber, melon, and bean plants are seriously checked in growth by transplanting unless it is done while the plants are small. A second transplanting of these plants is very injurious.

Difference in Response to Transplanting

Any of the common vegetable plants can be transplanted satisfactorily during the early stages of growth. With corn, beans, and the cucurbits, however, there is only a short period when they are not seriously injured by transplanting.

The recovery of the plant after transplanting is determined largely by its ability to obtain water, and this depends on the speed of root replacement (Fig. 7.9) . Plants seriously injured by transplanting normally have a rapid rate of top growth and a slow rate of root growth, while those that are not greatly checked in growth by transplanting have a relatively slow rate of top growth and a rapid rate of root replacement.

Figure 7.9 ilustrates the difference in rate of root replacement of cabbage and corn plants; cabbage is easy and corn difficult to transplant. Eight days after transplanting, the cabbage plant had a much greater root area than the nontransplanted plant. The nontransplanted corn plant, on the other hand, had a much greater absorbing surface than the transplanted one.

The rate of recovery from transplanting depends not only on the kind and age of the plant, but also on the quantity of stored food, especially carbohydrates. These enable the plant to replace its roots rapidly. There is evidence that the roots of some plants are suberized or cutinized at an early age and such plants are slow to recover following transplanting. Deposition of suberin or cutin in the endoderm or periderm hinders water absorption and branch-root formation.

HARDENING PLANTS

The term "hardening" is applied to any treatment that results in any firming or hardening of the tissues of plants. Hardening enables plants

Fig. 7.9—Root systems of cabbage plants (four on left) and corn plants (four on right) showing effect of transplanting on root branching. The plant on the left of each set of two is the non-transplanted plant and the one on the right is the transplanted one eight days after transplanting.

Cornell Univ. Agr. Exp. Sta.

to better withstand unfavorable environmental conditions, such as low temperatures, hot drying winds, certain types of insect injury, whipping in the wind, and injury from particles of soil and sand blown by the wind.

Methods Used

Any treatment that results in a check in growth increases hardiness, but plants differ in the degree of resistance to certain conditions following the hardening treatment. For example, cabbage and other cool-season plants can be hardened to such extent that they will withstand temperatures several degrees below freezing and will survive actual ice formation in their tissues. Warm-season plants, such as tomato, cucumber, melon, pepper, eggplant, and others, will not withstand ice formation, regardless of the degree of hardening. Checking growth of these results in only slight resistance to cold.

The usual methods of hardening plants are (1) exposing them to temperatures too low for good growth, (2) allowing the soil of the plant bed to become dry, and (3) a combination of these two. When plants are grown under protection during cool weather, it is easy to subject them to relatively low temperatures by reducing the heat in the greenhouse or hotbed, and by ventilation at the proper time.

If the plants are grown during warm weather, it is not possible to harden by low temperature, hence some other method must be used. Withholding water is the best method in this case, but when the plants are grown in outdoor beds, the success of this method is dependent on the weather. During a rainy period, hardening can be accomplished by lifting the plants slightly with a fork or by cutting the roots on both sides of the rows of plants. In both cases, the water-absorbing surface of the root system is reduced and, if the treatment is severe enough, growth is checked and hardening results.

Hardened plants develop new roots faster than do tender ones. It is better to maintain a moderate rate of growth throughout the plant-growing period than to permit rapid growth up to the last week or two and then check growth suddenly. Overhardening results in delayed growth when the plants are set out. Severe hardening of tomato plants decreases the early yield of fruit in the greenhouse. Overhardening will delay fruiting in the field and under some conditions reduce the total yield.

Changes During Hardening

Hardening is accompanied by (1) slowing up of the rate of growth; (2) thickening of the cuticle; (3) an increase in the waxy covering on the leaves of certain kinds of plants; (4) the development of a pink color, especially in the stems, petioles, and veins; (5) an increase in the dry matter; (6) an increase in the content of water-holding colloids; and (7) a decrease in the percentage of freezable water and other internal changes. Usually the leaves of hardened plants are deeper green and smaller than those of tender plants.

Hardened plants develop new roots faster than do tender ones and this is of special importance in plants that are grown in beds and later set in the field. The accumulation of food materials during the hardening treatment is important in new root formation. Hardening also increases the water retaining power of the cells and this is of importance in resistance to water loss incident to freezing and in transpiration. In the hardening of cabbage plants there is a change in the constituents of protoplasm which prevents their precipitation as a result of the physical changes incident to freezing. The proteins are changed to forms which are less easily precipitated.

SELECTED REFERENCES

Anonymous, "Hotbeds and Cold Frames," USDA Farmers' Bull. 1743, 1960.

Beattie, J. H., "Sash Greenhouses," USDA Leaflet 124, 1946.

Cates, F. B. and Spivey, C. D., "Grow Your Own Vegetable Transplants," Ga. Agr. Ser. Bull. 628, 1963.

Courter, J. W., "Plastic Greenhouses," Ill. Agr. Ext. Cir. 857, 1962.

Courter, J. W., and Vandemark, J. S., "Growing Vegetable Transplants," Ill. Agr. Exp. Sta. Cir. 884, 1964.

Dutt, J. O. and Fletcher, R. F., "Growing Good Vegetable Plants," Pa. Agr. Ext. Ser. Cir. 459, 1956.

Jones, T. H., and Shoemaker, J. S., "Growing Vegetable Transplants," Ontario Dept. Agr. Bull. 485, 1952.

Missley, C. H., "Vegetable Plants from Seedbed to Field," N. J. Agr. Ext. Leaflet 118, 1954.

Romshe, F. A., "Studies of Plant Production Methods for Vegetable Plants," Okla. Agr. Exp. Sta. Bull. B-421, 1954.

Stanley, J. M., "Electric Heating of Hotbeds," USDA Leaflet 445, 1959.

Watson, R. D., "Seed and Soil Treatments for Prevention of Diseases in Vegetables and Flowers," Idaho Agr. Exp. Sta. Cir. 127, 1953.

CHAPTER 8

Planting in the Open

The vegetable crops vary in their climatic requirements. Each must be planted at a time when it will have a good season for development or will mature at a good time for marketing. In some cases the seed can be sown directly in the field, but in others transplants have to be used. Along with timeliness, getting a stand of good plants is essential for successful vegetable production.

PLANTING SEED

Spacing the Rows

In the open field, 3 to 3½ feet is the usual width between rows for more than half of the common vegetables, including beans, peppers, eggplants, cabbage, corn, and potatoes. This width allows ample room for the use of equipment in cultivating, spraying, or harvesting, as well as space for top and root development of plants. When space is limited and hand labor is used, the width may be reduced.

Vegetables which have a narrow, spreading root system and small top, such as onions, lettuce, carrots, beets, radishes, and celery, will have ample room in 1½- to 2½-foot rows. These vegetables are usually intensely grown and it is necessary for economic reasons to produce a heavy yield from the land. Most of these will stand crowding and are not seriously injured by partial shade.

Plants with large leaves, trailing vines, or fruit which require direct sunlight for proper development must have more room. Among these are melons, squash, pumpkins, and cucumbers, which should be planted in rows 4 to 12 feet apart, depending on the kind of crop and local practice.

Preparing the Seedbed

In preparing the soil for planting, first remove anything that will interfere with plowing, spading, or hoeing the soil. If the soil contains sod or clay, it should be plowed to a depth of 6 inches at least a month before planting. Special care should be taken to remove from the land any portions of diseased plants which might infect the new plants.

About 2 weeks before planting, the soil should be harrowed, rolled, and dragged until it is smooth and mellow. It is then ready to be laid off in rows properly spaced to accommodate the vegetables to be grown. Preparation of beds will vary for seed of different kinds, specific directions for this being found in the special crop chapters.

Planting Methods

Vegetable seed are planted as follows: (1) by hand in hills, rows, or broadcast (Table 8.1); (2) with one-row hand seeders; and (3) with single- or multiple-row seeders drawn usually by tractors. The method of seeding depends largely on the quantity of seed to be planted and the rapidity with which the work must be done. Regardless of the method of planting, one should make sure that the seeds are planted at the proper depth and that the soil is left smooth and compact.

Melon, squash, and cucumber seed may be planted by hand or with drills of various kinds. They may be planted in hills or in continuous rows. On level land, the hills may be checked in order that cultivation can be carried on in both directions. After the land is prepared and laid off, a garden hoe is the only tool that is necessary. In some cases, corn or tomatoes may be checked also. Most winter-grown salad greens, including mustard, turnips, rape, tender greens, and spinach, may be sown by hand and covered with a garden rake. These very small seed are sown to advantage if mixed with four or five parts of fine soil.

Seeders vary from a simple bean dropper to complicated machines which have several attachments for manipulating the soil, fertilizer, and seed in the process of planting. One well-known planter performs the following operations simultaneously: (1) opens two furrows for placement of fertilizer, (2) deposits any desired quantity of fertilizer, (3) covers the fertilizer in the furrow, (4) makes up seedbed, (5) levels off bed at desired height, (6) opens the furrows for seed, (7) sows any quantity of seed, (8) covers the seeds to the proper depth, and (9) packs the soil over them. Seeders should not only space seeds properly but also should plant them without injury.

For most vegetables, seed must be fresh, and even then, a germination test is advisable. Soaking certain slow-germinating seeds, such as
beet, okra, celery, and pepper, in water overnight, just before planting,
increases the percentage and rapidity of germination. Seeds that have
been soaked are more difficult to sow with a seed drill than those that
have not been soaked.

Planting Dates

The time of planting vegetable seed is based on locality, hardiness,
length of season, and time of maturity. The earliest date for planting
winter crops is October or November in the extreme South. Following
the advance of the season northward, this date may be approximately
June 15 in the extreme northern portion of the country. The grower
should know the dates of the last killing frost in the spring (Fig. 8.1) and
the first killing frost in the fall (Fig. 8.2) for his particular locality, and
use these dates as the basis for planting crops that are sensitive to frost.
Local experience is usually a safeguard. Figure 8.1 and Table 8.2 show the

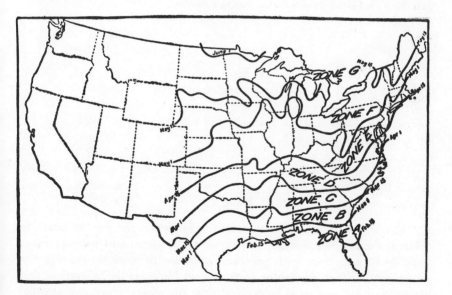

Fig. 8.1—Zone map of the United States, based on the average dates of the latest killing frost
in spring. By referring to Table 8.2, the earliest safe date of planting vegetables in the open in
the various zones may be determined.

USDA Farmers' Bull. 934

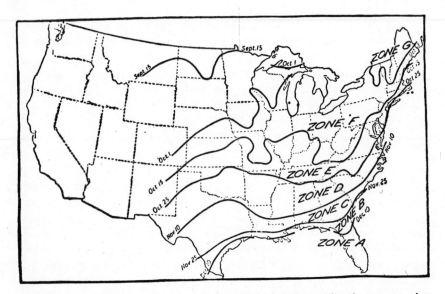

Fig. 8.2—Zone map of the central and eastern part of the United States based on average date of first killing frost in autumn. By referring to Table 8.3, the latest safe date for planting vegetables for the fall garden in various zones may be determined.

USDA Farmers' Bull. 934

earliest safe dates for planting vegetables in the spring; while Figure 8.2 and Table 8.3 give the latest safe dates for fall planting.

Hardy vegetables including beets, cabbage, carrots, collards, mustard, onions, peas, rape, shallots, spinach, and turnips, may be planted in the fall or winter in the South, because they are not easily injured by freezing. Semi-hardy vegetables, such as lettuce and radishes, must be planted in ice-free seasons, though they will stand frosts. Tender vegetables cannot be safely planted until all danger of frost is past and the ground becomes warm, as is shown in Table 8.1.

The length of season before maturity influences the time of planting different crops. Such vegetables as eggplants, peppers, and sweet potatoes are planted only once each year and continue to grow throughout the season, while other vegetables, such as snap beans, radishes, carrots, and lettuce, may be planted at intervals during the season. Tender vegetables which require 100 days or more to reach maturity must be planted in the spring, and as a rule, the earlier after the soil becomes warm, the better.

Table 8.1—Vegetable Crops Planting Chart.

KIND	Seeds for 100 Ft. Row	Seed for 1 Acre		*Approximate Number of Seeds per Pound	Distance Between Rows		Plants Apart in Rows	Depth of Planting	Time of Planting in Open Ground		Ready for Use from Date of Seeding
		Drilled in Field	If Transplanted		Machine Cultivation	Hand Cultivation			South	North	
Asparagus, seed	1 oz.	5 lbs.	1 lb.	22,400	30 to 36 in.	18 to 24 in.	3 in.	1 in.	Autumn or early spring	Early spring	1 or 2 yrs. (plants)
Asparagus, root	66 roots	—	6000	—	5 ft.	4 ft.	18 in.	2 in.	Autumn or early spring	Early spring	2 yrs.
Beans, dwarf	1 lb.	60 lbs.	—	1,200	30 to 36 in.	18 to 24 in.	2 in.	1 in.	Feb., Apr., (Aug., Sept.)	Apr. to July	42 to 75 days
Beans, pole	½ lb.	30 lbs.	—	1,200	3 to 4 ft.	3 to 4 ft.	3 to 4 ft.	1 in.	Late spring	May and June	65 to 90 days
Beet (and Swiss Chard)	1 oz.	10 lbs.	—	19,200	28 to 36 in.	12 to 18 in.	2 in.	1 in.	Feb., Apr., (Aug., Sept.)	April to Aug.	45 to 60 days
Beet, Mangel & Sugar	1 oz.	5 lbs.	—	24,000	28 to 36 in.	20 in.	4 in.	1 in.	Feb., Apr., (Aug., Sept.)	April to Aug.	90 to 120 days
Broccoli	¼ oz.	2 lbs.	4 oz.	160,000	30 to 40 in.	24 to 36 in.	18 to 24 in.	½ in.	Jan. to July	Mar. and Apr.	90 to 100 days
Brussels sprouts	¼ oz.	2 lbs.	4 oz.	136,000	30 to 36 in.	24 to 30 in.	12 to 16 in.	½ in.	Jan. to July	May and June	100 to 120 days
Cabbage, Chinese	¼ oz.	2 lbs.	4 oz.	152,000	30 to 36 in.	18 to 24 in.	10 to 12 in.	½ in.	July and Aug.	June and July	75 days
Cabbage, early	¼ oz.	2 lbs.	4 oz.	120,000	30 to 36 in.	24 to 30 in.	12 to 18 in.	½ in.	Oct. to Dec.	Mar. and Apr.	90 to 110 days
Cabbage, late	¼ oz.	2 lbs.	4 oz.	120,000	30 to 40 in.	24 to 36 in.	16 to 24 in.	½ in.	June and July	May and June	110 to 120 days
Cantaloup, Muskmelon	½ oz.	3 lbs.	—	16,000	6 to 8 ft.	6 to 8 ft.	4 every 4 ft.	1 in.	Feb. to Apr.	April to June	85 to 150 days
Carrot	½ oz.	3 lbs.	—	320,000	30 to 36 in.	12 to 18 in.	2 in.	½ in.	Mar. and Apr., (Sept.)	April to June	55 to 80 days
Cauliflower	¼ oz.	2 lbs.	4 oz.	160,000	30 to 36 in.	24 to 30 in.	14 to 18 in.	½ in.	Jan. and Feb. (June)	April to June	95 to 110 days
Celery	¼ oz.	1 lb.	4 oz.	1,280,000	3 to 6 ft.	18 to 36 in.	2 in.	½ in.	Aug. and Oct.	May and June	120 to 150 days
Chicory, Witloof	1 oz.	4 lbs.	1 lb.	256,000	30 in.	18 in.	4 in.*	⅛ in.	July and Aug.	Apr. to June	100 days
Chicory, Magdeburg	1 oz.	4 lbs.	—	256,000	30 in.	24 in.	6 in.	½ in.	March to July	Apr. to June	100 days
Collards	¼ oz.	2 lbs.	4 oz.	120,000	30 to 36 in.	24 to 30 in.	14 to 18 in.	½ in.	May and June	Late spring	100 to 120 days
Corn salad	1 oz.	8 lbs.	—	480,000	30 to 36 in.	12 to 18 in.	3 in.	½ in.	July and Aug.	June and July	60 days
Corn, sweet	¼ lb.	10 lbs.	—	3,520	36 to 42 in.	30 to 36 in.	4 every 3 ft.	1 in.	Feb. to April	May to July	55 to 90 days
Cress, water	½ oz.	—	—	2,400,000	Broadcast	—	—	water	Early spring	Apr. to Sept.	60 to 70 days
Cucumber	½ oz.	3 lbs.	—	16,000	4 to 6 ft.	4 to 6 ft.	4 every 3 ft.	1 in.	Feb. and Mar. (Sept.)	Apr. to July	50 to 70 days
Eggplant	⅛ oz.	2 lbs.	4 oz.	96,000	30 to 36 in.	24 to 30 in.	18 in.	½ in.	Feb. to Apr.	Apr. and May	125 to 140 days
Endive	1 oz.	4 lbs.	—	240,000	30 in.	18 in.	12 in.	½ in.	Feb. to Apr.	Apr. (July)	100 days
Kale or Borecole	¼ oz.	3 lbs.	1 lb.	144,000	30 to 36 in.	18 to 24 in.	18 in.	½ in.	Oct. to Feb.	Aug., Sept., (Mar., Apr.)	55 to 60 days
Kohlrabi	¼ oz.	4 lbs.	1 lb.	135,000	30 to 36 in.	18 to 24 in.	6 in.	½ in	Sept. to May	March to May	50 to 70 days
Leek	½ oz.	4 lbs.	—	176,000	30 to 36 in.	14 to 20 in.	4 in.	½ in	May to Sept.	March to May	120 to 150 days

(Continued)

Table 8.1—Vegetable Crop Planting Chart (Continued).

KIND	Seeds for 100 Ft. Row	Seed for 1 Acre — Drilled in Field	Seed for 1 Acre — If Transplanted	*Approximate Number of Seeds per Pound	Distance Between Rows — Machine Cultivation	Distance Between Rows — Hand Cultivation	Plants Apart in Rows	Depth of Planting	Time of Planting in Open Ground — South	Time of Planting in Open Ground — North	Ready for Use from Date of Seeding
Lettuce	1/4 oz.	3 lbs.	1 lb.	320,000	30 in.	12 to 18 in.	6 in.	1/2 in.	Sept. to Mar.	Mar. to Sept.	70 to 90 days
Mustard	1/4 oz.	4 lbs.	—	288,000	30 to 36 in.	12 to 18 in.	4 to 5 ft.	1/4 in.	Autumn or early spring	Mar. to May (Sept.)	60 to 90 days
Okra	2 oz.	8 lbs.	—	7,200	4 to 5 ft.	3 to 4 ft.	24 in.	1 in.	Feb. to Apr.	May and June	90 to 140 days
Onion, seed	1 oz.	4 lbs.	—	120,000	24 to 36 in.	12 to 18 in.	2 in.	1/2 in.	Oct. to Mar.	Apr. to May	125 to 150 days
Onion seed for sets	1 lb.	50 lbs.	—	120,000	24 to 36 in.	12 to 18 in.	1/2 in.	1/2 in.		Apr.	90 days
Onion sets	1 qt.	12 bu.	—	—	24 to 36 in.	12 to 18 in.	2 in.	1 in.	Early spring or autumn	Feb. to May	100 days
Parsley	1/4 oz.	3 lbs.	—	240,000	24 to 36 in.	12 to 18 in.	3 in.	1/8 in.	Sept. to May-Sept.	Mar.-Apr.	65 to 90 days
Parsnip	1/2 oz.	3 lbs.	—	112,000	30 to 36 in.	18 to 24 in.	2 in.	1/2 in.	Feb., Mar.	Mar.-Apr.	130 days
Peas	1 lb.	200 lbs.	—	2,000	3 to 4 ft.	30 to 36 in.	1 in.	2 in.	Sept. to Apr.	Mar. to June	45 to 75 days
Peas, Crowder	1/2 lb.	25 lbs.	—	2,800	3 to 4 ft.	3 ft.	4 to 6 in.	1 in.	Mar. to June	May	100 to 110 days
Pepper	1/8 oz.	2 lbs.	4 oz.	72,000	30 to 36 in.	18 to 24 in.	15 in.	1/2 in.	Early Spring	May and June	130 to 150 days
Pumpkin	1/2 oz.	4 lbs.	—	3,200	8 to 12 ft.	8 to 12 ft.	4 every 6 ft.	1 in.	Apr. and May	May to July	75 to 90 days
Radish	1 oz.	15 lbs.	—	64,000	24 to 36 in.	12 to 18 in.	1 in.	1 in.	Sept. to Apr.	Mar. to Sept.	20 to 75 days
Rhubarb, roots	40 roots	—	3500	—	5 ft.	4 ft.	30 in.	3 to 4 in.	Autumn or early spring	Early spring	2 or 3 yrs.
Rhubarb, seed	1/2 oz.	8 lbs.	2 lbs.	32,000	30 to 36 in.	18 to 24 in.	4 in.	1/2 in.	Early spring	Early spring	1 or 2 yrs. (plants)
Rutabaga	1/4 oz.	2 lbs.	—	64,000	30 to 36 in.	18 to 24 in.	6 in.	1/2 in.	Aug. and Sept.	June-July	90 days
Salsify	1 oz.	8 lbs.	—	48,000	30 to 36 in.	18 to 24 in.	2 in.	1/2 in.	Early spring	Early spring	150 days
Soybeans, Vegetable	1/2 lb.	30 lbs.	—	1,920	30 to 36 in.	16 to 36 in.	2 in.	1 in.	Apr.-May-June	May-June	90 to 120 days
Spinach	1 oz.	15 lbs.	—	48,000	30 to 36 in.	12 to 18 in.	2 in.	1/2 in.	Sept. to Mar.	Sept. & early spring	45 days is min.
Squash, summer	1/2 oz.	4 lbs.	—	4,800	3 to 4 ft.	3 to 4 ft.	4 every 4 ft.	1 in.	Spring	Apr. to June	65 to 70 days
Squash, winter	1/2 oz.	2 lbs.	—	2,000	7 to 10 ft.	7 to 10 ft.	4 every 6 ft.	1 in.	Spring	May to July	125 days
Tomato	1/8 oz.	2 lbs.	2 oz.	160,000	3 to 5 ft.	3 to 4 ft.	3 to 4 ft.	1/2 in.	Mar.-Apr.	May to June	125 to 150 days
Tomato, Pelleted	1 oz.	6 lbs.	12 lbs.	12,000	3 to 5 ft.	3 to 4 ft.	3 to 4 ft.	1/2 in.	Mar.-Apr.	May to June	125 to 150 days
Turnip	1/2 oz.	2 lbs.	—	208,000	24 to 36 in.	18 to 24 in.	2 in.	1/4 in.	Aug. to Oct.	Apr. and Aug.	45 to 90 days
Turnip, for greens	1 oz.	5 lbs.	—	208,000	Broadcast	12 to 18 in.	—	1/4 in.	Aug. to Oct.	Apr. and Aug.	45 to 50 days
Watermelon	1 oz.	3 lbs.	—	3,600	8 to 12 ft.	8 to 12 ft.	4 every 6 ft.	1 in.	Mar. to May	May and June	100 to 130 days

*The number of seeds per pound varies widely between varieties and lots of same species, but figures given are approximately average.
Data from Cornell Seed Co.

Table 8.2—Earliest Safe Dates for Planting in the Open in the Zones of the United States Illustrated in Fig. 8.1.

Crop	Zone A	Zone B	Zone C	Zone D	Zone E
Asparagus	(Not grown)	Feb. 15 to Mar. 1	Mar. 1 to 15	Mar. 15 to Apr. 15	Apr. 15 to May 1
Artichoke:					
Globe	Mar. 1 to Mar. 15	Mar. 15 to Apr. 1	Apr. 1 to 15	Apr. 15 to May 15	May 1 to 30
Jerusalem	Feb. 1 to 15	Feb. 15 to May 1	Mar. 1 to 15	Mar. 15 to Apr. 1	Apr. 1 to 15
Beans:					
Lima	Mar. 1 to 15	Mar. 15 to Apr. 1	Apr. 1 to 15	May 1 to 15	May 15 to June 1
Snap	Feb. 15 to Mar. 1	Mar. 1 to 15	Mar. 15 to 30	Apr. 1 to May 1	May 1 to 15
Beet	Feb. 1 to 15	Feb. 15 to Mar. 1	Mar. 1 to 15	Mar. 15 to Apr. 15	Apr. 15 to May 1
Brussels sprouts	Feb. 1 to 15	Feb. 15 to Mar. 1	Mar. 1 to 15	Mar. 15 to Apr. 15	Apr. 15 to May 1
Cabbage	Jan. 1 to Feb. 1	Jan. 15 to Feb. 15	Feb. 15 to Mar. 1	Mar. 1 to 15	Mar. 15 to Apr. 15
Carrot	Feb. 1 to 15	Feb. 15 to Mar. 1	Mar. 1 to 15	Mar. 15 to Apr. 15	Apr. 15 to May 1
Cauliflower	Feb. 1 to 15	Feb. 15 to Mar. 1	Mar. 1 to 15	Mar. 15 to Apr. 15	Apr. 15 to May 1
Celery	Feb. 1 to 15	Feb. 15 to Mar. 1	Mar. 1 to 15	Mar. 15 to Apr. 15	Apr. 15 to May 1
Chard	Feb. 1 to 15	Feb. 15 to Mar. 1	Mar. 1 to 15	Mar. 15 to Apr. 15	Apr. 15 to May 1
Collards	Jan. 1 to Feb. 1	Feb. 1 to 15	Feb. 15 to Mar. 1	Mar. 1 to 15	Mar. 15 to Apr. 15
Corn, sweet	Feb. 15 to Mar. 1	Mar. 1 to 15	Mar. 15 to Apr. 1	Apr. 1 to May 1	Apr. 15 to May 15
Cucumber	Mar. 1 to 15	Mar. 15 to Apr. 1	Apr. 1 to 15	Apr. 15 to May 15	May 1 to June 1
Eggplant	Mar. 1 to 15	Mar. 15 to Apr. 1	Apr. 1 to 15	Apr. 15 to May 15	May 1 to June 1
Garlic	Jan. 1 to Feb. 1	Feb. 1 to 15	Feb. 15 to Mar. 1	Mar. 1 to 15	Mar. 15 to Apr. 15
Kale	Jan. 1 to Feb. 1	Feb. 1 to 15	Feb. 15 to Mar. 1	Mar. 1 to 15	Mar. 15 to Apr. 15
Kohlrabi	Feb. 1 to 15	Feb. 15 to Mar. 1	Mar. 1 to 15	Mar. 1 to Apr. 1	Apr. 1 to May 1
Lettuce:					
Head	Feb. 1 to 15	Feb. 15 to Mar. 1	Mar. 1 to 15	Mar. 15 to Apr. 15	Apr. 1 to May 1
Leaf	Jan. 1 to Feb. 1	Feb. 1 to 15	Feb. 15 to Mar. 1	Mar. 1 to 15	Mar. 15 to Apr. 15

(Continued)

Table 8.2—Earliest Safe Dates for Planting in the Open in the Zones of the United States Illustrated in Fig. 8.1 (Continued).

Crop	Zone A	Zone B	Zone C	Zone D	Zone E
Melon	Mar. 1 to 15	Mar. 15 to Apr. 1	Apr. 1 to 15	Apr. 15 to May 1	May 1 to June 1
Mustard	Feb. 1 to 15	Feb. 15 to Mar. 1	Mar. 1 to 15	Mar. 15 to Apr. 1	Apr. 1 to May 1
Okra or gumbo	Feb. 15 to Mar. 1	Mar. 15 to Apr. 1	Mar. 15 to 30	Apr. 15 to May 1	May 1 to 15
Onion:					
Seed	Feb. 1 to 15	Feb. 15 to Mar. 1	Mar. 1 to 15	Mar. 15 to Apr. 1	Apr. 1 to May 1
Sets	Jan. 1 to Feb. 1	Feb. 1 to 15	Feb. 15 to Mar. 1	Mar. 1 to 15	Mar. 15 to Apr. 15
Parsley	Feb. 1 to 15	Feb. 15 to Mar. 1	Mar. 1 to 15	Mar. 15 to Apr. 1	Apr. 1 to May 1
Parsnip	Feb. 1 to 15	Feb. 15 to Mar. 1	Mar. 1 to 15	Mar. 15 to Apr. 1	Apr. 1 to May 1
Peas:					
Smooth	Jan. 1 to Feb. 1	Feb. 1 to 15	Feb. 15 to Mar. 1	Mar. 1 to 15	Mar. 15 to Apr. 15
Wrinkled	Feb. 1 to 15	Feb. 15 to Mar. 1	Mar. 1 to 15	Mar. 15 to Apr. 1	Apr. 1 to May 1
Pepper	Mar. 1 to 15	Mar. 15 to Apr. 1	Apr. 1 to 15	Apr. 15 to May 1	May 1 to June 1
Potato:					
Irish	Jan. 1 to Feb. 1	Feb. 1 to 15	Feb. 15 to Mar. 1	Mar. 1 to 15	Mar. 15 to Apr. 15
Sweet	Mar. 1 to 15	Mar. 15 to Apr. 1	Apr. 1 to 15	Apr. 15 to May 1	May 1 to June 1
Pumpkin	Mar. 1 to 15	Mar. 15 to Apr. 1	Apr. 1 to 15	Apr. 15 to May 1	May 1 to June 1
Radish	Jan. 1 to Feb. 1	Feb. 1 to 15	Feb. 15 to Mar. 1	Mar. 1 to 15	Mar. 15 to Apr. 15
Rhubarb	(Not grown)	(Not grown)	Mar. 1 to 15	Mar. 15 to Apr. 15	Apr. 15 to May 1
Salsify	Feb. 1 to 15	Feb. 15 to Mar. 1	Mar. 1 to 15	Mar. 15 to Apr. 15	Apr. 15 to May 1
Spinach	Feb. 1 to 15	Feb. 15 to Mar. 1	Mar. 1 to 15	Mar. 15 to Apr. 15	Apr. 15 to May 1
Squash	Mar. 1 to 15	Mar. 15 to Apr. 1	Apr. 1 to 15	Apr. 15 to May 1	May 1 to June 1
Tomato	Mar. 1 to 15	Mar. 15 to Apr. 1	Apr. 1 to 15	Apr. 15 to May 1	May 1 to June 1
Turnip	Jan. 1 to Feb. 1	Feb. 1 to 15	Feb. 15 to Mar. 1	Mar. 1 to 15	Mar. 15 to Apr. 15

Data from USDA Farmers' Bull. 934.

Table 8.3—Latest Safe Dates for Planting Vegetables for the Fall Garden
in the Zones of the United States Illustrated in Figure 8.2.

Crop	Zone B	Zone C	Zone D	Zone E
Beans, snap	Oct. 1 to 15	Sept. 15 to 30	Aug. 15 to 30	Aug. 1 to 30
Beet	Oct. 1 to 15	Sept. 15 to 30	Aug. 1 to 30	July 15 to Aug. 15
Cabbage		Sept. 1 to 15	Aug. 15 to Sept. 1	July 15 to Aug. 15
Carrot		Sept. 1 to 15	Aug. 15 to Sept. 1	July 15 to Aug. 15
Cauliflower		Sept. 1 to 15	Aug. 1 to Sept. 1	July 1 to Aug. 1
Celery		Oct. 1 to 15	Sept. 1 to 30	July 1 to Aug. 1
Corn, sweet		Aug. 15 to 30	Aug. 1 to 15	July 15 to Aug. 15
Cucumber		Aug. 15 to 30	Aug. 1 to 15	July 15 to Aug. 15
Kale		Oct. 15 to Nov. 15	Oct. 1 to 30	Sept. 1 to 30
Lettuce		Oct. 15 to Nov. 15	Oct. 1 to 15	Sept. 1 to 30
Mustard		Oct. 15 to Nov. 15	Oct. 1 to 15	Sept. 1 to 30
Parsley		Oct. 15 to Nov. 15	Oct. 1 to 15	Sept. 1 to 30
Peas		Oct. 15 to Nov. 15	Oct. 1 to 15	Aug. 15 to Sept. 15
Potato:				
Irish		Aug. 15 to 30	Aug. 1 to 15	July 1 to 30
Sweet	Aug. 15	Aug. 1 to 15	July 15 to 30	June 1 to 30
Spinach		Oct. 15 to 30	Oct. 1 to 15	Aug. 15 to Sept. 30
Tomato		Oct. 15 to 30	Oct. 1 to 15	Aug. 15 to Sept. 30
Turnip		Oct. 15 to 30	Oct. 1 to 15	Aug. 15 to Sept. 30

Data from USDA Farmers' Bull. 934.

Treating Seed

Vegetable seed for planting should be treated for the control of bacterial and fungus diseases. The organisms are carried either within the seed tissue or on the surface of the seed. The ideal treatment sterilizes the seed without injuring germination or retarding subsequent growth and, unless the seed is recontaminated, also prevents decay after planting and greatly reduces damping-off of seedlings.

Three types of seed treatment in common use are as follows: (1) The hot-water method is used to control disease organisms that reside within seed tissue. Usually, immediately before planting, the seed is immersed for about 10 minutes in water heated to 120° to 125° F. (Some hard seeds germinate more readily after this treatment.) (2) Liquid chemical treatment for the control of disease organisms on seed may be given immediately after harvest or just before planting. If given just after harvest, the seed should be dried, packaged, and stored in such a manner as to avoid recontamination. Chemicals and methods of treatment are discussed in Chapter 11. (3) Chemical dust treatments are similar to the above, with the exception that the material is applied in the form of a dust rather than in solution. These treatments may be given at any time before planting, and a residue of the chemical should remain on the seed.

The particular type of seed treatment to use depends on the disease or diseases involved and the susceptibility of the seed to injury. It has been found advisable to treat some seeds, such as pepper and tomato, as they are removed from the fruit, and before the seeds are dry. Information regarding seed treatment should be obtained from some reliable source, and should be followed carefully. Most commercial compounds carry detailed directions on the packages. Some states have laws requiring and regulating treatment of vegetable seed. In so far as possible, one should purchase only seed that have been properly treated for the control of seed-borne diseases.

Planting Depths

The depth of planting seed depends on a number of conditions, chief among which are the texture of the soil, the availability of moisture, and the length of time required for germination (Table 8.1). When conditions are ideal, seed will germinate best when planted at a depth about four times the diameter of the seed.

A sandy soil, which dries out readily and does not form a crust after each rain, requires that seed be planted about twice as deeply as soil with a clay surface. In times of drought, seed should be planted at about twice the depth as when the surface soil is moist. Seed which germinate slowly, such as okra, pepper, beet, and carrot, should be planted more deeply than those which germinate readily, such as cabbage, tomato, turnip, and mustard.

Regardless of the depth of planting or kind of seed, the surface of the soil should be leveled and firmly pressed above the seed in such a manner that rain water will neither wash down the bed nor puddle above the seed. While opening a furrow with a hoe and dropping and covering the seed by hand usually gives satisfactory results, a mechanical seeder is desirable because it is more economical of seed and covers them more uniformly.

Planting Rates

Quality of seed is the chief factor that determines rate of seeding. With most vegetables, seed is the cheapest of the five important items which constitute cost of production. The other four items—land, labor, fertilizer, and equipment—are almost the same for a poor stand of plants as for a full stand. It is thus poor economy to limit the quality or quantity of seed.

Table 8.1 shows the rate of seeding for most vegetables, but this is subject to wide variation, based largely on whether the seed is sown in drills, hills, or broadcast. Fully three times as much seed is required to broadcast an area as to plant it in rows. When seed is plentiful and space is limited, much more seed may be used than when seed is scarce and land is plentiful. Time may be the limiting factor and the gardener may use twice the normal amount of seed to make sure there will be no replanting or second planting. Unfavorable weather may make it necessary to greatly increase the quantity of seed.

Attending After Emergence

When properly treated seed is planted in clean soil, the young plants upon emergence will be without diseases and insects. Precautions should be taken to keep them free of pests by spraying at an early date. Colorado potato beetles attack potato and tomato plants as soon as they are well out of the ground, and Mexican bean beetles begin eating bean plants as soon as the fourth leaf is formed. Leaf-spot and other diseases become active at the same time.

If rain occurs between the time of planting and emergence of the seedlings, a crop of weeds and grass should be destroyed immediately by cultivation, hoeing, or hand pulling. Often, hand weeding can be eliminated by the use of herbicides (Table 9.2). If practiced, irrigation should begin after the rows and middles are weeded. An application of quick-acting fertilizer may be advantageous during the first 10 days to insure early rapid growth of the young plants.

SETTING PLANTS

If plant-growing directions given in Chapter 7 are followed, plants of broccoli, Brussels sprouts, cabbage, cauliflower, celery, collard, eggplant, lettuce, onion, pepper, sweet potato, and tomato will be ready to set in the field at the proper time.

Preparing the Plant Bed

The initial steps in preparing a plant bed are similar to those for a seedbed. Beds for setting long-rooted plants like tomatoes, sweet potatoes, and peppers should be higher (or opened deeper) than beds for short plants such as lettuce. Rows for setting onions or lettuce should be about 1½ or 2 feet apart, while 3 or 3½ feet are required for the other vegetables to be transplanted.

Setting Distances

The distance between plants in the row varies with the scarcity of land, fertility of land, and kind of vegetables. The total yield per acre of most vegetables is increased by close planting, up to the point where the tops receive insufficient sunlight; however, the size of the individual plants or fruits is usually smaller. Greater yields of pepper in Georgia were obtained when the plants were set 12 inches apart as compared with plantings of 18, 24, 30, or 36 inches, but the percentage of large specimens was reduced by crowding. Jumbo sweet potatoes can be practically eliminated by setting plants 16 inches or less apart rather than 24 inches or more.

With the exception of sweet potatoes, plants should be set close enough together that the mature specimens will touch without crowding.

Setting Methods

There are three general methods of setting plants—hand setting, hand-machine setting, and riding-machine setting.

Hand setting involves four distinct hand operations: Holes are dug with a hoe or dibble, the plants are dropped into the holes, ½ to 1 pint of water is applied, and the plants are set and packed. This is the best method of setting plants because each one can be given individual attention. After the water has soaked well into the soil, the surface around the plant should be covered with dry soil.

In hand-machine setting, holes are made with the point of the plant setter and plants are placed in the holes from the machine. A quantity of water is poured by pressing a lever with the thumb, and the plant roots are covered with dry soil, all in one operation. This method is little used because hand setters are slow and difficult to operate.

In riding-machine setting, a machine opens a furrow into which a riding boy drops a plant. Water is immediately released from a barrel, and two curved slides cover the plant roots by raking soil from either side. This is a rapid method of setting plants and is quite satisfactory when the soil is well prepared and not too dry. With such a machine, one careful driver and two boys may plant as much as 10 acres a day.

Plants do best when set on a cloudy day, late in the afternoon, just after a rain, or just before a rain. Plants moved with the roots intact are less seriously injured than plants whose root systems are largely lost in transplanting; also, young plants whose tissues have not begun to appreciably suberize are less injured by transplanting than older plants.

Tomato, cabbage, eggplant, and pepper plants are sometimes checked to permit cultivation in both directions.

Size and Quality of Plants

With the exception of lettuce and celery, most plants to be set in the field should be about 6 inches long, equally divided between top and root, and from 6 to 10 weeks old. Larger and older plants are often used to advantage, but those more than 8 inches long are difficult to transplant and the mortality rate is higher.

Freedom from disease, freshness, vigor, and trueness to variety and type are more important than size. In so far as possible, plants should be set in the field on the same day they are pulled from the beds, discarding all that show abnormalities. During the interval that they are out of the ground the roots should be kept moist and the tops relatively dry and in the shade. The roots of plants held overnight should be wrapped in wet sphagnum moss.

Setting Dates

Tomato, eggplant, pepper, and sweet potato plants grow only during the warm season and should be set in the field only when the soil is warm. Lettuce, onion, cabbage, and related plants are semi-hardy and live through the winter in the lower South. Farther north, they are grown as spring or fall crops, not being able to stand either the extreme heat of summer or cold of winter.

The exact time to set plants depends on (1) the condition of the plants, (2) the condition of the soil, and (3) prevailing weather. Often it is profitable to postpone planting until a time when conditions are suitable. Only when plants are plentiful and the season is well advanced is it advisable to plant on poorly prepared land or under adverse weather conditions.

Setting Rates and Depths

Plants should be set in the field in about the same manner as they grew in the cold frame, but farther apart and from $\frac{1}{2}$ to 1 inch deeper.

Setting should be shallow enough to expose fully the bud and deep enough to prevent the plant from falling over and exposing the stem to the sun. About 4 inches of stem should be left above ground in setting tomato, pepper, cabbage, eggplant, and sweet potato plants, even if the below-ground portion is much more than this.

Attending After Setting

When only a few plants are set, they can be protected from the midday sun by putting a shingle on the south side of each plant. Paper or cardboard protectors are also used to shield newly set plants from drying winds and sun.

Except in arid or semi-arid regions, most vegetables usually need no watering other than at the time of setting. Certain intensely cultivated vegetables such as onions, lettuce, and celery, however, are sometimes grown under irrigation even in humid regions, in which case watering should be started immediately after the plants are set.

With summer vegetables such as tomatoes, peppers, and celery, the soil is sometimes mulched with fine straw, decayed manure, or treated paper. The soil should be thoroughly cultivated just before mulching. Chapter 10, "Irrigating and Mulching," gives full information on these practices.

If a rapid growth is desired early in the spring, as with lettuce, cabbage, celery, and others, a side dressing of readily soluble nitrogenous fertilizer is recommended.

SELECTED REFERENCES

Anonymous, "Usual Planting and Harvesting Dates," USDA *Handbook No. 251*, 1963.
Dethier, B. E. and Vittum, M. T., "Growing Degree Days," N. Y. State Exp. Sta. Bull. 801, 1963.
Hayslip, N. C., "Spacing of Vegetable Crop Plants," A. R. Fla. Agr. Exp. Sta. 1963-1964, p. 268.
Minges, P. A., "New Vegetable Varieties," Proc. Amer. Soc. Hort. Sci. 86, 1965.
Seaton, H. L., "Scheduling Plantings and Predicting Harvest Maturities for Processing Vegetables," *Food Technology* 9: 202-209, 1955.

CHAPTER 9

Cultivating and Rotating

Cultivation and rotation requirements of different vegetables vary considerably in different sections of the country according to climate, soil type, availability of labor, and other factors. The burden of cultivation has been materially decreased in recent years by the use of improved mechanization and chemicals, but some vegetable crops still require considerable hand work (Table 1.4).

CULTIVATING

Cultivation or intertillage of crops is a very old agricultural practice and its benefits are well recognized. The main benefits derived from cultivation are: (1) weed control, which aids in conserving moisture and nutrients; (2) conservation of moisture through the formation and maintenance of a soil mulch; and (3) increased aeration, which favors nitrification and other chemical changes in the soil. Special cultivation practices employed in producing different vegetables are discussed in the special crop chapters in Section Two, so this chapter deals primarily with basic principles.

Effects of Cultivation on Yield

Under most conditions, cultivation increases the yield of crop plants. This increase in yield results mainly from weed control, but the formation and maintenance of a soil mulch sometimes may be an important factor. Data from experiments carried on at Ithaca, New York, on a sandy loam soil show clearly that weed control is of major importance.

They show also that the maintenance of a soil mulch is of value to all crops under some conditions and of no benefit under other conditions. Similar results were obtained with experiments at Riverhead, New York, on a sassafras loam soil. In the experiments at Riverhead, cultivation once a week throughout the season was compared with cultivation once a week until the crops were about half grown, and with scraping the surface of the soil to control weeds. In one set of plots, the weeds were allowed to grow in order to determine their effect on the yield of the various crops. By comparing the yields of the cultivated and the scraped plots, the value of the soil mulch is shown, since weeds were eliminated as a factor in the two treatments. A summary of the results of experiments at Riverhead is given in Table 9.1.

Table 9.1—Effect of Cultivation on Yield.

Kind of Crop	Average Yield of Marketable Portion of Crop in Pounds per Plot			
	Cultivated All Season	Cultivated Half of Season	Scraped	Weeds Allowed to Grow
Carrot	505.3	506.4	519.5	27.9
Beet	240.3	239.7	233.2	45.6
Cabbage	233.6	234.6	207.5	129.1
Onion	67.7	69.6	64.3	3.6
Tomato	164.0	166.6	166.8	23.3
Potato	148.3	150.4	158.8	52.7

Data from Cornell Univ. Exp. Sta. Bull. 521.

A study of the data in Table 9.1 will show only slight differences in yield between the two sets of cultivated plots and between these and the scraped plots. In no case is the difference in average yields between the two sets of cultivated plots significant. The cultivated plots of cabbage produced a higher average yield than did the scraped plots, but the difference is not statistically significant. The scraped plots of potatoes consistently produced a slightly larger yield than the cultivated plots and the difference is statistically significant. Results somewhat similar to these were reported in Pennsylvania with corn, beans, potatoes, mangel beets, and cabbage.

Effects of Cultivation on Soil Moisture

Cultivation nearly always results in moisture conservation through the destruction of weeds. The formation of a soil mulch may also conserve moisture by preventing surface run-off and by slowing up the movement of water to the surface, where it evaporates. However, the benefits derived from the soil mulch have been greatly overemphasized. Results of many experiments have shown much less conservation of moisture than is commonly believed, For example, the study at Ithaca, New York, comparing cultivation with scraping the soil to control weeds shows that cultivation resulted in moisture conservation in about two-thirds of the comparisons, but most of the differences were slight. In the other comparisons, cultivation resulted in no conservation of moisture or even in actual loss.

It is important to know under what conditions stirring the soil is likely to result in loss of moisture and when in conservation. In general, when the soil is cultivated soon after a rain of ½ inch or less, moisture is likely to be lost because evaporation is hastened by exposing more surface to the drying action of the air. In many instances, practically all of the moisture from a light rain is lost by cultivating. Even if the moisture from a light rain were not lost, it would not be available to the plants because the cultivator destroys the roots to the depth cultivated. Moisture is lost also if cultivation is done when a mulch is already present. The mulch is deepened and moist soil from below is brought to the surface, where the moisture is lost by evaporation.

Not only does cultivation sometimes cause loss of moisture at critical periods, but it may also conserve moisture when a lower water content would be an advantage. It should be noted also that cultivation for the purpose of maintaining a mulch does not always increase yields, even if moisture is conserved. Destruction of roots by the cultivator may more than offset the benefits from moisture conservation. Knowledge of these facts enables one to time his cultivating intelligently and to reduce the detrimental effects.

There is no justification for the practice of cultivating at regular intervals regardless of the conditions. When there are no weeds and a soil mulch is present, cultivation is not only an unnecessary expense, but it is usually injurious. When 3 or 4 inches of the surface soil are kept stirred, most of the roots are destroyed so that it is impossible for the plants to get moisture and nutrients in the cultivated zone (Fig. 9.1).

Effects of Cultivation on Soil Temperature

It is often stated that cultivation increases the absorption and retention of heat. This belief is based on the fact that heat is used in the evaporation of water. If this were the only factor involved, stirring the soil would raise the temperature whenever it resulted in conserving

Fig. 9.1—Roots of beet plants at depth of 2 to 3 inches. Cultivation to depth of 3 inches would have destroyed all of these roots.

Cornell Univ. Agr. Exp. Sta.

moisture, and would lower the temperature when cultivation increased the loss of moisture. Many investigators have shown that during the growing season, cultivation reduces the temperature. Usually the reduction is small and probably of little practical significance. The compactness of the surface of the uncultivated soil probably accounts for the higher temperature. A compact soil has been shown to be a better heat conductor than a loose, dry layer of soil.

Effects of Cultivation on Nitrification

Many studies have been made on the effects of cultivation on nitrification, and the results are somewhat conflicting. In some cases, nitrification was increased by stirring the soil, and in other cases, there was no significant difference between cultivated and uncultivated soil. In the studies on a sandy loam soil at Ithaca, New York, there was no consistent advantage in favor of cultivation as compared with scraping the soil, as far as nitrification was concerned. Investigations with a Hagerstown silt-loam soil in Pennsylvania show that nitrification proceeded as rapidly on the scraped plots as on plots that were cultivated three to eight times. On the other hand, nitrates have averaged higher on cultivated plots than on comparable scraped plots of Dunkirk silty clay soil at Ithaca, New York.

Any increase in nitrification resulting from cultivation would be brought about by increasing aeration, or by providing better moisture or better temperature conditions for the growth of nitrifying bacteria. Some investigators have shown a positive correlation between soil moisture and nitrates, while others have shown no relation. Since the soil mulch does not always have the same effect on moisture conservation, one might expect that its effect on nitrification would vary with conditions. On heavy soils, cultivation to break the surface crust usually increases aeration and this frequently results in increasing nitrification. On most vegetable soils, cultivation is seldom of much importance from the standpoint of soil aeration.

Cultivating Implements and Tools

Vegetables are cultivated by all types of equipment that are used for cultivating other intertilled crops and, in addition, hand cultivators and special garden tractors are used. Hand cultivators, of the wheel-hoe type, are used mainly for cultivating small growing crops produced intensively and for home gardens. Tractor cultivators range in size from the small garden tractor to the large farm tractors (Fig. 9.2). The heaviest tractors are not well suited to cultivation of most vegetables. Some of the smaller farm tractors are satisfactory for cultivating potatoes, cabbage, tomatoes, and other crops that are grown in rows far enough apart to give ample space for wheels. When garden tractors are used to pull gang seeders, all rows in one operation are equally spaced. The same group of rows can then be carefully cultivated with a tractor pulling a gang cultivator.

Various kinds of attachments are used on all types of cultivators mentioned. The sweep, commonly used in the South, and the blade attachments, such as are employed on hand cultivators, are efficient in controlling weeds and are less destructive to the roots than the shovel and teeth attachments.

Fig. 9.2—Cultivating and fertilizing tomatoes in Puerto Rico.

When and How to Cultivate

Weed control is the most important function of cultivation; therefore, the work should be done at the time most favorable for killing weeds. The best time is before the weeds have become established, since they are more easily killed when they are small. Also, it is important to destroy the weeds before they compete seriously with vegetable plants for moisture, nutrients, light, and air. Cultivation when the weeds are breaking through the surface is most efficient, since at this time they are not well established, and merely breaking the surface of the soil will destroy them.

Cultivating should be done as often as necessary to prevent weeds from injuring the crop. This requires frequent cultivation when conditions are favorable for the germination of weed seeds, as after a rain or after the application of irrigation water. The best time to cultivate after a rain, as after the application of water, is when the soil is dry enough to crumble and not so dry as to break up into lumps. If cultivated when too wet, most classes of soils, except the sands and loose mucks and peats, will

Table 9.2—Suggestions for Herbicides in 1967.

Crop	Herbicide	Rate of Active Ingredient per Acre Actually Covered*	Weeds Controlled	Best Time of Application (Based on Crop Stage)	Remarks, Cautions, Limitations
Asparagus (seedlings)	Amiben	3 lb.	Annuals	Immediately after seeding.	Irrigation or rainfall after treatment will give maximum control.
Asparagus (established planting)	Dowpon	5-10 lb.	Perennial grass	End of harvest season following disking.	Apply when grass weeds are 3 to 4 inches tall.
	Telvar	3 lb.	Annuals	In spring before spears emerge and immediately following harvest.	Apply Telvar after disking. Do not exceed 6 lb. per growing season.
	Karmex	3 lb.	Annuals		Apply Karmex after disking. Do not exceed 4.8 lb. per growing season. Do not replant treated area to any other crop for 2 years after last application.
	Simazine	3-4 lb.	Annuals	In spring and after harvest.	Apply after disking. Apply only once a year after first year. Do not treat during last year in asparagus because of residue.
Beans, lima	Amiben	3-4 lb.	Annuals	Immediately after seeding.	Field may be rotary-hoed without destroying herbicide action. Do not feed foliage to livestock.
	Amiben plus Randox	2 lb. +2 lb.	Annuals	Immediately after seeding.	Gives sustained annual grass control.
	Treflan	0.5 to 0.75 lb.	Primarily annual grasses	Preplant soil application. Incorporate with soil immediately.	Plant crop immediately or within 3 weeks after application. Do not feed foliage to livestock.
Beans, snap	Sinox PE** or Premerge**		Annuals	Pre-emergence.	
	Eptam	4 lb.	Annual grasses and nutgrass	Preplant soil application. Incorporate with soil immediately.	Use ⅔ rate on light sandy soil. Do not feed foliage to livestock.
	Treflan	0.5 to 0.75 lb.	Primary annual grasses	Preplant soil application. Incorporate with soil immediately.	Plant crop immediately or within 3 weeks after application. Do not feed forage to livestock.

(Continued)

Table 9.2—Suggestions for Herbicides in 1967 (Continued).

Crop	Herbicide	Rate of Active Ingredient per Acre Actually Covered*	Weeds Controlled	Best Time of Application (Based on Crop Stage)	Remarks, Cautions, Limitations
Beets, garden and sugar	Endothal	4-6 lb.	Annuals	Pre-emergence.	Rainfall or irrigation after treatment and before weeds emerge gives maximum control.
	TCA	8 lb.	Annual grasses	Pre-emergence.	Do not use treated tops for food.
	(Endothal-TCA is available as a commercailly prepared mixture of 2% endothal and 4% TCA for a mixture of weed populations. Use at same rate as individual chemicals alone.)				
	Pyramin	4 lb.	Annuals	Pre-emergence or after beets emerge and before weeds have 2 true leaves.	Where grasses are a severe problem, use 4 lb. Pyramin + 4-6 lb. TCA.
Broccoli Brussels sprouts Cabbage Cauliflower	Treflan	1 lb.	Primarily annual grasses	Preplant soil application. Incorporate with soil immediately.	Transplant after application to 3 weeks later.
	Vegadex	4-6 lb.	Annuals	Immediately before or after seeding or transplanting.	Direct spray to base of transplants. Do not use when temperature is above 80° F. Use lower rates when temperature is below 60°. Irrigation or rainfall after application is beneficial.
Carrots Celery Dill Parsnips Parsley	Stoddard Solvent	60-80 gal.	Annuals	After two true leaves have appeared. (Do not apply to carrots or parsnips after they are ¼ inch in diameter, because an oily taste may result.)	Most effective when sprayed on cloudy days or during high humidity, and when weeds are not more than 2 inches high. May not control ragweed.
Carrots Parsnips	Lorox	2 lb. 1½ lb.	Annuals	Pre-emergence.	Do not feed treated foliage to livestock or replant treated area for 4 months. Do not use on parsnips on sandy soil. Use ⅔ rate on carrots.

Crop	Chemical	Rate	Weeds controlled	Time of application	Remarks
Cucumbers Muskmelons	Alanap	3-5 lb. / 3-3.5 lb.	Annuals	Immediately after seeding or transplanting. After transplanting or vining.	Do not use on cold soil. Rainfall or irrigation after treatment gives maximum control. Use granular form. Keep away from foliage.
Onions	Dacthal	8-10 lb.	Annuals	Immediately after seeding or transplanting.	May not kill smartweed or common ragweed. Can be used on seeds, sets, or seedlings. CIPC can be used for smartweed or common ragweed.
	Chloro-IPC	3-6 lb.	Use to enhance broad leaf control	On seeded onions: loop stage or after 3- to 4-leaf stage.	In the later sprays, direct at base of onion plant. If more than one application is applied do not exceed 6 lb. per acre for the season. **Use lower rates in cool, wet weather.** Use no later than 30 days before harvest.
	Randox	4-6 lb.	Annuals	After 3 or more true leaves.	Heavy rainfall may reduce stand. Very effective on purslane and pigweed. Use no later than 45 days before harvest. Direct application to base of plant in later treatment.
Peas	Sinox PE[2] or Premerge[2]	1-1¼ lb.	Annuals	Post-emergence: Before peas are 6 inches tall.	Apply in at least 20 gal. of water per acre. Use lower rate when temperature is 80°. Do not graze or use for stock for 60 days.
	MCPB	1 lb.	Broad-leaved weeds and Canada thistle	When peas are 3-7 inches tall and no later than 4 nodes prior to pea blossom.	May delay maturity 1 to 4 days. Use at least 20 gal. of water per acre. Do not feed vines to livestock. MCPA is more effective on mustard. MCPB is less injurious to peas.
	MCPA	¼-½ lb.			
Peppers	Dymid, Enide	4-5 lb.	Annuals	Pre-emergence or after transplanting.	Do not plant another food crop on treated areas for 6 months. Use 4 lb. on light soil.
	Vegiben	3-4 lb.	Annuals	Within 2 to 3 days after transplanting or immediately after lay-by.	Apply only once during growing season. Apply when foliage is dry. Rainfall or irrigation after application will give best results. Use granular formulation only. Do not feed foliage to livestock.
	Treflan	1 lb.	Primarily annual grasses	Preplant soil application. Incorporate with soil immediately.	Use on transplants only. Do not feed foliage to livestock.

(Continued)

Table 9.2—Suggestions for Herbicides in 1967.

Crop	Herbicide	Rate of Active Ingredient per Acre Actually Covered*	Weeds Controlled	Best Time of Application (Based on Crop Stage)	Remarks, Cautions, Limitations
Potatoes, Irish	Eptam	3-5 lb.	Annual grasses and nutgrass	Preplant soil application. Incorporate with soil immediately.	Use lower rate on sandy soil.
	Lorox	2 lb.	Annuals	Pre-emergence.	Use ⅔ rate on light sandy soil. Plant tubers at least 2 inches deep. Do not replant treated area to other crops for 4 months after treatment.
	Dowpon	4 lb.	Annual grasses and quackgrass	Just before emergence.	Do not use on red-skinned varieties. Do not use if a preplant treatment was used.
		6 lb.	Quackgrass	Before plowing in spring; wait 4 days before plowing and planting.	Not for fields intended for red-skinned varieties.
Potatoes, sweet	Dacthal	8-10 lb.	Annuals	Immediately after planting.	May not control smartweed or common ragweed. Preferred on sandy soils.
	Amiben	3 lb.	Annuals	Immediately after planting.	Preferred on loam soils. Do not feed foliage to livestock.
Spinach	Chloro-IPC	1-3 lb.	Annuals	Immediately after seeding.	Use 1 lb. if the temperature is below 60° Do not apply if temperature is above 80°. Irrigation or rainfall after treatment gives best results.
	Vegadex	3-4 lb.	Annuals	Immediately after seeding.	
Squash Pumpkins	Alanap	3-3.5 lb	Annuals	Immediately after seeding.	Use granular form on transplants. Do not use early when soil is cold. Moisture is necessary for good control. Use 3-lb. rate on sandy soils. Use on loam soils.
	Amiben	3-4 lb.	Annuals	As soon after seeding as possible.	

Crop	Herbicide	Rate	Weeds controlled	Time of application	Remarks
Sweet corn	Randox	5 lb.	Annuals	Pre-emergence.	Not effective on sandy soils.
	Atrazine	2-3 lb.	Annuals, annual and perennial grasses	Pre-emergence; apply no later than 3 weeks after seeding. Shallow cultivation may improve weed control during dry weather.	Grow corn a second year without treatment. This chemical has a high soil residue. Do not plant other vegetable crops on a sprayed area until a second year of corn has been grown. Use Atrazine only where quackgrass is a problem. Residue hazard decreased when banded or in combination with Lorox.
	Atrazine plus Lorox	1.5 lb. + 1 lb.	Annuals and perennial grasses	Pre-emergence.	Use to reduce Atrazine residue. Plant seeds 1.75 inches deep.
	2,4-D (amine)	½ lb.	Annuals	Post-emergence.	Preferably, apply before corn is 6 inches tall. If corn is over 12 inches reduce rate to ¼ lb.
Tomatoes, direct-seeded	Dymid, Enide	4-6 lb.	Annuals	Pre-emergence.	Do not plant other food crops on treated areas for 6 months.
Tomatoes, transplanted	Dymid, Enide	4-6 lb.	Annuals	After transplanting.	Do not plant other food crops on treated areas for 6 months. Use 4 lb. on light soils.
	Vegiben	3-4 lb.	Annuals	Within 2 to 3 days after transplanting or immediately after lay-by.	Use granular formulation only. Do not use on sandy soils.
	Treflan	1 lb.	Primarily annual grasses	Preplant soil application. Incorporate with soil immediately.	Granular formulation can be used on all soils. Apply only once during growing season. Do not feed foliage to livestock.
Watermelon	Alanap	3-5 lb.	Annuals	Immediately after seeding.	Do not use on cold soil. Use low rates on sandy soil. Rainfall or irrigation after treatment gives maximum control.
		3-3.5 lb.		After transplanting or vining.	Granular form preferred. Keep material away from foliage.

* Based on active ingredients (actual amount of active herbicide in material or acid equivalent). Use lower rate on sandy soil and higher rate on clay and loam soils. When using a band application over the row, adjust amount of material applied to the part of an acre treated. See Illinois Circular 791.

** May not control smartweed and annual grasses.

Data from Ill. Agr. Ext. Cir. 907 by H. J. Hopen and J. S. Vandemark.

bake on drying; and, if allowed to get too dry, the surface will have already become baked and hard and will not crumble when broken up.

Shallow cultivation is preferable to deep cultivation under most conditions. Practically all of the benefits derived from cultivation are obtained through shallow tillage, and such tillage results in a minimum of destruction to the roots. Some vegetable growers practice deep cultivation when the plants are small, with the idea that the breaking of the roots near the surface will result in greater development of roots below the depth cultivated. Experimental evidence with potatoes indicates that this is a mistake and that destroying the surface roots does not make the roots go deeper.

Under most conditions, if sufficient cultivation is given to control weeds, it will be enough to accomplish all other purposes. Cultivation to form a mulch may be desirable when a hard crust forms on the surface and when cracks develop; however, deep cultivation may do more harm than good, even under such conditions. It is certain that no good is accomplished by cultivating when there are no weeds and a mulch is already present.

CONTROLLING WEEDS WITH CHEMICALS

In certain cases the cost of controlling weeds can be reduced by the use of chemicals. They may be used advantageously where weed seeds germinate before the crop plants emerge. A particular chemical can be used to kill infesting weeds when the crop plant is tolerant to the herbicide. Perennial weeds, which are difficult to eradicate by cultivation, can often be controlled by spraying or treating the soil. Chemical herbicides can be used along fence rows or irrigation ditches where cultivation is impossible.

The effectiveness of a herbicide often depends upon the care exercised in following the directions for its use. The rate and timeliness of application, soil type, weather conditions, and the kind of crop and weeds on which a herbicide is used should be considered. Practices suggested for the control of weeds are given in Table 9.2.

ROTATING

Crop rotation may be defined as the growing of two or more crops in regular sequence on the same land during a period of years. Rotation may cover a period of two, three, or more years. When two or more crops are grown in sequence on the same land in one year, the term "successive cropping" is used. Crop rotation is of importance in disease and insect control and in making the best use of the resources of the soil.

This chapter discusses the principles of rotation primarily, while the chapters on special crops contain specific recommendations concerning this subject.

Rotation as a Factor in Disease and Insect Control

Some diseases can be controlled by a system of rotation in which the host plants are grown on the same land only once in a period of three, four, or more years. Rotation is most effective in disease control when the organisms causing the disease live in the soil only one or two years. Club root of cabbage and other cruciferous plants, for example, can be controlled by rotation, provided no cruciferous crops or cruciferous weeds are allowed to grow for at least three years; a longer rotation is desirable, however, where club root is serious. Some diseases, such as potato scab and onion smut, cannot be controlled by ordinary rotation as the organisms involved live in the soil for many years.

In planning a rotation system, one needs to know what kinds of plants are attacked by a given organism. Some organisms attack only one kind of host plant; others attack all kinds of plants within a genus; and still others are not limited to a given family of plants. Club root affects many kinds of cruciferous plants, and the nematode disease is serious on a large number of crops representing many families.

Rotation helps to control insects, especially those that feed on one kind of crop only and those that are unable to move very far. A short rotation is as good as a long one for controlling most insects, since they die soon after emergence if the food plants are absent.

Rotation as a Factor in Soil Management

Rotation is of importance in soil management, since crops differ in their requirements for nutrients, in the extent and distribution of their root systems, and in their effects on soil acidity and on other factors. It is a fairly common belief that certain crops are "hard on land," and it is well known that crops differ in their effects on the yield of those which follow. Hartwell and his co-workers, under Rhode Island conditions, have shown that onions produced a small yield following certain crops such as mangel beets, rutabagas, cabbage, buckwheat, and potatoes, and a relatively large yield following red top, timothy, and a combination of these. Buckwheat, on the other hand, produced a very large yield following rutabagas and a very small yield following corn and millet. In general, the crops which had the most depressing effect on the yield of onions had the opposite effect on buckwheat. The large difference in yield of these two crops is probably due to the varying effects of the preceding crops on soil acidity and on the quantity of nutrients removed. It was found that the lowest yield of onions followed those crops which removed the largest quantity of the deficient nutrients and the largest yield followed the crop which removed the smallest quantity of nitrogen and phosphorus. It was not universally true, however, that the crops which removed the largest quantities of the deficient nutrients were the ones which had the greatest depressing effect on the succeeding crop.

Soil acidity is affected differently by different crops and this may account for considerable variation in yield of succeeding crops that are sensitive to acidity or conditions associated with it. It was found in the Rhode Island studies, mentioned above, that the yield of onions was highest following those crops giving rise to the least acidity. When the acidity was reduced by liming, the effects of various crops on the yield of onions following was much less divergent. With optimum quantities of nutrients and with favorable soil reaction, a large part of the depressing effects of the crops on the yield of those following largely disappeared. It appears, therefore, that supplying adequate quantities of nutrients and maintaining a favorable soil reaction would eliminate much of the depressing effect of a given crop on the one following.

Order of Crop Rotation

No definite system of rotation can be given that would be satisfactory under a wide range of conditions, but there are a few principles which should be observed. In order to utilize fully the resources of the soil, it is desirable to alternate shallow-rooted plants with deep-rooted ones, and to follow crops that supply organic matter to the soil with those that favor its decomposition. The rotation should be so planned as to give as much time as feasible to the growing of soil-improving crops between the time of harvesting one crop and the planting of the next one on the same land. Where soil erosion is a serious problem, it is important to have a soil-improving crop on the land whenever it is not occupied by a money crop. This is especially important in regions where the land is idle during the winter. In most of the large commercial vegetable-growing regions of the South, the soil-improving crop should be grown in the summer, and turned under in preparation for fall or winter crops.

Where vegetables are grown in rotation with general farm crops, it is advisable to follow a hay or pasture crop with corn or cotton rather than with vegetable crops. Small growing crops, such as lettuce, celery, and beets, carrots, and other root crops, should be preceded by a cultivated crop. Weeds are less likely to be serious following a clean-cultivated crop than following a hay or pasture crop.

In planning the order of crop rotation, attention should be given also to disease and insect control as mentioned in a previous paragraph.

SELECTED REFERENCES

Anonymous, "Chemical Weed Control Recommendations for Vegetable Crops," Wisc. Ext. Ser. Cir. 55, 1966.

Audus, L. J., *The Physiology and Biochemistry of Herbicides*, London and New York: Academic Press, 1964.

Hopen, H. J. and Vandemark, J. S, "Herbicide Guide for Commercial Vegetable Growers," Ill. Agr. Ext. Cir. 907, 1967.

Janes, B. E., "Vegetable Rotation Studies in Connecticut, II," *Proc. Amer. Soc. Hort. Sci.* 57: 252-258, 1951.

Odland, T. E. and Smith, J. B., "Further Studies on the Effect of Certain Crops on Succeeding Crops," *Jour. Amer. Soc. Agronomy* 40: 99-107, 1948.

Odland, T. E., Bell, R. S., and Smith, J. B., "The Influence of Crop Plants on Those Which Follow, V," R. I. Agr. Exp. Sta. Bull. 309, 1950.

Thompson, H. C., Wessels, P. H., and Mills, H. S., "Cultivation Experiments with Certain Vegetable Crops on Long Island," Cornell Univ. Exp. Sta. Bull. 521, 1931.

CHAPTER 10

Irrigating and Mulching

Adequate soil moisture is essential to the production of most vegetable crops. In addition to the direct effect on plant growth, water often aids in dissolving fertilizers and soil nutrients, and plays an important part in biological activities. Sources of the soil's water supply are: (1) direct precipitation, (2) surface drainage water, and (3) underground water, the first being by far the most important. Man has supplemented these natural sources with various forms of irrigation, by which the grower practically controls moisture conditions of the soil in arid and semi-arid regions. Besides irrigation, other means of moisture control are: (1) the addition of organic matter, which increases the water-holding capacity of the soil, and (2) the use of mulches, which usually retard evaporation.

IRRIGATING

Rainfall even in the humid regions of the country is often inadequate or poorly distributed for vegetable production. If a drought occurs during a critical period of a crop's growth, the yield may be decreased and quality lowered. Irrigation and moisture control are important for both yield and quality of most vegetable crops. For many years most vegetables in California and other arid and semi-arid regions of the country have been irrigated. Irrigation of vegetables has increased rapidly in the 28 so-called humid states during the last 30 years. Approximately 40 percent of all vegetables produced in the United States in 1949 were irrigated. The U.S. Agricultural Census reported that 70 percent of all vegetables except sweet potatoes in 1954 and 76 percent in 1959 were irrigated. This increase is expected to continue.

145

Sources of Water

Water for irrigation may be obtained from streams, lakes, wells, springs, and stored storm water. In most states where irrigation is practiced, definite laws and regulations pertaining to the use of water for irrigation purposes have been set up. These regulations should be known and understood before a grower proceeds to spend money on irrigation equipment.

Water may be diverted from streams, lakes, or reservoirs through gravitation or by means of pumps. Some wells are overflowing, while others require pumps to lift the water. A farmer may use one or more sources and systems in obtaining water for irrigation.

Costs obviously vary greatly, and they may be divided into two parts: (1) the costs of initial purchase and installation of equipment, and (2) costs connected with actual application of the water to the land. Where water is obtained from flowing wells or springs, or diverted from streams or lakes, the initial expense may be comparatively low. The expense of stream diversion is often borne by a group of people. However, when powerful pumps are required to raise the water, initial expenses become high. The cost of drilling a well and installing a pump and motor, as well as building a reservoir for temporary storage, may easily amount to a substantial investment. The expense of applying water to the land is more or less constant every year.

Applying Water

Water can be applied usually by one of three systems: (1) surface irrigation, (2) subirrigation, and (3) spraying. The first is by far the most common, and is practically the only method used on the irrigated lands listed by the Bureau of the Census. Subirrigation is feasible only under certain soil conditions, and is not commonly practiced. As an insurance against drought, spray irrigation is used more in the eastern states than in other sections. Since care in choosing equipment may reduce initial cost and insure practical results, a grower should determine which system best suits his particular condition, and should insist that it be laid out to the best advantage. The source and amount of water available, topography of the farm, soil type, and prevailing climatic conditions are some of the factors to be considered.

The actual application of water also requires special training on the part of the grower. The amount of water to apply, the frequency of its application, and the various methods best suited to the different crops, as well as soil management, are important considerations. The mere application of water to the soil far from solves a grower's problems; indeed, it may add to them. For example, irrigation sometimes leads to drainage difficulties and to salt accumulation; therefore, adequate drainage is just as necessary as a sufficient water supply. On farms where irrigation is consistently practiced, there is a danger that salts, harmful to plant growth, may gradually accumulate in the surface layer of soil. Various factors such as poor drainage, water with a high salt content, and too frequent light irrigations may all contribute to this condition. While proper methods of soil and irrigation management aid in preventing such salt accumulations, they tend to occur under some conditions, regardless of precautions taken. However, in many locations such difficulties are not encountered, and through intelligent management, some soils retain their productive qualities after many years of irrigation.

In general, regardless of the method of irrigation, sufficient water should be applied to moisten the ground thoroughly. Frequent inadequate irrigations should be avoided unless the primary purpose of the irrigation is to cool the soil. In actual practice, the quantity of water applied and the frequency of irrigation will depend on several interacting factors involving the crop, the soil, and the weather. In surface irrigation, the furrows or the areas between the borders are usually made of sufficient length to allow proper penetration and horizontal movement of water by the time it reaches the lower end. A common application is equivalent to a solid sheet of water 3 to 4 inches deep, which is usually more than sufficient.

Surface Irrigation

As the name implies, in surface irrigation the water is made to flow over the soil surface. Wherever vegetable crops are irrigated by this system, either the border or the furrow method is generally used. In the former system, which is more adapted to land having a gentle slope, borders 6 to 8 inches high and 150 to 300 feet long are thrown up every 5 to 12 feet apart. These borders follow the general contour of the land, and the entire area between them is flooded during irrigations. With more rolling pieces of ground, the ridge and furrow system is usually more desirable (Fig. 10.1).

Correct preparation of the soil surface is most essential in any method of surface irrigation. It saves loss of time during actual irrigation, results in a more even distribution of water, reduces waste, and leads to the production of larger crops of better quality. Grading after plowing reduces the soil to an even plane surface, by removing the knolls and fill-

Fig. 10.1—Setting out plastic syphon spiles for surface irrigation.

USDA Photograph

ing the depressions, but the entire area is not reduced to the same level. A general slope is desirable, the amount varying with each locality. Manufactured levelers as well as homemade wooden floats or drags are commonly used for this final smoothing process.

When the initial cost for wells, pumps, and accompanying equipment is not so large, surface irrigation requires only a moderate investment. If the supply of water is sufficient, this method is excellently adapted to irrigating immense areas of ground. Among the disadvantages are: (1) the necessity for constant attention, (2) the tendency for soils to crust and bake, and (3) the tremendous losses of water by seepage in supply ditches.

Subirrigation

In subirrigation, water is added to the soil in such a way that it permeates the soil from below. Subirrigation requires an abundance of water, a sandy loam topsoil through which water will move freely by capillary attraction, and an impervious subsoil which will hold the water. At the same time, adequate drainage is necessary. The large amount of water required and the great expense involved in the laying of the tile pipes (although subirrigation does not necessarily involve the laying of any structures) are disadvantages of this system. Advantages include the maintenance of an undisturbed soil mulch, and lack of trouble from soil baking. In actual practice, subirrigation is sometimes difficult, justifying considerable investigation of existing soil conditions and the water supply before such a system is installed.

Spray Irrigation

Spray irrigation involves the use of a system of pipes in which the water is conveyed to the fields under pressure, and there sprayed on the crops (Fig. 10.2). Advantages of this system include: (1) adaptability to

Fig. 10.2—A crop of cabbage under overhead spray irrigation. The lines of parallel pipes are placed so that there will be complete coverage between each pair, but with a minimum overlapping of spray.

Progressive Farmer and Southern Ruralist

all soils and soil surfaces, (2) utilization of amounts of water entirely inadequate for surface or subirrigation, and (3) minimum attention requirements. A spray irrigation system is often excellent insurance against drought in humid regions, where the crops being grown warrant the heavy expense of installation and the cost of water itself. It is not successful under ordinary arid climatic conditions as it delivers water too slowly and in insufficient quantities.

MULCHING

A mulch is created whenever the soil surface is artificially modified. Coverings of straw, leaves, refuse, or paper, and even a loose layer of soil produced by cultivation, are all mulches. Mulching with materials other than the soil itself is not very extensively practiced. In the nonirrigated sections of the South, straw and pine needles are commonly used as mulches for strawberries. In recent years, polyethylene as well as paper has received considerable attention as a mulch for various vegetable crops, especially in the North.

Purpose of Mulching

The chief purpose of mulches is to conserve moisture, but they are also used to insure clean fruit, control weeds, hasten maturity, and increase yields. Paper mulch, more than any other kind, is reported to be effective for all of these uses.

Effect of Mulching

Because of the interest in paper mulch, numerous observations have been made as to its effect on soil moisture, soil temperature, and soil nitrates, as well as its influence on weed growth, and the various processes and characteristics of the crop.

EFFECT ON THE SOIL. Most workers have found that the mulch conserves moisture directly by preventing evaporation, and indirectly by controlling weeds. In arid and semi-arid regions, where the soil moisture is low to begin with, mulch is no substitute for irrigation and in some cases makes irrigation difficult.

Experiments in three widely separated localities have indicated that there is increased nitrification under mulch paper. Soil temperatures are usually several degrees higher under ordinary black paper mulches than under similar unmulched conditions. With papers of lighter color, and under certain climatic conditions, temperatures under a mulch may be lower. They may average as much as 10 degrees F. lower under a straw mulch. Since soil and most other mulches are not so impervious as paper mulch, their effects on soil conditions are probably not so striking.

EFFECT ON THE CROP. Warm-season crops, such as cucumbers, musk-melons, eggplants, and peppers, usually respond to paper mulch by maturing earlier and by yielding more. Quick-maturing spring crops also are often benefited. The response of both these types of crops is probably due to higher soil temperatures. The quality of such crops may be improved by paper mulch, the products being larger and cleaner and containing fewer culls. When growing conditions are already favorable, however, paper mulch rarely improves them, and may indeed affect the crop adversely. Such cool-weather crops as onions, lettuce, beets, cabbage, and cauliflower have been reported as responding rather poorly to paper mulch. The yield and keeping quality of early potatoes may be improved by straw mulch.

Making the Mulch

The time at which mulches are made depends on the type of mulch as well as the kind of crop. In general, most mulches are made after the crop is planted.

PAPER MULCH. Paper mulch can be laid strip by strip as the rows of seeds or plants are set out. It is usually laid first, and then the planting done through the paper (Figs. 10.3 and 10.4). Special equipment has been developed to lay the paper and cover the edges with a narrow bank of earth, all in one operation. The cost of paper mulch is very high, especially with complete coverage, and its use is warranted only on crops of high value which are known to respond well. The heavier grades of paper should be used to exclude light, and paper containing volatile or water-soluble materials which are harmful to the plant should be avoided. The paper is usually impregnated with a fungicide to prevent early decay.

POLYETHYLENE MULCHES. Good results have been reported from the use of black polyethylene. However, this material is expensive and does not decay readily. It must be removed from the field, and this operation is also expensive. Clear polyethylene is most effective in increasing soil temperature. Sunlight transmitted by the film is absorbed by the soil and converted to heat which is not readily reradiated through the film. Since it transmits light, its use is dependent upon soil fumigation or a herbicide to prevent weed growth. An extremely thin polyethylene coating on paper seems to have possibilities as a soil mulch. It breaks up and does not cause a removal problem.

Fig. 10.3—Laying paper mulch by machine.

Univ. of Ill. Photograph

OTHER MULCHES. Straw, leaves, pine needles, and similar mulches are usually applied after the crop is well established. Such mulches are not commonly used with vegetable crops. However, many growers like to maintain a good soil mulch, which is fully discussed in Chapter 9.

SELECTED REFERENCES

Barr, W. L. and Thomas, D. W., "Irrigation on Pennsylvania Farms," Pa. Agr. Exp. Sta. Bull. 562, 1953.
Bradley, G. A. and Pratt, A. J., "Irrigation to Make a Crop—Not to Save It," N. Y. State Farm Research 20, No. 2, 1954.
Campbell, J. A., "Irrigation for Vegetable Crops," Miss. Agr. Exp. Sta. Cir. 182, 1953.
Davis, J. R., "Irrigating Small Acreages," Mich. Agr. Ext. Bull. 320, 1953.

Fig. 10.4—Seeding through paper mulch.

Univ. of Ill. Photograph

Nettles, V. F, Jamison, F. S., and Jones, B. E., "Irrigation and other Cultural Studies with Cabbage, Sweet Corn, Snap Beans, Onions, Tomatoes, and Cucumbers," Fla. Agr. Exp. Sta. Bull. 495, 1952.

Schoenemann, J. A., et al., "Chemical Weed Control Recommendations for Vegetable Crops, 1962," Wisc. Agr. Exp. Sta. Spec. Cir. 55, 1962.

Schwalen, H. C., Frost, K. R., and Hinz, W. W., "Sprinkler Irrigation," Ariz. Agr. Exp. Sta. Bull. 250, 1953.

Waggoner, P. E., Miller, P. M., and DeRoo, H. C., "Plastic Mulching: Principles and Benefits," Conn. Agr. Exp. Sta. Bull. 634, 1960.

CHAPTER 11

Controlling Insects and Diseases

Never before in world history have people been so well fed by so few farmers as in this country today. With only 8 percent of our population farming, the remaining 92 percent are fed, while nearly all of the population of some of the developing countries work at producing food. The American farmer is establishing the world pace partly because he uses all of the available tools of present-day farming—chemical and mechanical. He relies heavily on the chemical tools to control insects and diseases in order to produce high-quality food at low prices.

Fortunately, at our disposal we have more than 100 pesticidal chemicals which will control insect and disease pests. We need only to learn how to use these chemical tools properly to continue producing the wholesome, nutritious food we are accustomed to producing, regardless of destructive pests.

Importance of Pest Control

Insect and disease infestations in vegetable crops bring about heavy losses through: (1) reduced yields, (2) lowered quality of produce, (3) increased costs of production and harvesting, and (4) required expenditures for materials and equipment to apply control measures. These losses are important because they affect you, the prospective vegetable grower, through reduced income and lowered living standards.

The insect- and disease-control picture in vegetable production has changed considerably over the past 20 years. This change has been the result of two important developments: (1) new organic pesticides, and (2) low-gallonage, high-pressure spray equipment. In this chapter we will be concerned with materials, especially the new organic pesticides, rather than equipment.

The suggestions made here are summarized from information available in publications of the U.S. Department of Agriculture and state agricultural experiment stations and are presented only as indications of current practices. The reader is reminded that any use made of the control measures suggested are at his own risk, and he is urged to consult his local state experiment station or county agricultural agent for detailed information concerning the proper way to control insect and disease pests in his locality as well as to follow carefully the directions given by the manufacturer on the label of any pesticide to be applied.

General Control Measures

The new organic pesticides are by no means the complete and final answer to insect and disease problems which arise in vegetable production. True, they represent a magnificent improvement over the materials which were available only 20 years ago, and will control a large majority of the problems which may be encountered. However, much remains to be learned about the physiological actions of these materials, as well as the pests being controlled.

Several "common sense" practices, when incorporated into the insecticide-fungicide program, will improve yield, increase produce quality, and in the long run increase profits. These fundamentals can be found in almost any text devoted to the art and science of vegetable production as well as in publications of the U.S. Department of Agriculture and of the state experiment stations and extension services. They are included here for the convenience of the reader.

1. Plant the best quality seed. This means that the seed should be (a) disease-free and (b) certified when possible.
2. Select crops which are best suited to your soil and climate. Because a crop isn't grown in your area doesn't mean it cannot be grown there, but it is usually a good indication.
3. Cultivate regularly. Grass and weeds compete strongly with crops for soil moisture and plant nutrients, and they frequently harbor or attract insects which may later attack the crop and may also serve as disease reservoirs.
4. Select plots of land that are fertile and well drained. Substandard land will produce substandard yields while poorly drained areas will invariably result in sparse stands, damping off and seed-decay problems.

5. Use only the best quality fertilizers. Soil tests will indicate what fertilizer combination is needed and whether or not liming is necessary. Bargains in fertilizer are seldom found.

6. Buy plants as you would seed—disease-free and certified—when possible.

7. Use disease-resistant varieties if they are available. At present these include varieties that are resistant to only a few diseases of specified crops. The degree of resistance varies considerably through the range of available varieties.

8. When harvest is completed, destroy the remains of annual crops as soon as practical. Stems, leaves, and roots can serve as disease reservoirs and insect harbors for the following year.

9. Rotate crops. Planting the same crop in a field year after year may eventually result in severe soil-borne diseases and insect or nematode infestations. All of these can be held in check to some degree by crop rotation.

10. Follow recommended planting dates. Some crops can be planted so that they will mature before diseases strike and before or after certain insects begin their attack. Planting dates are usually issued by the state experiment stations or the agricultural extension service.

CONTROLLING INSECTS

New Kinds of Insecticides and Miticides

The use of organic insecticides (materials used to kill insects) began in 1945, when DDT was released for civilian use, following its famous role in disease-vector control during World War II. After DDT came many other useful chlorinated organic materials, such as aldrin, BHC, chlordane, dieldrin, endrin, heptachlor, lindane, methoxychlor, TDE, toxaphene, and endosulfan. All of these, with the exception of BHC, are currently approved by the Federal government for controlling insects on vegetables in *specified instances.*

In the midst of this great surge of new insecticides came the development and use of the organic phosphorus insecticides, such as parathion, demeton, TEPP, methyl parathion, EPN, schradan, potasan, meta-systox, malathion, chlorthion, diazinon, and thrichlorfon. Those which are currently accepted for use on vegetables include demeton, malathion, parathion, TEPP, di-syston, guthion, diazinon, mevinphos, ethion, and naled. A new class of insecticides known as the carbamates has appeared. The only representative of this class which has broad usage on vegetables is carbaryl. It is effective against a great many pests and has a very low toxicity to man and other warm-blooded animals.

MITICIDES. Miticides are those materials which are used primarily to control spider mites and in some instances their eggs as well. Currently approved for specified use on vegetables are ovex, demeton, and kelthane. Several of the organic phosphate insecticides control spider mites with equal effectiveness. Some of these are malathion, carbophenothion, mevinphos, parathion, and EPN.

OLDER MATERIALS. The older insecticides which have been successfully used for several decades and will undoubtedly be useful for years to come include the two general classifications: (1) botanical insecticides and (2) inorganic insecticides.

Botanical insecticides are derived from plants or plant parts. Those presently accepted for use on vegetables are rotenone, pyrethrum, nicotine sulfate, sabadilla, and ryania.

The inorganic materials acceptable for use are cryolite, sulfur, and calcium arsenate. The latter is applied only to the foliage of plants whose edible parts are underground—for example, potatoes.

BIOLOGICAL CONTROL. Although an old concept, a bacterial culture for the control of certain caterpillars has been available only during the last few years. The scientific name of this bacteria is *Bacillus thuringiensis*, and it is sold under several trade names, usually in the form of a wettable powder to be sprayed on infested plants. This form of insect control has two advantages: (1) insect predators are not killed, and (2) no harmful chemical residues remain on the produce at the time of harvest.

Public Law 518—The Miller Bill

With the passage of Public Law 518 (commonly referred to as the "Miller Bill") in 1954, and its subsequent enforcement in 1956, insect and disease control in vegetable production has become a serious venture for the producer as well as for the pesticide manufacturer. This is explained by the fact that this law places limits on the amounts of insecticides and fungicides which can remain as *residues* in or on raw agricultural commodities. These limits are known as *tolerances.*

Public Law 518 was designed primarily to protect the consumer, but it also protects the vegetable producer and the pesticide manufacturer.

The producer needs only to follow the directions for rate and time of application, which by requirement of law appear on every pesticide container label if the pesticide enters interstate commerce. Most states now have laws which require that pesticides be properly labeled for safe use. By adhering to the manufacturer's directions, the grower is assured of placing produce on the market which will meet with tolerances established by the Food and Drug Administration. On the other hand, if the grower does not follow label directions, his produce may be confiscated during interstate commerce for having pesticide residues higher than the permitted tolerances. Under these conditions the grower must assume complete responsibility for residues in excess of the tolerances. Consequently, it is important to read and follow the directions on the label.

FORMS OF INSECTICIDES. Most of the commonly used insecticides are sold in three forms: (1) dust, (2) emulsible concentrate, and (3) wettable powder. Dusts are used in standard hand and power dusting equipment in the form in which they are purchased. The emulsible concentrates and wettable powders are manufactured to be diluted with water to the desired concentration and sprayed with hand or power equipment. All three forms have their advantage depending on the insect to be controlled, terrain, weather and ground conditions, and equipment available.

The granular material is another form of insecticide which has become popular in recent years. Small clay pellets are evenly impregnated with insecticide and can be distributed by aircraft, fertilizer and seeding equipment, or with equipment made especially for granular application.

Granulars have been used for both soil and foliage applications. One outstanding feature of granular insecticides is their low residues compared to sprays and dusts.

In certain areas of the United States, several insecticides can be purchased already mixed with standard forms of commercial fertilizer. These are used specifically for soil-dwelling insects such as wireworms and white grubs. The fertilizer-insecticide mixtures have one notable advantage in that they can be applied in one application without the use or need for special equipment.

The Critical Period

With few exceptions, vegetable crops represent the highest acre investment of all forms of agricultural endeavor. In the value of the harvested crop they again take the dollar lead. Each year's harvest usually represents an enormous number of man-hours and a tremendous investment in irrigation equipment, fertilizer, and special planting, harvesting, and processing machinery. Considering the expense and effort involved in preparing a crop for market, it would seem unreasonable to permit an insect infestation to lower the market grade or even, as occasionally happens, destroy the crop.

Yet this very tragedy does occur, not because of the producer's failure to apply insecticides, but because of several other factors. These include: (1) poor timing of insecticide application, (2) improper selection of insecticide, (3) unfavorable weather conditions, (4) low rate of application, (5) equipment failure, and (6) operator negligence. Timing of application is the most important and probably the least attended of these factors.

Every insect pest usually has a time in its development which can be referred to as the "critical period"—that is, a time in which it is most vulnerable to control by chemicals. The term "critical period," could also be applied to some stage in the growth of the plant, or even to the minimum number of days a material can be applied to crops before harvest, according to regulations of the Miller Bill. All three "critical periods" should be taken into consideration when planning insect control.

Scouting for Insect Pests

Vegetable producers should check or scout their crops every two or three days, carefully examining them for signs of insect infestations, such as eggs, insect frass, and damaged leaves or fruits. In this way, most insect pests can be discovered and control measures can be applied before the problem becomes serious.

The value of scouting fields to determine the proper time for control applications cannot be overemphasized. A knowledge of the extent of infestation and the stage of insect development will in the long run save the producer time, money, and worry.

Table 11.1—Insects Which Commonly Attack Vegetable Crops.

Vegetable	Insect Pest
Asparagus	Asparagus beetle, cutworm, thrips, wireworm
Beans	Aphid, bean leaf beetle, cornear worm, cutworm, leaf hopper, Mexican bean beetle, root maggot, spider mite, cucumber beetle, western bean cutworm, wireworm, lygus bug, flea beetle
Beet	Beet webworm, blister beetle, cutworm, flea beetle, wireworm, white-fringed beetle grub
Cabbage, Broccoli, Cauliflower, Kale	Aphid, cabbage looper and caterpillars, cutworm, flea beetle, harlequin bug, mole cricket, root maggot, vegetable weevil, white-fringed beetle grub, wireworm
Carrot	Carrot rust fly, leaf hopper, vegetable weevil, wireworm
Celery	Aphid, celery leaf tier, cutworm, lygus bug, spider mite
Cucumber and Melons	Aphid, cucumber beetle, leaf hopper, leaf miner, pickleworm, spider mite, thrips, wireworm
Eggplant	Colorado potato beetle, cutworm, eggplant lace bug, flea beetle, hornworm, spider mite, whitefly, wireworm
Lettuce	Aphid, army worm, cutworm, caterpillars, leaf hopper, mole cricket, wireworm
Onion	Onion maggot, thrips, wireworm, leaf miner
Peas (garden)	Aphid, pea weevil, alfalfa and celery loopers
Pepper	Aphid, cutworm, flea beetle, hornworm, leaf miner, pepper maggot, pepper weevil, spider mite, wireworm
Potato	Aphid, army worm, blister beetle, Colorado potato beetle, cutworm, European corn borer, flea beetle, grasshopper, leaf hopper, mole cricket, plant bug, potato psyllid, potato tuberworm, vegetable weevil, white-fringed beetle grub, white grub, wireworm
Pumpkin and Squash	Aphid, cucumber beetle, cutworm, squash bug, squash vine borer, pickleworm
Spinach	Alfalfa looper, aphid, beet webworm, leaf miner
Sweet corn	Cornear worm, European corn borer, Japanese beetle, wireworm
Sweet potato	Sweet potato weevil, wireworm, white-fringed beetle grub
Tomato	Aphid, army worm, blister beetle, Colorado potato beetle, cutworm, drosophila, flea beetle, hornworm, leaf miner, spider mite, tomato fruitworm, tomato pinworm, tomato psyllid, tomato russet mite
Turnip	Aphid, caterpillars, flea beetle, root maggot, vegetable weevil, wireworm, white-fringed beetle grub

Table 11.2—Insect Control Recommendations.

Insect Pest	Insecticide	Active Ingredient per Acre	Application	Min. Days from Last Application to Harvest
Aphid	Malathion 5% D 25% WP 50% EC	1¼ lb.	On foliage.	1-7
	40% Nicotine Sulfate	2 pt.	On foliage.	3
	Diazinon D, EC, WP	1 lb.	On foliage.	5-14
Army worm	DDT D, WP, EC	1½-2 lb.	To nearby infested vegetation before worms reach crops.	—
	Carbaryl D, WP, EC	2 lb.	On foliage.	1
	Toxaphene D, WP, ED	1½-2 lb.	Same as DDT.	
Bean leaf beetle	DDT D, EC, WP	1 lb.	On foliage (Caution: DDT may injure beans).	7
	Rotenone D, EC, or powder	¼ lb.	On foliage.	1
	Carbaryl D, WP	½-1 lb.	On foliage.	1
Blister beetle	DDT D, WP, EC	1½ lb.	On beetles.	7
	Methoxychlor D, WP, EC	1½ lb.	On beetles.	7-14
	Carbaryl D, WP	2 lb.	On beetles.	1

(Continued)

Table 11.2—Insect Control Recommendations (Continued).

Insect Pest	Insecticide	Active Ingredient per Acre	Application	Min. Days from Last Application to Harvest
Caterpillars	Rotenone D, EC, or powder	¼ lb.	On foliage.	1
	Toxaphene D, WP, EC	2-3 lb.	On foliage before heads or fruit have formed.	—
	Malathion D, WP, EC	1¼ lb.	On foliage.	7
	Endosulfan D, EC	1 lb.	On foliage.	7
Colorado potato beetle (on potatoes)	Calcium Arsenate 25% D in lime or talc	20-35 lb.	On foliage.	—
	Carbaryl D, WP	1-1½ lb.	On foliage.	—
	Cryolite 50-90% D	12 lb. (Spray) 20-30 lb.	On foliage.	5
(on tomatoes)	Carbaryl D, WP	1-2 lb.	On foliage.	1
	DDT D, WP, EC	1½ lb.	On foliage.	5
	Endosulfan D, EC	1 lb.	On foliage.	1
Cornear worm on sweet corn	DDT	2 lb./ 25 gal.	Apply 5 times at 3 day intervals. Begin day after silks appear. Wet silks thoroughly.	—
	Carbaryl WP	1½ lb./ 25 gal.	On larvae in whorl.	1

(Continued)

Table 11.2—Insect Control Recommendations (Continued).

Insect Pest	Insecticide	Active Ingredient per Acre	Application	Min. Days from Last Application to Harvest
Cucumber beetle	Malathion EC, WP	1-1½ lb.	On foliage.	1
	Methoxychlor D, WP	1-2 lb.	On foliage.	1
	Carbaryl	1 lb.	On foliage.	1
Cutworm (in soil)	DDT D, WP, EC	2 lb.	Broadcast on soil surface.	Depends on the crop. See label
	Toxaphene D, WP, EC 3% bait	2 lb. 1.2 lb.	Broadcast on soil surface.	Same as above
Flea beetle	DDT D, WP, EC	1¼ lb.	On foliage before edible parts are formed.	—
	Methoxychlor D, WP	1½ lb.	On foliage.	7
	Carbaryl D, WP	1-2 lb.	On foliage.	1
Grasshoppers (on potatoes)	Toxaphene D, WP, EC	2½ lb. 1½ lb. in WP or EC	On foliage and margins as needed.	—
	Malathion	0.4-0.8 lb.		
Hornworm and tomato fruit worm	TDE D, WP	2-3 lb.	On foliage as needed.	1
	Carbaryl D, WP	2-4 lb.	On foliage as needed.	1

(Continued)

Table 11.2—Insect Control Recommendations (Continued).

Insect Pest	Insecticide	Active Ingredient per Acre	Application	Min. Days from Last Application to Harvest
Japanese beetle	DDT D, EC, WP	1-1½ lb.	On foliage.	7
	Methoxychlor D, EC, WP	1½ lb.	On foliage.	7
	Carbaryl WP	1-2 lb.	On foliage.	1
Leaf hopper (except on potatoes)	DDT D, EC, WP	1-1¼ lb.	On foliage.	7
	Malathion D, EC, WP	1½ lb.	On foliage.	8
	Carbaryl D, WP	1-2 lb.	On foliage.	1-14
Mexican bean beetle	Malathion 5% D 50% EC	1½ lb.	On foliage.	1
	Methoxychlor 5% D 50% WP	1½ lb.	On foliage.	7
Root maggot (on crucifers)	Chlordane D, WP, EC	1½ lb.	To soil around seedlings. Repeat after thinning.	—
Slug and snail	Commercial Metaldehyde bait 2.5%	30-40 lb.	Apply to infested areas following rain.	—

(Continued)

Table 11.2—Insect Control Recommendations (Continued).

Insect Pest	Insecticide	Active Ingredient per Acre	Application	Min. Days from Last Application to Harvest
Spider mite (on tomatoes and celery)	Malathion D, WP, EC	1¼ lb.	On foliage.	1 on tomatoes 7 on celery
(on tomatoes, beans, cucumbers, melons)	Kelthane EC, WP	3/5-1 lb.	On foliage.	2-7
Vegetable weevil	Rotenone D, EC, Powder	¼ lb.	On foliage.	1
	DDT D, EC, WP	1½ lb.	On foliage not on edible parts.	—
	Dieldrin D, EC, WP	¼-½ lb.	On foliage not on edible parts.	3
White grub	Chlordane D, WP, EC	4-10 lb.	Work in top 3 inches of soil before planting.	—
	DDT EC, G, WP	10 lb.		

(Continued)

Table 11.2—Insect Control Recommendations (Continued).

Insect Pest	Insecticide	Active Ingredient per Acre	Application	Min. Days from Last Application to Harvest
White-fringed beetle and grub	DDT D, G, WP, EC	10 lb.	Work in top 3 inches of soil before planting.	—
	Chlordane D, G, WP, EC	4-6 lb.	Same as above.	—
	Aldrin D, G, WP, EC	2 lb.	Same as above.	—
Wireworm	Chlordane D, WP, EC	4-10 lb.	To soil surface and work in top 6-9 in. Before planting or after harvesting.	—
	DDT D, WP, EC	10-20 lb.	Same as above (only in West).	—
	Diazinon	3-4 lb.		
	Dieldrin D, WP, EC	2-3 lb.	Same as above.	—
	Ethylene Dibromide 40% Soln. 83% Soln.	10 gal. 3 gal.	Inject 8 in. deep in fallow soil every 12 in. 3 wks. before planting.	—

Insect control recommendations modified from "Suggested Guide tor the Use of Insecticides," **Agriculture Handbook No. 120,** Agricultural Research Service and Forest Service, USDA, June, 1966.

    D   Dust
    EC   Emulsible Concentrate
    WP Wettable Powder
    G   Granular

NOTE: Further information on the identification of these insects may be found in the chapters discussing the crops which the insects attack.

CAUTION: These recommendations are general. Before applying material to a crop, you should check carefully the state recommendations which are available through your local county agricultural extension agent, and READ THE LABEL.

CONTROLLING VEGETABLE DISEASES

As with insect control, disease control is an important phase of vegetable production. Disease-control measures must begin BEFORE the disease is observed in the field. In contrast, measures for controlling insects are usually withheld until insects or their damage is observed.

Disease control begins with soil sterilization and seed treatment and continues with applications of fungicides (materials used to kill or control plant diseases) to the growing plant. Even though disease control appears more complicated with the ever-increasing number of new fungicides, the task has actually become more simplified. Most vegetable diseases can now be prevented before they strike. Where fungicides have not been applied in time to prevent disease, they may, in some circumstances, be used to decrease the severity of damage after the disease has become established.

All new organic fungicides are included in the Miller Bill. This law limits the amount of chemicals that can remain as residues on or in crops at the time of harvest. The slogan, READ THE LABEL, cannot be overemphasized with respect to fungicide and insecticide applications.

Soil Sterilization and Seed Treatment

If possible, the soil should be sterilized to kill fungi, bacterial spores, and weed seeds. This can be done by using a formaldehyde drench, treating with chloropicrin (a tear gas), dipping bagged soil in boiling water for several minutes, or heating the soil with live steam. Where live steam is available, as in steam-heated greenhouses, steam treatment is the most practical method.

For best results, soil sterilization should be combined with seed treatment. While sterilization of the soil will control many diseases which begin with seed germination, it will not control those which are seed-borne rather than soil-borne. These are controlled by coating the seeds with a good seed protectant, either as a dust or a slurry. Seed treatment is especially important where soil sterilization is not feasible, such as in field seedings.

Seed can be purchased already treated at the packaging house, or it can be treated by the vegetable grower, usually without any special equipment. Some of the materials which are commonly used for seed treatment are captan, chloranil, dichlone, ferbam, Semesan, thiram, and Vapam.

After seedlings have been transplanted in the field or field seedlings have sprouted and begun to develop, the next stage of disease prevention must be considered. Occasionally some seedlings such as cabbage and pepper can be dipped in a fungicide solution just before transplanting to provide further protection while the plants are adjusting to climatic and soil changes.

"Preventive" Applications of Fungicides

Best results are obtained when the fungicides are applied before there is any evidence of plant damage. Fungicides should be applied to protect the plants during the stage when they are susceptible to pathogens. In some rare instances, applications can be delayed until disease symptoms appear without seriously affecting the crop. However, with crops whose sale value depends strongly on appearance, such as celery and lettuce, this cannot become the practice.

Usually, fungicides can be applied as dusts or sprays, but sprays are generally preferable because the films stick more readily, remain longer, and can be applied during any time of day. Dusts can be applied only when there is little or no wind. In applying a fungicide, one important fact should be kept in mind—only that portion of a plant which has a coating of dust or spray film is protected from disease (Fig. 11.1).

Applications must be repeated whenever the coating or film wears off. In common practice applications are made at 7- to 10-day intervals. In wet weather more frequent applications may be necessary for two reasons: (1) the fungicide may be washed off by the rain, and (2) some disease pathogens survive better during wet or damp weather than during dry weather.

Failure to obtain good disease control can be due to one or a combination of the factors previously listed as responsible for insect-control failures.

The list of fungicides given below will familiarize the reader with the names and uses of the materials most commonly used in vegetable production. Table 11.3 on general control measures will satisfy the needs of most crops grown extensively in the United States. Vegetable diseases on crops of lesser importance have been excluded for simplicity and space conservation.

FUNGICIDES USED IN VEGETABLE PRODUCTION

Copper Fungicides

Bordeaux mixture is an old and effective material seldom found on today's market. It is only mentioned as a fungicidal "classic" in that it is no longer recommended for disease control in this text.

Copper-zinc chromate, a "fixed" or insoluble copper, is sometimes used on potatoes, tomatoes, cucurbits, peanuts, and citrus, at the rate of

Fig. 11.1—Spraying potatoes for disease and insect control.

Firestone Tire and Rubber Co. Photograph

1½ to 2 pounds in 100 gallons of water. It is not likely to cause plant injury.

Monobasic copper sulfate, a soluble copper, is used to control diseases on hardy vegetable crops. Late blight of tomatoes is controlled by a dust containing 6 to 7 percent metallic copper at 40 to 50 pounds to the acre.

Dusting and spraying *sulfurs* generally tend to increase in effectiveness with decrease in particle size. In order of decreasing size they are (a) ground, (b) sublimed, (c) flotation, and (d) colloidal. Some diseases for which sulfur is used are rusts, especially asparagus and bean rust, and powdery mildews. Generally speaking, sulfur is only partially effective against plant diseases.

Formaldehyde has been long and widely used as a drench to disinfect seedbeds and greenhouse soil. It is very economical, but its sharp, penetrating odor makes it disagreeable to use. It is still used as a potato dip for rhizoctonia and potato scab just before planting. Seed potatoes are dipped for two to four minutes in a diluted solution heated to 124° F.

Mercury

Mercuric chloride is an old stand-by used to control diseases borne on seeds, corms, tubers, and bulbs. These are dipped in a 1/1000 solution from 10 to 90 minutes, depending on size.

Organic mercury compounds are not as toxic as the inorganic mercury materials. They are available in a variety of trade names usually as sprays, but dusts are also manufactured. All mercury compounds have a zero tolerance.

Organic Fungicides

Ferbam is used as a spray or dust to control damping off of vegetable seedlings and tomato leaf spot. It is used at the rate of 1½ to 2 pounds in 100 gallons of water. A tolerance of seven parts per million has been set on vegetable crops.

Zineb is sold as a spray or dust. It is effective against many vegetable diseases including early and late blight of tomatoes, potatoes, and celery; rust, anthracnose, and downy mildew on beans; and downy mildew on cucumbers and melons. Recommended rates vary from 1½ to 2 pounds in 100 gallons of water. A tolerance of 7 to 25 parts per million is established on several vegetables.

Ziram is effective against tomato early blight, anthracnose, and septoria leaf spot; potato early blight; celery early and late blight; cucurbit leaf diseases (except powdery mildew) ; bean anthracnose; leaf spots of carrots, beets, and peppers; and for Phomopis canker and fruit rot of eggplant. It is used chiefly as a spray and has a tolerance of seven parts per million on several vegetable crops.

Nabam is sold as a liquid and as a powder. It is useful in control of some vegetable diseases. Its effectiveness increases with the addition of zinc sulfate to the spray (see disease-control chart) . Diseases controlled include: celery, potato, and tomato early blight; beet and carrot leaf spot; downy mildew and some leaf diseases of cucumbers, cantaloups, and melons; and downy mildew of onions. Generally Nabam is mixed with zinc or other mineral salts.

Karathane was originally marketed as a miticide, but has recently been sold as a specific control for powdery mildew of several vegetable crops. No tolerance for residues is established.

Thiram (50 and 75) is used as a seed treatment for corn, sorghum, peanuts, soybeans, peas, and other vegetables, as well as for a sweet potato sprout dip for the control of stem rot and scurf. It is used as a foliage spray for apples, peaches, strawberries, celery, and tomatoes. There is a tolerance of seven parts per million on strawberries and tomatoes.

Maneb is very effective against potato and tomato early and late blights and leaf spots. It has limited use on cucumber anthracnose, Lima bean downy mildew, and spinach blue mold. It is used at the rate of $1\frac{1}{2}$ to 2 pounds in 100 gallons of water. A tolerance of 7 to 10 parts per million is set for most of the above crops.

Captan is effective against a wide variety of common vegetable diseases, both as a plant and a seed treatment. One outstanding quality is its low toxicity to warm-blooded animals. It is usually recommended at 2 pounds in 100 gallons of water. A tolerance of 100 parts per million is set for vegetable crops.

Chloranil is used extensively as a seed protectant, especially against damping off diseases of peas, beans, and soybeans, and as a sweet potato and bulb dip. The newer materials such as captan and thiram are in many cases more effective.

Dichlone is useful in the control of celery and tomato blights and as a vegetable seed treatment. This material may cause injury to foliage under certain conditions. A tolerance of three parts per million is established for vegetables.

Pentachloronitrobenzene (PCNB) is used as a soil treatment for root and stem rot and damping off of beans, when applied just before or at the time of planting. It is worked into the top 4 to 6 inches of soil. It has limited use for lettuce drop and bottom rot when applied to seedling plants and soil. Potato scab and rhizoctonia are reduced when this material is applied broadcast or in the row before planting. There is no tolerance set for this compound; when it is applied at the time of planting there seems to be no need of a tolerance.

Dyrene is a chlorinated organic fungicide effective against celery blights. It is also used on melons, tomatoes, potatoes, and onions. The tolerance varies from 1 to 10 parts per million depending on the crop.

Folpet is a new arrival belonging to the class of chlorinated organic fungicides, and is used on potatoes, onions, and melons for the control of powdery mildew. No tolerance is established for its present usage recommendations.

Antibiotics

Antibiotics are a new concept in plant disease control. Strangely enough they are produced by living fungi. At present streptomycin is used primarily on bacterial diseases such as bacterial spot of peppers and bacterial bean blight, but occasionally it is effective against some fungus diseases. There are no tolerances set on vegetable crops as of 1966.

Table 11.3—Recommended Control Measures for Vegetable Diseases.

Crop and Disease	Materials and Rates per Acre	Instructions
Asparagus Rust	Grow rust-resistant varieties. Spray with Zineb, 3 lb., or Sulfur.	Cut and burn diseased tops in fall.
Beans Bacterial blights and anthracnose	Spray with Zineb, Ferbam, or Ziram, 3 lb.	Apply at 7-day intervals.
Beet **Cercospora** leaf spot	Fixed copper, 6 lb., or Maneb or Zineb, 3 lb.	Apply at 10-day intervals—use crop rotation.
Carrot **Cercospora** and **Macrosporium** leaf spots	Maneb, Ziram or Zineb, 3 lb.	Apply at 10-day intervals.
Cabbage and other Crucifers Club root	Use PCNB in transplant water.	Raising soil alkalinity helps—use disease-free seed and plants.
Yellows	No chemical control available.	Plant yellows-resistant varieties, and plant in new location.
Celery **Cercospora** (early) and **Septoria** (late) blights	Fixed copper, 6 lb. or Ziram, Zineb, Dyrene or Maneb, 3 lb.	Apply at 6-day intervals (if severe, shorten to 4-day intervals).
Cucumber and Muskmelon Bacterial blight, leaf and fruit spots (anthracnose, angular leaf spot, scab and **Macrosporium**	Sevin, 1 lb. A. Rotenone 4% powder, 6 lb. Purified DDT, 1 lb. Methoxychlor, 1.75 lb., or Dieldrin, 0.5 lb. B. Fixed copper, 6 lb., or Ziram, 3 lb.	Treat seed, rotate crops, combine one of group A with one of group B; leaf-fruit spots, at 7-day intervals—bacterial blight, at 5-day intervals.
Powdery mildews	Karathane, 0.5 lb.	

(Continued)

Table 11.3—Recommended Control Measures for Vegetable Diseases (Continued).

Crop and Disease	Materials and Rates per Acre	Instructions
Eggplant and Pepper Leaf and fruit spots	Fixed copper, 4.5 lb., or Ziram, Zineb, or Maneb, 3 lb.	Treat seed—apply at 7-day intervals.
Onion Mildew	Spray with fixed copper or Maneb or Zineb, 3 lb.	Apply at 10-day intervals.
Lettuce Tipburn	Grow tipburn-resistant varieties.	
Yellows	Control leafhoppers (vectors) with malathion, 1 lb., or Sevin 1.5 lb., or methoxychlor, 2 lb.	Begin when ½ inch high, and repeat weekly—control border weeds around fields.
Potato Early blight (Alternaria)	Fixed copper, 6 lb.	Apply at 10-day intervals (if late blight is epidemic, every 4 days)—plant disease-free tubers, and partly resistant varieties.
Late blight (Phytophthora)	Zineb or Maneb, 3 lb. Spray or dust.	
Spinach Blue mold	Maneb, 3 lb.	Apply at 7-day intervals.
Yellows (blight)	Grow resistant varieties, and control aphids (vectors) with malathion, 1 lb., or Diazinon, 0.5 lb.	

(Continued)

Nematodes

Nematodes are neither insects nor fungi, but they do injure all vegetable crops to some degree, depending on the crop, soil type, and the consecutive number of years a crop has been planted on the same field.

Nematodes are small eelworms, usually less than 1/16 inch long, which live in and on the roots and surrounding soil of all vegetable crops. One nematode is probably familiar to the reader—the root knot nematode. It receives its name from the small, distinct galls that it causes on the roots of cabbage and other crucifers. These galls vary from the size of a pinhead to an inch in diameter.

Nematodes usually feed and produce their young on roots of a great

Table 11.3—Recommended Control Measures for Vegetable Diseases (Continued).

Crop and Disease	Materials and Rates per Acre	Instructions
Sweet corn Bacterial wilt	DDT, 1-1.5 lb. to control corn flea beetle (vector)—Sevin, 1.5 lb. for beetle control.	Apply at seedling emergence and 3- to 4-day intervals as needed.
Sweet potatoes Stem rot and scurf	Thiram solution.	As sprout dip before planting.
Tomato Leaf blights, early (Alternaria) late (Phytophthora) and Septoria	Fixed copper, 6 lb. Maneb or Zineb, 3 lb. Nabam, 3 qts./1.5 lb. $ZnSO_4$ or Ziram, 3 lb. alternated with 6 lb. fixed copper to control leaf spots and fruit rots.	Apply at 7- to 10-day intervals.
Fruit rots	Maneb, Ziram, or Dyrene, 3 lb.	Apply at 10-day intervals.
Watermelon Anthracnose leaf and fruit spot	Fixed copper, 6 lb. Ziram, 3 lb.	Begin after vining, continue at 7-day intervals until mid-harvest.

Adapted in part from the Ohio Agr. Exp. Sta. Publication Series No. 11 of the Departments of Entomology, Botany, and Plant Pathology, Feb. 1964, and Bulletin 434, "Plant Disease Control in the Garden," Cooperative Extension Service, The Ohio State Univ., Columbus, July 1963.

number of plants. They live in the soil and in decaying vegetable material from one year to the next. The importance of their damage has just been recognized in the past few years.

These tiny pests can be controlled in two major ways: (1) A nematode-resistant crop can be included in the rotation. (2) The soil can be fumigated. A fumigant (nematocide) applied several inches deep will spread evenly through the soil and kill the nematodes.

Combining Insecticides with Fungicides

Disease and insect problems frequently occur at the same time. Under such circumstances, both insecticide and fungicide may be applied together in one operation—provided they are compatible. Some materials, however, are not compatible with others. Applying incompatible materials together can reduce control of the insect, the disease, or both. This happens through chemical action or breakdown of the compounds in the spray tank.

To be certain that two materials can be mixed in the same spray application, compatibility charts should be consulted. These are charts that show which materials can and which cannot be mixed together. They are usually available on request from your pesticide dealer.

SAFE HANDLING OF INSECTICIDES AND FUNGICIDES

Practically all of the insecticides and fungicides commercially available are toxic to man and animals. The persons most likely to encounter these hazards are the operators and applicators.

Insecticides and fungicides can enter the body through three routes: (1) ingesting or swallowing, (2) breathing the dusts or vapors, and (3) absorption or penetration through the skin. One form can prove just as fatal as the other, but most cases of poisoning occur through accidental eating or drinking of materials which have lost their labels or have been placed in other containers. Unfortunately children are the most frequent victims of such adult carelessness. Because of this, all materials should be kept in their original containers and locked up or placed out of the reach of children.

There are 12 general rules to follow when handling any of these materials:

1. Read carefully the warning statement and directions for use on the container BEFORE beginning the operation, and use only as recommended.
2. Become familiar with the antidote in case of accidental ingestion.
3. Wear the prescribed clothing for the material, such as rubber gloves, respirator, coveralls, or a rubber suit with such extremely toxic materials as parathion, TEPP, Di-Syston, and mevinphos.
4. Wash hands before smoking or eating.
5. If clothing becomes saturated with liquid or dust, remove it immediately, take a bath or shower, and change into clean clothes.
6. Keep a special set of old clothes on hand just for handling and applying these materials.
7. At the end of each day's work with these materials take a bath

or shower and make a complete change of clothing.

8. Fill tanks and hoppers, treat seeds, make dilutions, etc., in well-ventilated places.
9. Do not walk or ride in the downwind trail of dust or spray applications without protective clothing and respirators.
10. Burn or destroy empty containers of highly toxic insecticides and stay out of the smoke.
11. Keep these materials out of reach of children and do not use on warm-blooded animals, in the house, etc.
12. Call a physician if poisoning symptoms occur after handling toxic materials. Such symptoms might be: headaches, dizziness, nausea, and vomiting.

WARNING: Parathion, TEPP, Thimet, endrin, Guthion, Di-Syston, phosphamidon, Trithion, demeton, and mevinphos are extremely effective insecticides, BUT they are also highly poisonous to human beings if inhaled, absorbed through the skin, or swallowed. They are not, therefore, used in the recommendations of this text. They should be applied only by professional applicators who have the experience, knowledge, and safety equipment necessary to protect all concerned. Danger may be minimized when applying the pesticides recommended here only by rigidly and constantly following the safety precautions listed above.

Sources of Control Recommendations

By the time any publication on insect or disease control reaches the user it has become outdated by more recent results of research. Such is the case with recommendations in this chapter, and accounts for the general rather than the specific control measures found here. For a specific insect or a disease on a certain crop, the reader should consult more detailed information from reliable sources.

Insect and disease control recommendations come from many sources, but the most dependable are issued by the U.S. Department of Agriculture, state experiment stations, and the agricultural extension service. The latter is represented by the county agricultural agents and the extension entomologist and plant pathologist. Most control recommendations can be obtained through the county agent's office. U.S. Department of Agriculture publications not available from him can be purchased from the Superintendent of Documents, U.S. Government Printing Office, Washington 25, D.C.

Sources of Insect and Disease Identification

Frequently vegetable producers find insects or diseased plants which they cannot identify. These problems should be carried to the local county agricultural agent or sent to the extension specialists concerned who are located at Land Grant Universities and Colleges.

Insect pests, including immature stages if possible, should be carefully wrapped in soft tissue paper (soft-bodied insects such as caterpillars preserved in 70 percent alcohol), packaged in a small can, plastic box, or other strong container and sent by first class mail to the extension entomologist.

Plant disease specimens should include entire plants, when possible, with the roots wrapped in moist soil, peat moss, or sawdust. They should be carefully packed in a strong container and mailed first class to the extension plant pathologist. *A letter should always be attached to the package describing the crop, area, fungicide or insecticide history, location, and type of damage. The more information given the specialist, the easier it will be for him to identify the specimens.*

SELECTED REFERENCES

Anonymous, "Controlling Tomato Diseases," USDA Farmer's Bull. 2200, 1964.

Boswell, V. R., *et al.*, "Pepper Production, Disease and Insect Control," USDA Farmer's Bull. 2051, 1959.

Gunther, F. A. and Jeppson, L. R., *Modern Insecticides and World Food Production*, New York: John Wiley & Sons, Inc., 1959.

Linn, M. B., "Vegetable Diseases," Ill. Agr. Exp. Sta. Cir. 802, 1958.

Metcalf, C. L. and Flint, W. P., *Destructive and Useful Insects*, 4th ed., New York: McGraw-Hill, 1962.

Peairs, L. M. and Davidson, R. H., *Insect Pests of Farm, Garden, and Orchard*, 5th ed., New York: John Wiley & Sons, Inc., 1956.

Reed, L. B. and Doolittle, S. P., "Insects and Diseases of Vegetables in the Home Garden," USDA Home and Garden Bull. 46, 1961.

Reid, W. J., Jr. and Cuthbert, F. P., "Control of Caterpillars," USDA Farmer's Bull. 2099, 1960.

Shands, W. A., Landis, B. J. and Reid, W. J., Jr., "Controlling Potato Insects," USDA Farmer's Bull. 2168, 1963.

Smith, F. F., "Control of Insect Pest of Greenhouse Vegetables," USDA *Agr. Handbook 142*, 1959.

Smith, M. A., *et al.*, "Market Diseases of Asparagus, Onions, Beans, Peas, Carrots, Celery, and Related Vegetables," USDA *Agr. Handbook 303*, 1966.

CHAPTER 12

Storing Vegetables

Storage is important in order to prolong the season of certain vegetables and to maintain prices at levels that will be beneficial to both producer and consumer. While the consumer pays lower prices during periods of surpluses, these are more than offset by higher prices when demand exceeds supply.

Due to the large increase in vegetable production in the South, winter storage has greatly decreased in importance. It is limited primarily to crops such as potatoes, sweet potatoes, onions, and winter pumpkins and squashes. Many crops may be stored for short periods to facilitate orderly marketing. When vegetables are grown for home use, it may be necessary to store some of them so they can be used over a longer period.

Vegetable products must be in good condition to be stored successfully. Usually stored vegetables should be as nearly like freshly harvested ones as possible. Information concerning changes that are likely to take place in storage is important. All vegetables stored at temperatures above their freezing point are alive and life activities continue, though they may be slowed down by storage conditions. During the storage period a certain amount of physiological shrinkage takes place. This is caused largely by loss of moisture, but is due also to the loss of solids which are used up in the process of respiration. Sometimes the loss of moisture increases the dry-matter content of the stored product, as often occurs with sweet potatoes during the curing period. The change in moisture content is not nearly so great as is indicated by loss in weight. Cucumbers which had a moisture content of 95 percent when harvested were kept at a room temperature of 70° to 80° F. for two weeks, and, though the shrinkage in weight was 7 to 8 percent, the moisture content actually increased from 95 to 96 percent. This is an unusual case, but it emphasizes what may take place in physiological shrinkage. Watermelons kept at room temperatures behave somewhat similarly. The importance of physiological shrinkage is often underrated by those storing vegetables. As far as food value is concerned, there may be little or no loss in many stored products. In some cases, as with the sweet potato, storage may be an actual advantage in food value as well as in quality.

Loss from rot or decay is entirely different from physiological shrinkage, and it is often much more serious from an economic standpoint. Physiological shrinkage exacts a more or less definite toll, depending on the condition of the product and storage conditions, while losses from rot may vary from nothing to 100 percent. It is the object of proper storage to reduce both types of shrinkage to a minimum while maintaining the quality of the product stored.

STORAGE REQUIREMENTS

Temperature

One of the most important factors to be considered in connection with storage is temperature. In general, life activities in vegetables increase with the rise of temperature from the freezing point to the maximum temperatures ordinarily encountered. With a few exceptions, including sweet potatoes and pumpkins, loss from decay organisms is lessened as the temperature is lowered. This means that the storage temperature should be kept low for most material without allowing it to freeze. Most vegetables freeze at temperatures varying from 28° to 30° F. If only one storage room is available and the temperature may be controlled, the best temperature for general home storage of vegetables is probably between 36° and 40° F. Many vegetables, however, prefer a lower and some a higher temperature (Table 12.1).

The response of Irish potatoes to cold storage temperatures is different from that of most vegetables. With a drop in temperature from 40° to 32° F., the respiration rate does not decrease, but may even increase. Below 40° F., sugars accumulate in appreciable amounts and the starch content is reduced. If much sugar is present in potatoes, their cooking quality is greatly impaired. If potatoes with a high sugar content are taken from cold storage, and are kept for about two weeks at room temperatures, the sugars will largely revert to starch. When potatoes are removed from cold storage to a higher temperature, the respiration rate is higher for a few days than is normal for that temperature. The lower the storage temperature and the higher the temperature after removal, the greater the abnormal respiration rate. This means that potatoes re-

Table 12.1—Commercial Storage Requirements and Approximate Maximum Storage Period for Vegetables.

Vegetable	Temperature, Degrees F.	Relative Humidity Percent	Maximum Storage Period*
Asparagus	32	95–98	1 week
Beans, snap	40	90–98	12 days
Beans, lima	32	90–95	2–3 weeks
Beet	32–40	90–95	4–5 months
Broccoli, sprouting	32	95–98	10 days
Brussels sprouts	32	95–98	2 months
Cabbage	32–40	90–98	5 months
Carrot	32–40	90–95	6 months
Cauliflower	32	90–98	30–40 days
Celery	32	90–98	3–5 months
Cucumber	32–40	95–98	4–5 weeks
Eggplant	32	90–95	3–4 weeks
Kale	32	95–98	1 month
Lettuce	32	95–98	3–4 weeks
Muskmelon, immature	50	80–90	2 weeks
Muskmelon, mature	32	80–90	1 month
Onion and onion sets	31–32	80–95	5 months
Parsnip	32	90–95	5 months
Peas, green	32	95–98	2 weeks
Pepper	32	95–98	40 days
Potato	38–40	85–90	5–6 months
Pumpkin	40	50–70	2–3 months
Rutabaga	32–40	90–95	3–4 months
Squash	40	50–70	5 months
Sweet corn	32	90–98	3–4 weeks
Sweet potato	55–60	80–85	4–6 months
Tomato, green ripe	50–60	95–98	1 month
Tomato, ripe	40	95–98	10 days

*The length of time during which vegetables may be kept in cold storage depends on differences in growing conditions, state of maturity, the variety of the vegetable, disease infection, and other factors.

moved from storage at low temperatures should receive special care as to ventilation, for a few days at least.

Sweet potatoes should be kept at temperatures from 80° to 85° F. for about two weeks after digging. During this so-called curing period, wounds of the sweet potato heal, the most rapid loss of moisture for the storage period takes place, and the sugar content, especially sucrose, increases. Artificial heat is usually necessary to maintain high enough temperatures for curing, but, in the far South, this has been found unnecessary if potatoes are dug during dry, warm weather. What is meant by a cured potato is very indefinite, as there is no reliable test for this condition.

During the storage period of sweet potatoes (after curing), the temperature is kept as near 50° to 55° F. as possible. Sweet potatoes become more susceptible to injury from certain rot organisms at temperatures much below 50° F. Low temperatures seem to reduce the resistance of the roots to the decay organisms. Sweet potatoes will stand low temperatures, above the freezing point, for short periods of time without serious injury, but exposure to low temperature for extended periods is sure to result in injury.

Pumpkins and winter squash require storage conditions somewhat similar to those of sweet potatoes; curing is necessary before storage for best keeping quality.

Moisture

Relative humidity of the storage place has an important bearing on moisture loss. In general, the higher the humidity of storage, the lower the water loss, and this is beneficial with many vegetable products. High humidity, however, tends to increase growth of molds and other decay organisms, and for this reason may be very harmful. Moisture should not be allowed to accumulate on the walls, containers, or the stored product. Onions, sweet potatoes, and pumpkins require a dry atmosphere, 60 to 75 percent of saturation, while the ordinary root crops and celery keep best under high humidity. The humidity of storage rooms may be controlled to some extent by regulating ventilation and temperature.

Aeration

Oxygen in fresh air is necessary for respiration in the stored material. The higher the respiration rate, the greater the need of fresh air. The respiration rate of Irish potatoes is high for a few days immediately after digging, so proper aeration is especially important at that time. Black heart, a breakdown of center tissue in Irish potatoes, is caused by a lack of oxygen, and occurs when potatoes are kept at temperatures as low as 32° F. without enough fresh air.

When vegetables are put in storage, the containers should be so arranged that there is free access of air to all the stored material. A ventilated false floor should be used where most produce is stored. As previously stated, ventilation is also important in helping control the humidity of the storage atmosphere.

Light

Most vegetables should be stored in the dark or at least in very reduced light; but some light does not seem to harm sweet potatoes, pumpkins, or shallots. Direct sunlight is generally injurious to stored material, but is not often an important factor.

Condition of Crop

The physical condition of stored vegetables does not improve in storage, but usually depreciates to some extent in spite of the best of care. This means that only the best products possible should be stored. They should be handled very carefully and bruises or other mechanical injuries kept at a minimum. No decay or rot should be present, as this is likely to injure the healthy vegetables as well as those that are infected.

Sweet potatoes that are to be stored should be dug before the vines are killed by frost, if successful storage is expected. Before spring- or summer-dug Irish potatoes are placed in cold storage, they should be kept for 10 to 14 days at normal temperatures. The reason for this is that wounds will heal and the skins suberize much more readily at the higher temperatures when the relative humidity is high than they will at cold-storage temperatures. Another advantage of waiting is that the most rapid shrinkage occurs during the first few days and the amount of material on which storage will have to be paid will be reduced.

If Irish potatoes have been exposed to enough sun at digging time to cause injury, there is no use in attempting to store them. It is unwise to take a chance on storing vegetables in questionable condition.

Sanitation

It is very unwise to store excellent produce in places overrun with sources of rot infection. Sanitation is good storage insurance—it does not often entirely prevent rot, but it does help to keep rot at a minimum. The storage room should be kept as clean as possible, and when empty it should be thoroughly disinfected from time to time.

Protection from Rodents

Storage houses should be constructed as nearly rat-proof as possible. If rodents enter the house by coming from the field in storage containers or otherwise, they should be killed the easiest available way. Rats and mice not only directly destroy considerable produce or render it unmarketable, but they also increase loss from decay, since decay organisms find ready entrance to stored vegetables that have been gnawed by rodents.

STORAGE METHODS AND STRUCTURES

Storing in the Field

Vegetables such as cabbage and most of the root crops can be stored in the field in trenches, pits, or mounds. When freezing weather approaches, a well-drained place is selected. The vegetables may be placed in piles surrounded with straw and covered with just enough soil to prevent freezing injury. Ventilation can be provided by placing a flue in the center of the pile and extending it above the cover. In severe weather it can be closed.

Field storage is generally unsatisfactory. Temperature and moisture cannot be controlled, the produce is difficult to remove in disagreeable weather, and a large amount of labor is required.

Storing in Cellars

Where drainage permits, unheated cellars are used to some extent for storing some types of vegetables. Special attention should be given to ventilation, for, at best, cellars will usually have high humidities. Root crops may be successfully stored in them and potatoes may be kept with fair success.

Storing in Above-Ground Houses

Storage houses can be used advantageously for such crops as onions and sweet potatoes that require a dry atmosphere. The storage can be readily ventilated providing some control of temperature and humidity, and the produce can be conveniently handled. Construction of the house may be varied depending upon the product and the climate.

Cold Storage

In this type of storage, produce is stored at fairly well-controlled low temperatures, and, in some storage houses, the humidity is also controlled. With a few exceptions, this is the ideal type of storage, especially in the South, where even in the winter great fluctuations in temperature and humidity cause considerable variation in most other types of storage. The disadvantages of this type of storage are its high cost and distance from the farm. However, the larger market gardeners may rent or own cold storage units and thus extend the marketing seasons.

Most vegetables will keep for a time in cold storage, and many are easily kept. Cucumbers, however, will soon shrivel badly if kept under ordinary cold storage conditions. Most vegetables are kept in cold storage with temperatures ranging from 32° to 40° F. as shown in Table 12.1. Onions will keep best if stored in a dry atmosphere at a temperature of about 32° F. For root crops and cabbage, 33° to 35° F. is probably low enough, as too low temperatures may be injurious. Sometimes the temperature, even in controlled cold storage rooms, will vary, and if produce is being kept at 32° F., injury may occur if the temperature goes lower. Potatoes, sweet potatoes, pumpkin, squash, and tomatoes require higher temperatures, as shown in Table 12.1.

SELECTED REFERENCES

McColloch, L. P., "Home Storage of Vegetables and Fruits," USDA Farmers' Bull. 1939, 1960.

Platenius, H., Jamison, F. S., and Thompson, H. C., "Studies on Cold Storage of Vegetables," Cornell Uni. Exp. Sta. Bull. 602, 1934.

Wright, R. C., Rose, D. H., and Whiteman, T. M., "The Commercial Storage of Fruits, Vegetables and Florist and Nursery Stock," USDA *Handbook 66*, 1954.

CHAPTER 13

Harvesting, Handling, and Marketing

Growing and harvesting vegetables are the primary responsibilities of farmers, who must necessarily be adept at this special phase of agriculture. The overall harvesting, handling, and marketing of vegetables are an involved series of procedures which tax the skills and ingenuity of people in the vegetable industry. After vegetables reach harvest maturity, speedy operations are required by growers, handlers, marketing specialists, wholesalers, and retailers to move produce from the farm to the consumer. The various procedures are discussed in this chapter in their sequence.

MAINTAINING QUALITY

The maintenance of quality from farm to consumer is perhaps the most important requisite in vegetable marketing. To begin with, it is usually necessary to have vegetables with good shipping and handling characteristics, which include harvesting at the proper stage of maturity. Tomatoes harvested when red ripe may be suitable for local market or processing but not for shipment.

Appearance

From the standpoint of sales, appearance is the most important factor in products that can be seen at the time of selection for purchase. Indeed, it may be the only basis that the buyer has for evaluation. Particular attention should be given to uniformity of size, shape, color, and freedom from blemishes, wilting, and dirt.

Texture

Although texture of produce may not be apparent at the time of purchase, the consumer may subsequently be impressed with its importance. Imagine the disappointment in buying a nice-appearing bunch of asparagus only to find it so fibrous as to be inedible. Equally undesirable is stringiness in celery and snap beans or toughness in corn and peas. A slice of red tomato should enhance the appearance of a salad, but will not when it is so soft that it falls apart when sliced. It is amazing that so many consumers have never eaten garden-fresh sweet corn or vine-ripened tomatoes and melons. Proper texture in fresh vegetables depends upon variety, stage of maturity, cultural conditions, and handling. These factors are discussed in the corresponding crop chapters of Section Two.

Flavor

In spite of the desirability of good flavor, this factor of quality plays only a minor role in the marketing of vegetables. It is less apparent than either appearance or texture, and the consumer usually has no standard by which to judge flavor. People differ in their tastes and usually prefer flavors to which they are accustomed. In many cases the natural flavors of vegetables are masked by the additives used in their preparation for the table. Such undesirable characteristics as off-flavors, bitterness, astringency, and pungency in vegetable products are easily recognized and generally affect consumer demand.

HARVESTING

When to Harvest

Some crops such as beets and carrots may be harvested over a period of several weeks, depending upon market demand. Others like asparagus, sweet corn, peas, and okra quickly pass through the stage of optimum edible maturity. Frequent and timely harvests of these crops are necessary if the growers wish to supply a discriminating market with high quality produce. In crops such as pickling cucumbers and snap beans, high quality but not high yields, result from early harvesting. The time of harvesting will depend upon the desired quality and the premium paid for it.

Harvesting a crop before it is of acceptable quality in order to take advantage of a good market may reduce the demand for a product later in the season. However, early harvesting of some crops may also decrease field and handling losses. High temperatures hasten maturity and necessitate more frequent and timely harvesting of some crops.

Time of Day

Those vegetables which lose quality rapidly at high temperatures should be harvested in the early morning and kept as cool as possible. While the quality of snap beans, for example, may be reduced by high temperatures, a small degree of wilting may prevent breakage in spinach and asparagus and actually be beneficial.

Preventing Injury

Vegetables are subject to harvesting and handling damages, which may result in substantial losses. Organisms enter broken areas and cause decay and spoilage. Even slight bruises may darken the produce and present an unsightly appearance. Injuries also increase respiration and loss of weight and constituents of quality.

PREPARING FOR MARKET

Trimming

The appearance of vegetables may be improved by removing damaged, diseased, dead, or discolored parts. In some cases, however, the outer leaves offer protection and may even enhance the appearance of the product. Some field trimming is desirable for most vegetables, but sufficient wrapper leaves should be left on such crops as lettuce, cabbage, and celery for protection. Damaged and discolored leaves can be removed in the market as desired.

Washing

The market demands clean produce, so most vegetables should be washed after harvesting. Washing removes dirt, freshens the produce, and may remove spray residues. After the produce is washed, it should be kept cool to prevent the development of rot organisms. Most of the root crops should not be washed until they are marketed. Muskmelons, cucumbers, and sweet potatoes are usually cleaned by brushing or wiping dry, rather than by washing.

Grading

Grading, the sorting of vegetables so that the contents of each package will be fairly uniform, makes produce more salable and is usually a paying operation. Even products of second quality will present a better appearance when packed by themselves, with no first-class products in the same package. Uniformity appeals to the eye and suggests that the vegetables have been carefully handled (Fig. 13.1).

Fig. 13.1—Packing trays of tomatoes at wholesale fruit and vegetable terminal.

USDA Photograph

Broadly speaking, the further the grower is from market or the greater his marketing costs, the more carefully he must grade and pack and the less likely he is to be able to sell culls and over-matured products. The nearer the grower is to market and the smaller the market costs, the better are his chances to sell low grades for something more than the cost of handling.

The U.S. Department of Agriculture has established uniform grades for each important vegetable, as discussed under the "Standardization and Inspection" section of this chapter.

Packing

Most vegetables are packed in local or shipping-point packing sheds. Increasing attention is being given to standard uniform packs in sufficient quantity to attract volume buyers. Many large central packing operations have increased their facilities and production to such volume and efficiency that numerous small packing sheds have been forced to close.

Table 13.1—Approximate Unit Weights and Specifications of Common Containers Used in Packaging Commercial Vegetables.*

Principal Vegetables	Common Units or Packs and Specifications	Approximate Net Weight in Pounds	Approximate No. of Containers (Units) per Railroad Car
Asparagus	Pyramid crate	26-32	950
Beans, all types	Bu. basket, hamper, or crate	28-30	750
Beet (bunched)	½ WGA crate or 10-inch W. B.	45-50	640
Broccoli	½ crate and pony crate	20 & 40	800 & 420
Brussels sprouts	Drum	25	900
Cabbage	Sack or carton	60-50	550-700
Cantaloup (melon)	Crate & hamper or bu. basket	47 & 70	850 & 550
Carrot (bunched)	2/3 WGA crate	45-50	520
Carrot (topped)	Bu. basket, crate, or sack	48-50	760
Cauliflower	Carton & LA or WGA crate	23 & 50	950 & 500
Celery	16-inch crate	55-60	640
Corn, green	Crate or sack	40-60	725
Cucumber	Bu. basket, carton, or hamper	47-55	650
Eggplant	Bu. basket, hamper, or crate	30-34	775
Garlic	Sack & box or carton	50 & 30	600 & 1,000
Kohlrabi	Bu. basket & 2/3 WGA crate	30 & 51	650 & 400
Lettuce and Romaine	Carton or crate	40-45	825
Okra	Bu. basket, hamper, or crate	30	750
Onion, dry	50 lb. sack or carton	50	800
Onion, green	Lug or WGA 16-inch crate and cartons	60 & 35	350 & 550
Peas, green		15-18	1,200-1,500
Peas, field	Bu. basket, hamper, or tub	28-30	720
Pepper, green, all	Bu. basket, hamper, or crate	30	750
Potato	Bu. basket, hamper, or crate	28-30	775
Radish, bunched	All size and type packages	Various	48,000-56,000 lbs.
Spinach and greens	Crate or carton	30-40	1,800
Squash (summer), soft	Basket, hamper, or crate	18-25	850
Squash and Pumpkins	Bu. basket, hamper, or crate	40-45	750
Sweet potato	Bu. basket, hamper, or crate	50	650
Tomato	Bu. basket, hamper, or crate	50	600
Watermelon	Crate and carton	60 & 40	600 & 900
Misc. topped vegetables	Loaded in bulk, averaging Bu. basket or sack	20-25 ea. 50	34,000-41,000 lbs. 700-800

*The packages and net weights listed are commonly used in the important producing areas of the United States. Other packages of different types, material, and volume are used under various circumstances in different parts of the country. Because of the variable size of railroad cars and prevailing regulations and loading incentives in different areas, the number of containers per car varies.

Information adapted from "Table of Carlot and Conversion Factors," Consumer and Marketing Service, USDA, effective January 1, 1966.

Farmers have found that the most economical packing can be done by cooperatives or large private packing facilities. Table 13.1 lists the types and respective net weights of the most common containers for various vegetables.

Considerable packaging of some products is now being done in convenient-size consumer units, which are packed in larger containers for shipment. This type of operation is increasing rapidly, and consumers now are able to buy many products in a variety of small attractive packages of fiberboard, polyethylene, shrink-film overwrap, and other materials.

Prepackaging

In recent years there has been a marked development of consumer packages (Fig. 13.2). These can be used in self-service stores to decrease

Fig. 13.2—A U.S. Department of Agriculture inspector examining prepackaged spinach before package is heat sealed.

USDA Photograph

the cost of retail merchandising. The packages protect the product against loss of water, dust, dirt, and handling by customers. Also, brand names placed on the small packages get to the consumer. Prepackaging is a specialized business, usually requiring elaborate equipment and cold storage. Vegetables or soup and salad mixes of them, inclosed in film bags, must be kept cool to prevent decay and loss of quality.

HARVESTING AND HANDLING EQUIPMENT

Harvesting Equipment

While much of the harvesting or certain aspects thereof is still done by hand, there is a rapid increase in mechanical harvesting of potatoes, sweet potatoes, celery, lettuce, green beans, tomatoes, and some other vegetables. Machinery is used extensively for harvesting crops, especially those for processing. Machines reduce costs but may cause more injury, which is disadvantageous for produce intended for the fresh market. Conveyors and other labor-saving aids are frequently used in the harvesting of such crops as tomatoes, asparagus, potatoes, and sweet potatoes. Information on the increased efficiency in the use of labor is provided in Table 1.4, Chapter 1, and in the specific vegetable chapters of Section Two.

Grading and Packing Equipment

Equipment for grading and packing may be comparatively simple for the small grower. On the other hand, much of the harvested produce is taken to central packing sheds, which are well equipped to provide all the grading and packing services. Produce harvested in the rough is conveyed, trimmed, washed, sometimes waxed, graded, and labeled in a production-line process. Central packing usually produces a more uniform and salable product in attractive packages.

A consolidated mobile grading and packing unit, referred to as the "mule train," is coming into prominence in many sections for such crops as celery and sweet corn. The harvested produce is fed into this large machine as it passes through the field. The produce comes out washed, trimmed, and packaged ready for shipment (Figs. 13.3 and 13.4).

Cooling

A number of methods may be used to remove field heat from pro-

Fig. 13.3—Harvesting and field packing of celery.

USDA Photograph

duce. It can be stored in a refrigerated space but this method is slow. Some products can be dipped in cold water and cooled rapidly. Others may be subject to decay when wet. A recent development is vacuum cooling, commonly used for lettuce. The lettuce is packed in fiberboard boxes, placed in a chamber, and evacuated. Cooling, but not serious wilting, results from the rapid evaporation of water from the leaves. Only produce subject to rapid water loss can be cooled in this manner.

COOPERATIVE MARKETING ASSOCIATIONS

The Farmer Cooperative Service of the U.S. Department of Agriculture reported in 1966 that fruit, vegetable, and nut growers marketed more than $1 billion of products annually through some 700 cooperative associations. Nearly 600 of these cooperatives specialized primarily in

Fig. 13.4—View of wholesale market in Washington, D.C.

USDA Photograph

marketing fruits, vegetables and nuts, accounting for less than 5 percent of all marketing cooperative memberships, but more than 10 percent of the value of all farm products marketed cooperatively.

About 150 associations were marketing primarily fresh vegetables in 1964. Potatoes were the primary product handled by 35 of these cooperatives. Most of the 20 or more associations that process vegetables also process fruit.

Organizations and Services Vary

Cooperatives vary considerably in organization, membership, and services, but basically all are designed to improve the farmers' incomes. This is done through the voluntary joining together of physical, financial, and human resources in associations which provide marketing services and production supplies at cost. The services of cooperative vegetable associations range from cleaning, grading, packing, and storing to more complete marketing services including processing, selling, and merchandising under cooperative labels.

Location and Volume of Business

Cooperatives serve vegetable growers throughout the country but are concentrated in areas known for volume production of high quality vegetables. California and Florida lead in number of fresh vegetable marketing associations. California, Oregon, and Washington are important for vegetable processing cooperatives.

The trend in recent years has been toward a reduction in the number of vegetable associations and an increase in the volume of business and number of services offered. Volume of produce handled varies from a few hundred truck or carlots to 5,000 or more carlots in some of the major areas of production.

Basic Cooperative Principles

Principles that distinguish farmer cooperatives from other types of free enterprise businesses are: (1) democratic control by producer-members, (2) returns on capital invested are limited, usually to not more than 8 percent, and (3) service is provided at cost with any savings distributed in direct proportion to the patronage of each member.

TRANSPORTING

Year-round availability of fresh vegetables has become an essential feature of the American life. Without the growth of a vast transportation system linking specialized growing areas with centers of population, this availability would be impossible. Production is concentrated in a few high-yield areas with suitable yearly climates. Today, California and Florida produce almost half of the nation's commercial vegetables.

Transportation Requirements

The transportation of vegetables involves special considerations not required in the movement of nonperishable commodities. Shipments must be moved rapidly enough to preserve the natural freshness of the produce, a major factor affecting the market price. The cost of movement per pound must be commensurate with the relatively low unit value of vegetables in comparison with finished goods and other commodities. Transportation facilities must be adequate and flexible enough to accommodate the highly seasonal and fluctuating demands. These special requirements continue to tax the ingenuity of growers, transportation companies, and dealers in determining the most desirable means of transport.

Principal Modes of Transportation

Most vegetables move to market by rail or motor trucks. During recent years, the share moved by trucks increased, while that carried by railroads declined. The railroads dominated volume movements of vegetables for many years before trucks were able to offer serious competition.

Trends in Transportation

With the improvement in the size, speed, and refrigeration of trucks (Fig. 1.1) and the development of farm-to-market roads, trucks are increasing in popularity. Trucks now carry larger amounts of vegetables moving long distances, most moving mid-distances, and practically all transported short distances to market (Fig. 13.5). Movements of produce by truck from Texas to California and the reverse, from Florida to Texas and vice versa, and even between California and Florida are common.

The annual share of California-Arizona fruits and vegetables moving to interstate markets by rail decreased from 87 to 70 percent between 1951 and 1960. During this period the rail share of shipments of potatoes from the bi-state area to U.S. markets declined from 95 to 83 percent, tomatoes from 87 to 70 percent, lettuce from 87 to 66 percent, and carrots from 65 to 35 percent. The trend still continues but has slowed down considerably since 1961. A major portion of the vegetables shipped from California, Arizona, and other Western and Southwestern regions to points west of the Mississippi River are now hauled by trucks. Despite the increasing use of trucks, railroads still transport a major portion of vegetables on the longest hauls.

Other Means of Transportation

Quantities of the less perishable "hardware" type vegetables have been transported by inland and ocean going ships for many years, but this mode of movement is generally not suitable for the more perishable vegetables. Refrigerated transports and the recent introduction of the

Fig. 13.5—Truck trailers ride piggyback on railroad car to destination.

USDA Photograph

"fishy-back" container for use on water vessels make low-cost water movement practical and promising under favorable circumstances.

The increasing use of air transportation for "gourmet" and some high-value vegetables has focused attention on the maintenance of quality by high-speed transit. However, cargo planes are not all equipped with flexible refrigeration devices, thereby limiting their handling of certain vegetable types. Until refrigeration and other facilities are improved and costs are reduced, air movement of vegetables will be restricted to those high-priced items which are in short supply in discriminating markets. The future growth of air transportation, which appears promising, will depend not only upon its own improvement but also upon technological and economical developments in the competing methods of transportation.

Developments in Transportation

Experience and research are improving all types of transportation. For example, van containers are being used more and more. These large mobile trailer units equipped with self-contained refrigeration are loaded on railroad flatcars for long distance movement by rail, or placed aboard ships for movement by water transports. Upon arrival in market centers, the units are unloaded and usually trucked to terminal warehouses, distribution points, or retail outlets. This innovation, which developed in a small way in the Rio Grande Valley of Texas in 1957, has increased rapidly, and promises to provide a major link in transportation.

Competition among the various means of transportation will force continuing improvements in the economical dispatch of commodities.

MARKETING

Marketing is the performance of services required to move commodities from farms into the possession of consumers—in the form, at the time, and to the places desired. Agricultural products move from many growers to a much smaller number of buyers, then through trade channels to retailers and on to millions of consumers.

Marketing Objectives

The objectives of a good marketing program are to: (1) move produce with the least loss of quality to consumers, (2) provide sales appeal by attractive and convenient packaging, (3) keep marketing cost at a minimum, and thereby, (4) provide both producers and consumers fair prices. In order to accomplish these objectives, careful and efficient handling, preparing, transportation, and the other marketing requirements discussed herein must necessarily be observed by all involved.

Marketing Services

Agricultural marketing services may include assembling, grading and standardizing, storing, packaging, processing, transporting, financing, advertising, risk-sharing, and wholesaling and retailing. Some of these operations may be performed more than once in the marketing process; while others, such as storing, processing, and packaging, are not involved with certain vegetables.

Marketing Procedures

Marketing procedures are expensive and technical and these functions are performed more and more by specialists and less and less by producers. Perishables, the stepchildren of food merchandising, belong in the most difficult category of commodities to market. Growers, who frequently complain of their small share of the consumer's dollar, have been generally willing to relinquish the complex marketing responsibility to a vast marketing industry, which employs millions of people and requires extensive technological and physical facilities. Continuing research and experience will no doubt improve the methods and quality of this service.

RETAILING PRACTICES AND TRENDS

More and more sales in fewer and fewer stores is the trend of the nation's grocery business in recent years according to a 1965 survey by the Ohio State Extension Service. The 1964 Annual Report of the Grocery Industry Magazine, reveals that retail food stores in the United States realized sales of $67.7 billion in 1964. Just a decade prior, total sales were $43.6 billion. During this period food store sales increased nearly 60 percent while food prices increased about 12 percent. "Grocery stores" captured 92 percent of the total food store sales while "speciality markets" realized 8 percent in 1964. Ten years ago, speciality markets captured 15 percent of all food store sales. During this same period, the number of grocery stores in the United States decreased from 355,000 to 228,000, a reduction of 36 percent. This decline has started to level off in recent years, however, and will likely begin to increase in the future.

Significant changes have also occurred in the structure of food retailing. Of all grocery stores, 14 percent were large enough to be classified as supermarkets (annual sales in excess of $500,000) in 1964, yet they made 70 percent of all grocery store sales. Approximately one-half of these supermarkets were owned by corporate chain companies and one-half by independent retailers.

Paralleling the increase in numbers and size of supermarkets and superettes is a trend toward complete self-service in food stores. Increased prepackaging of produce is a part of this trend (Fig. 13.2), as a majority of the supermarkets are selling many fruits and vegetables prepackaged.

Few consumers are aware of the overall coordinated operations involved in supplying grocery stores with a wide variety of good quality, attractively packaged vegetables. Little do they realize that many of these vegetables were fresh from the fields, ran the complicated gauntlet of marketing, and were delivered to the grocery stores the night before being retailed (Fig. 13.6).

Fig. 13.6—Discriminating customers selecting vegetables in a retail market.

USDA Photograph

EXPORTING AND IMPORTING

Of the large volume of commercial vegetables produced in this country (Table 1.3), variable quantities of some fresh and processed items are exported to many countries throughout the world.

The United States exported a record of $5.6 billion of farm products in 1963. Of this amount, vegetables (excluding dried beans and peas) accounted for approximately $71,000,000 as shown in Table 13.2. In 1963, United States imports of farm products totaled approximately $4 billion, of which about $58,500,000 were for fresh vegetables and their products (Table 13.2).

Canada is by far the most important fresh vegetable export market of the United States. For many years, large quantities of potatoes, lettuce, celery, tomatoes, carrots, and cabbage; and sizable amounts of green beans, peppers, and cantaloups have been shipped to Canada, the sum total amounting to about $60,000,000 in 1963. Processed and fresh vegetables approximating $18,000,000 in value were also exported, mostly to western European countries and Mexico.

Almost two-thirds of the fresh vegetables imported by the United States came from Mexico. Large quantities of tomatoes, muskmelons or cantaloups, watermelons, onions, and sizable amounts of cucumbers, peppers, beans, garlic, and squash are imported annually. Canada is the second largest supplier, providing the United States with considerable quantities of table and seed potatoes, turnips, rutabagas, carrots, and variable amounts of lettuce, tomatoes, cucumbers, and some other vegetables.

The quantities exported and the principal countries to which exports were made are discussed separately in the chapters on individual vegetables (Section Two) under "Marketing." Considerable quantities of canned tomatoes, tomato paste, and puree are imported from Italy, and limited amounts of canned peas and other items come from Canada and other countries. International trade in vegetables will likely continue on a large scale.

FEDERAL-STATE MARKETING SERVICES

The U.S. Department of Agriculture alone or in cooperation with the state departments of agriculture has provided research, reporting, news, inspection, standardization, and regulatory services on the major crops for many years. Such information and control services are tailored to the need and designed to protect both the growers and the consumers. Those services which deal with fruits and vegetables are discussed briefly in order for readers to make use of their provisions when desired. Detailed information on each of these services can be obtained from the Consumer and Marketing Service, U.S. Department of Agriculture, Washington, D.C., or from one of its state, regional, or field offices.

Market News Service

The "Market News Service" is simply an exchange of information on fruit and vegetable supplies, relating to the demand and prices between growers, shippers, wholesalers, and others in the produce industry. This information is gathered by skilled market reporters and flashed to all parts of the country over a nationwide teletype system provided by the U.S. Department of Agriculture and the state departments of agriculture. These market news reporters serve as the "eyes and ears" of the produce industry, and provide valuable information on supply and demand, the basic factors in determining prices.

The Market News Service issues: (1) shipping point reports which show all rail movements, available truck shipments, and prices received

Table 13.2—U.S. Exports and Imports of Principal Fresh and Processed Vegetables in 1963.

Fresh and Processed Vegetables	Unit	Exports Quantity	Exports Value, $1,000	Imports Quantity	Imports Value, $1,000
Asparagus, canned	cases	2,074,881	15,100	—	—
Beans (green), canned	case	565,692	1,786	8,196	55
Beans (green), fresh	cwt	184,954	1,592	85,244	1,269
Cabbage, fresh	cwt.	547,099	1,721	14,651	51
Carrot, fresh	cwt.	1,346,532	5,308	388,495	1,304
Celery, fresh	cwt.	1,002,429	4,403	—	—
Corn, canned	case	267,646	1,101	NSC	NSC
Cucumber, fresh	cwt.	NSC	NSC	611,547	3,707
Eggplant, fresh	cwt.	NSC	NSC	46,630	312
Lettuce, fresh	cwt.	1,644,499	7,578	5,460	29
Muskmelon (cantaloups)	cwt.	NSC	NSC	1,111,467	8,492
Onion, fresh	cwt.	1,318,890	5,988	441,740	2,374
Peas, canned	cases	198,957	975	24,622	151
Peas, fresh	cwt.	NSC	NSC	59,984	594
Pepper, fresh	cwt.	115,080	999	166,515	2,213
Potato, fresh	cwt.	3,259,116	7,207	445,259	1,844
Radish, fresh	cwt.	NSC	NSC	66,136	119
Spinach, canned	cases	43,536	139	NSC	NSC
Sweet potato	cwt.	57,062	303	NSC	NSC
Turnip and Rutabaga	cwt.	NSC	NSC	383,864	1,683
Tomato, canned (all)	cases	1,614,545	6,246	3,880,994	12,194
Tomato, fresh	cwt.	1,001,465	8,975	2,419,742	20,926
Watermelon, fresh	cwt.	842,343	1,952	663,032	1,212
Total		16,084,726	71,373	10,823,578	58,529

Cases—30 pounds net
NSC—not separately classified.
Export and import data from the USDA, Foreign Agricultural Service.

by producers and shippers for various commodities; (2) terminal market reports which provide rail and truck receipts in the 23 largest cities of the country and prices received by wholesalers; and (3) Washington reports which show nationwide rail and available truck movements for all commodities, annual summaries of produce prices, and other special reports. Detailed market reports are mailed free upon request from shipping point and terminal market offices.

Many newspapers and trade journals such as *The Packer* and *The Produce News*, hundreds of radio stations, and many TV stations carry market news information from the Federal-State News Service.

Standardization and Inspection Services

The packing of vegetables according to the requirements of official standards is the first step for orderly marketing and efficient buying and selling. Official standards provide a yardstick for measuring variations in quality and serve as a basis for dealing at long distance. Clear and definite standards are indispensible in the settlement of disputes between buyers and sellers.

The separation of products into standard grades makes equitable distribution according to demand possible. Separate grades also provide small and large growers an opportunity to pool their products in cooperative marketing associations, provide a continuity of supply, and attract volume buyers.

The number of grades and the grade names included in a standard vary depending upon the number of distinct quality gradations. Two or three distinct grades are usually enough to meet normal trading demands for most vegetables. Usual grades are designed as U.S. Fancy, U.S. No. 1, and U.S. No. 2. Some commodities, however, lend themselves to separation into several quality classes. For these, a greater number of grades and grade names are provided.

Standardization and inspection services are applicable to vegetables for processing as well as those for fresh market. United States standards for fresh market vegetables not only apply to quality and size, but they also provide standards for bunching in case of bunched vegetables, arrangement of items in containers, uniformity of size, and tightness of pack. In addition, they specify permissible tolerances which allow for variations incident to grading and packing. Thus, upon inspection a product might meet the requirements of grade and fail to meet the standards of packing, or vice versa.

Generally speaking, U.S. standards are permissive, their use by producers and buyers being optional under the law authorizing such. Certain other Federal and state laws, however, grant authority for compulsory grading of produce under certain circumstances. The grading of some products is compulsory in those areas which have adopted marketing agreements and orders. Compulsory grading is also required by the provisions of many state laws; and a few states require compulsory inspection of some products, either by law or by regulations.

For established fees, trained inspectors at shipping points (Fig. 13.2) or in terminal markets inspect commodities and issue certificates stating their quality or condition and whether or not such comply with designated grades or specifications. The inspection certificate can be based on the official U.S. grade standards, a state grade, or on other written specifications designated by the buyer or seller. These certificates are accepted by law as *prima facie* evidence in all Federal courts and in nearly all state courts.

To provide inspection services nationwide, the U.S. Department of Agriculture has cooperative agreements with the state departments of agriculture or other cooperating state agencies in 50 states and Puerto Rico. Under these agreements, approximately 3,800 Federally-licensed inspectors perform the inspection work at points of origin. Inspectors are stationed throughout the country to provide fast, efficient service to growers, shippers, receivers, processors, repackers, and institutions, including government procurement agencies.

The inspection service performed under these cooperative agreements is operated jointly by the Consumer and Marketing Service of the U.S. Department of Agriculture and the cooperating state agencies, and is known as the Federal-State Inspection Service. The Consumer and Marketing Service establishes basic inspection policies and procedures and furnishes overall direction.

Federal inspection services are provided in 78 of the largest terminal markets in the country. Assistance from cooperating state agencies is available at some of these markets.

Federal Marketing Orders

Produce growers face major marketing problems, often too great for each to solve individually. Many growers are now overcoming their big marketing problems by pooling their interests and working together through "Federal Marketing Orders."

The marketing-order program is simply a partnership between industry and government. If a two-thirds majority of the growers (either by number of growers voting in a referendum or by volume of production) favor a marketing order, the Secretary of Agriculture can issue an order, binding on the whole industry in the producing area. The industry can then, through its administrative committee, tailor a marketing plan to fit its needs and initiate regulations under the authorized marketing order. The administrative committee is responsible for expenditures and must keep books, which are subject to annual audit.

The number of marketing orders and their volume of sales have increased considerably in recent years. Details on the establishment, needs and advantages, and methods of operating and financing marketing-order programs are available upon request from the U.S. Department of Agriculture.

The Perishable Agricultural Commodities Act

The "Perishable Agricultural Commodities Act" (PACA) is designed to encourage fair trading practices in the marketing of fresh and frozen fruits and vegetables in interstate and foreign commerce. Certain unfair and fraudulent practices are prohibited and penalties are provided for violation. The Act also provides for the award of damages against those who fail to live up to contract obligations.

The produce industry realized the importance of a code of fair trading standards and the PACA was passed by Congress in 1930 at the industry's request. It has been amended a number of times to keep it up to date with changing trade practices. The U.S. Department of Agriculture is responsible for administering this Act.

The regulations under PACA include definitions of standard trade terms which have been used by the industry for many years. The PACA is primarily concerned in prohibiting (without reasonable cause) sellers from failing to deliver purchases, buyers from refusing to accept purchased produce, failures to make payments as agreed, the dumping or destroying of produce by consignees, failures to render correct accounting, and misrepresentations concerning the grade, brand, quality, weight, state of origin, and related violations.

Commission merchants, dealers, brokers, and others involved in handling fresh or frozen fruits or vegetables in interstate or foreign commerce are required to be licensed under this Act. Farmers or growers selling only fruits and vegetables they grow are not subject to license. However, if they also sell in interstate or foreign commerce produce by other farmers, they are required to have a license. Truckers are not required to be licensed if they merely haul produce for freight charges, but if they buy and sell fruits and vegetables in interstate or foreign commerce, they must obtain a license.

All of the expenses of administering the Act, except for the cost of legal services, are financed by the revenue from license fees. Annual license fees vary with the cost of operation up to a legal maximum of $50 per individual firm. The penalty for operating without a license when one is required is not more than $500 for each offense and not more than $25 for each day the offense continues. Other violations of the Act can result in the suspension or revocation of a license issued under the Act.

Inquiries on licensing or requests for license applications and additional information on this and other acts designed to regulate and control fair trade practices should be directed to one of the PACA regional offices or to the Consumer and Marketing Service, U.S. Department of Agriculture, Washington, D.C.

Other Federal-State Marketing Service Programs

Marketing service programs conducted by state departments of agriculture under the matching-fund authority of the Agricultural Marketing Act of 1946 were started in 1947 with 21 states participating. Programs on various farm products were carried on in 41 states in 1960-61. The office of this Matching-Fund Program, in the Consumer and Marketing Service, provides guidance and assistance to the states in conducting this work.

These programs are designed to: (1) help marketing agencies at the various levels of distribution adopt new techniques and methods for performing marketing operations discovered or developed through research, (2) show these marketing agencies and producers how to improve or maintain the quality of farm products during marketing, (3) provide producers and marketing agencies with new or more timely and complete marketing facts and information, and (4) expand markets for farm products.

General guidance to the Matching-Fund Program is provided by the Advisory Committee on Cooperative Work under the Agricultural Marketing Act with state departments of agriculture. To improve the operation of their programs and prevent duplication of effort, the state departments of agriculture maintain close cooperation with industry and trade groups, state extension services, agricultural experiment stations, vocational education agencies, and the U.S. Department of Agriculture.

These programs are conducted under cooperative agreements between the state departments of agriculture or similar agencies responsible for marketing service work and the U.S. Department of Agriculture. Individual projects are initiated by the states and approved by the Consumer and Marketing Service. The types of vegetable marketing services provided by this Federal-State Matching-Fund Program include: (1) projects on improving quality, (2) expanding outlets, (3) improving marketing efficiency, and (4) providing basic data and marketing information. More than 30 states including Alaska are participating in most of these programs. Detailed information, including projects by states, are provided in USDA Publication AMS-56.

SELECTED REFERENCES

Anonymous, "Consumer and Marketing Service," USDA, PA-661, 1965.
Anonymous, "Conversion Factors and Weights and Measures," USDA, ERS Statistical Bull. 362, 1965.

Anonymous, "Federal Marketing Orders and Agreements," USDA, AMS PA-506, 1962.

Anonymous, "Foreign Agricultural Trade of the United States," USDA, ERS Report, 1965.

Anonymous, "Loading Out Fruits and Vegetables in Wholesale Warehouses," USDA, AMS Report No. 282, 1959.

Anonymous, "The Market News Service," USDA, AMS-99, 1963.

Anonymous, "Marketing and Transportation Situation," USDA, MTS-151, 1963.

Anonymous, "Marketing Service Programs," USDA, AMS-56, 1962.

Anonymous, "Official Grade Standards and Inspection for Fresh Fruits and Vegetables," USDA, AMS-520, 1963.

Anonymous, "Perishable Agricultural Commodities Act," USDA, C & MS, 1965.

Anonymous, "Receiving Fruits and Vegetables in Wholesale Warehouses," USDA, MRR-478, 1961.

Anonymous, "Shifts in Rail and Truck Transportation of Fresh Fruits and Vegetables," USDA, MRR-237, 1958.

Anonymous, "Tips on Selecting Fruits and Vegetables," USDA Marketing Bulletin No. 13, 1961.

Anonymous, "Truck-Rail and Sea-Land Shipping Tests With Texas Fruits and Vegetables," USDA, MRR-589, 1963.

Futrell, G. and Kolmer, L., "Consumers Marketing Handbook, Fruits and Vegetables," Ia. Ext. Ser., Part I, 1961.

Seelig, R. A., "Marketing Fresh Vegetables," Fresh Market Fruit and Vegetable Association, Washington, D.C., 1963.

Section Two
PRACTICES

INTRODUCTION TO SECTION TWO

Chapters 14 through 33 of Section Two deal with the economic importance and specific "practices" involved in the production, harvesting, handling, and marketing of the principal vegetable crops. These chapters contain the most applicable information on each vegetable crop.

In discussing the culture of different crops, it is assumed that the reader is familiar with the principles underlying the various operations as discussed in the first 13 chapters. An understanding of these principles will be a considerable aid in applications of the different jobs.

In view of the fact that the botanical and horticultural relationships of the various vegetables were fully discussed in Chapter 2, "Classification of Vegetables," the arrangement of the crop production chapters is alphabetical by crops, rather than by botanical relationships. This arrangement provides for convenient reference, and should not discourage the student from studying or comparing related vegetables.

Each chapter is complete in itself, but references are made to similar discussions elsewhere in order to supplement information or to conserve space. Pertinent facts on the crop under discussion, including botanical classification, history, production, economic importance, and climatic requirements, are systematically given at the beginning of the chapter.

The subject matter of the vegetable chapters is treated according to the job-analysis plan. Each vegetable enterprise is divided into jobs or teaching units, covering the subject in order of seasonal sequence. The jobs are further subdivided into special operations.

A typical outline showing the job-analysis treatment used in the chapter of each vegetable enterprise is given below:

JOB 1. SELECTING VARIETIES AND SEED
       Determining Varieties
       Securing Seed

JOB 2. PREPARING THE SOIL
       Soil Preference
       Preparing the Seedbed

JOB 3. FERTILIZING, MANURING, AND LIMING
            Fertilizing
            Manuring
            Liming
JOB 4. PLANTING AND PROTECTING
            Starting Plants Under Protection
            Seeding in the Field
JOB 5. CULTIVATING AND IRRIGATING
            Cultivating
            Irrigating
            Thinning and Weeding
            Training
JOB 6. CONTROLLING DISEASES AND INSECTS
            Controlling Diseases
            Controlling Insects
JOB 7. HARVESTING, HANDLING, AND MARKETING
            Harvesting
            Grading
            Packing
            Storing
            Marketing

The statistics on each crop, including acreage, acre yield, production, unit price, farm value, and comparative growing seasons by leading states, have not appeared in similar form elsewhere. The student will find many interesting comparisons in these tables, which were prepared from reports supplied by the Crop Reporting Board of the Statistical Reporting Service, U.S. Department of Agriculture.

The dot maps, prepared by the U.S. Department of Commerce, are only approximate as production and related values are constantly shifting. Beginning in 1964, the Crop Reporting Board of the U.S. Department of Agriculture revised its system of computing crop values. The 1965 values of "fresh market vegetables" herein are based on the "f.o.b. values at the shipping point"; while those of "vegetables for processing" are based on values at the "processing plant door." Consequently, 1965 values are relative and not precisely comparable to farm values reported in previous years.

Readers should bear in mind that vegetable acreage, yields, production, and value vary considerably from year to year. Consequently, the 1965 data appearing in the vegetable chapters should be considered on an annual basis and not as an average or trend.

Diseases and insects have been discussed somewhat in detail, because they are of great economic importance; and because their control is closely associated with production, and, in many cases, with transportation and marketing.

For completeness and convenient reference, scientific names of plants, diseases, and insects appear in parentheses following the common names.

Another feature contained in the crop chapters is the parallel description of the outstanding characteristics of some of the principal varieties.

CHAPTER 14

Asparagus

Classification, Origin, and History

Asparagus (*Asparagus officinalis*) is a member of the lily family and is indigenous to parts of Russia, the Mediterranean region, and the British Isles. It was used for food by the Romans and other ancient peoples, and was also highly regarded for medicinal purposes. The plant was brought to America by the early colonists.

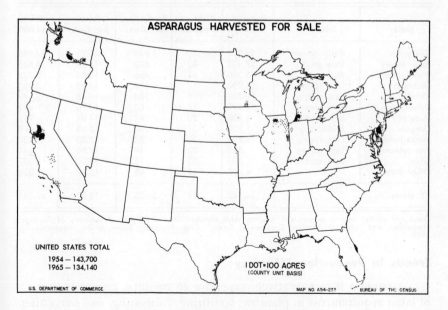

ASPARAGUS HARVESTED FOR SALE

UNITED STATES TOTAL
1954 — 143,700
1965 — 134,140

I DOT=I00 ACRES
(COUNTY UNIT BASIS)

U.S. DEPARTMENT OF COMMERCE   MAP NO. A54-233   BUREAU OF THE CENSUS

Fig. 14.1—Acreage and distribution of asparagus.

215

Scope and Importance

Commercial asparagus production is concentrated mainly along the west and east coasts and in the Great Lakes region. It is a popular early spring crop and is grown for local market and home use in many parts of the United States. Asparagus ranked 10th in acreage and 14th in value among the 22 principal vegetables in 1965.

Asparagus acreage increased from 124,440 in 1939 to about 161,000 in 1959 and then declined to an estimated 134,140 acres in 1965. Acre yields increased insignificantly during this period. The farm value of asparagus for fresh market and processing was $13,205,000 in 1939 and approximated $50,000,000 in recent years. California is by far the leading state in asparagus production, followed by New Jersey, Washington, and Michigan. The distribution of asparagus production is shown in Fig. 14.1 while the acreage, production, and value of these and other principal producing states are presented in Table 14.1.

Table 14.1—Asparagus for Fresh Market and Processing: Shipping Season and Estimated Commercial Acreage, Yield, Production, and Value in Leading States, 1965.

State	Season	Harvested Acreage	Yield per Acre, Cwt.	Production, per Cwt.	Price, per Cwt.	Value, $1,000
California	Early spring	54,900	30	1,647	$15.75	24,056
New Jersey	Late spring	27,400	22	603	14.70	8,865
Washington	Mid-spring	15,200	32	486	13.83	6,722
Michigan	Late spring	11,200	17	190	16.35	3,107
Illinois	Late spring	10,200	18	184	11.68	2,149
Delaware	Late spring	3,500	17	60	14.70	882
Maryland	Late spring	3,400	20	68	14.04	955
Oregon	Mid-spring	1,300	31	40	12.98	519
Massachusetts	Late spring	1,200	20	24	17.50	420
Pennsylvania	Late spring	850	22	19	17.90	340
Ohio	Late spring	500	32	16	19.20	307
Other states		4,490	15	68	15.12	1,028
All states		134,140	25	3,405	15.02	49,350

These and similar data in subsequent chapters were obtained from the "Annual Summary of Acreage, Production, and Value of Principal Commercial Crops," Crop Reporting Board, USDA, December 20, 1965.

Trends in Production Efficiency

Asparagus is comparatively expensive to produce, primarily because of labor requirements in planting, fertilizing, cultivating, and harvesting. Fresh market asparagus required 173 man-hours per acre for growing and harvesting in 1959, while the processed crop averaged 130 man-hours. The average acre yield of asparagus did not rise during the 1939-1959 period but has increased since. The unit output per man-hour for fresh market asparagus rose only 8 percent during this period, while that for the processed crop actually decreased 18 percent according to a 1964 report by the Economic Research Service, U.S. Department of Agriculture (Table 1.4).

Mechanization of the asparagus harvest may soon be a reality as the University of California at Davis has developed a non-selective harvester which appears competitive with hand cutting.[1]

Climatic Requirements

Asparagus grows best where cool temperatures prevail during the growing season and where adequate moisture is available. The high summer temperatures occurring in the southern states do not favor maximum production of spears; but where there is sufficient cold in winter to render the plants dormant for a considerable period, profitable yields are possible if the crop is well fertilized and properly cultivated. The crowns are very hardy and are seldom injured by the cold winters of the northern states. Winter injury is usually restricted to fields where the tops of the plants have been removed in the fall.

JOB 1. SELECTING VARIETIES AND SEED

Varieties

The Mary Washington is the only variety grown to any extent in the South, and it is by far the most important in the whole country. The closely related variety, Waltham Washington, is grown to some extent, particularly in the northeastern part of the United States. Both of these varieties are relatively rust-resistant. The latter is somewhat more resistant than the Mary Washington, but it does not produce as desirable spears. In South Carolina, the full-grown stalks of Martha Washington have been reported to blow over badly during high winds.

In addition to the Washington varieties, a number of other promising ones have recently been introduced. They include Eden, Viking, California 500, Waltham Washington, Raritan, and Seneca Washington. All except Eden were selected from the Washington strains.

---

[1]See article in "California Agriculture," Vol. 19, No. 1, January, 1965.

Securing Seed

Some asparagus seed is saved in most of the areas where the crop is grown commercially. California, New Jersey, and South Carolina are the sources of considerable quantities of seed. Prices of seed vary depending upon its source. Seed saved in the fall from a planting which produces good-quality asparagus is probably about as satisfactory as any.

JOB 2. GROWING AND SELECTING CROWNS

Asparagus plants are grown in a nursery for one season, and then set in permanent fields. The grower may buy crowns or grow them at home. If home-grown crowns are used, production of a crop will be delayed one year; but the cost of establishing may be less and the grower will have more opportunity to practice crown selection.

In growing crowns, the seed is usually planted on sandy loam soil as soon as the soil is warm in the spring, with the rows 24 to 30 inches apart. Garden seed drills or other planters provided with special plates are commonly used for planting. Preferably, seeds are dropped singly 2 or 3 inches apart and covered 1 to 1½ inches deep. Thinning is difficult, and the crowns are hard to separate after digging if they are grown so close together that the roots are interwoven. Since the seed is slow to germinate at low temperatures, it is difficult to get early uniform seedling development. This can best be done by germinating the seed at high temperatures (80° to 90° F.) and transplanting the seedlings. Such a practice would be expensive and therefore applicable only to a small-scale operation. The practice of soaking the seed is of doubtful value. Delayed plantings germinate promptly without treatment.

In growing crowns on a large scale, the seed is usually planted at the rate of four or five pounds per acre. This quantity of seed will, according to nurserymen, produce about 30,000 or more plants.

Ordinarily the soil used for growing asparagus crowns should be well fertilized at planting time. The plants are cultivated during the season as any other row crop. It is preferable to dig the crowns shortly before planting in the spring, and the digging should be done in such manner as to injure the storage roots as little as possible. Although the results of experiments are somewhat conflicting, it is probably advisable to use only the larger crowns for planting.

Crowns may be purchased from plant growers and the price is usually dependent upon size. The cheaper crowns should weigh 75 to 80 pounds per 1,000, while well-grown ones may weigh as much as 150 pounds or more per 1,000.

JOB 3. PREPARING THE SOIL AND PLANTING THE CROWNS

Soil Preferences

Asparagus may be grown on a wide variety of soils, but, for best results, they should be well drained, deep, loose, and light. Mucks and light sandy loams favor the development of healthy root systems and unblemished spears. Light sandy or gravelly soils having porous subsoils should be avoided because of their low moisture-holding capacities.

Preparing the Soil for Planting

Preparation of the soil for planting asparagus is usually best done in early spring. Since asparagus occupies the land for 15 years or longer, the soil should be put in good condition at the start. It is desirable to plow under a green manure crop in the fall before planting. The land should be free from stumps and from coarse rubbish which might cause crooked spears. It should also be as free as possible of weeds, particularly perennial weeds. Since deep planting of the crowns is commonly practiced, the soil should be plowed rather deeply.

Planting the Crowns

Asparagus crowns are usually set in the field as soon as the soil can be worked in the spring, and before shoot development has begun. In mild regions they may be planted in the late fall or winter after they have become dormant. Furrows should be plowed out to a depth of 8 or 10 inches with a turning plow, or middle buster. In these, the crowns are placed with buds 6 to 8 inches below the general ground level, and are covered about 2 inches deep. As the tops grow, the soil is gradually worked toward the plants until the furrows have been entirely filled. In some parts of the country shallow planting is recommended, especially on heavy soils. Better stands are obtained, but shallow crowns may be injured by disking and freezing so that they produce small spears.

The spacing of asparagus plants varies considerably in different sections of the country. Close planting may be practiced in home gardens, but plantings for commercial production usually consist of rows 6 to 7 feet apart with the plants 12 to 18 inches apart in the row. However, according to observations made by the South Carolina Experiment Station over a period of eight years, a spacing of 2 by 5 feet, or not more than 2 by 6 feet, gave better yields, quantity and quality considered, than either a 2-by-4- or 2-by-8-feet spacing. These results are in line with similar data secured in Iowa and California. With a spacing of 2 by 5 feet, 4,356 crowns are required to plant an acre.

JOB 4. FERTILIZING, LIMING, AND MANURING

Fertilizing

The cost of fertilizing asparagus is the largest single item of expense in its production. Fertilizer practices should therefore be carefully considered so that the outlay may be no more than is necessary. Because of the premium paid for the colossal grade, growers have a tendency to adjust fertilizer and other practices so as to secure as much of this grade as possible, without due regard for the economics involved. If the increased yields from excessive amounts of fertilizer are not enough to off-set the extra cost as compared with that of a moderate application, the use of the larger amount of fertilizer should be discontinued.

KIND AND AMOUNT OF FERTILIZER. It is important to have the soil well fertilized, especially with phosphorus and potassium, before setting the crowns. These elements do not move readily in the soil, and efforts to place them down to the feeding roots after the plants are established results in injury and reduced yields. Surface applications, on the other hand, are not very effective. If the soil is well supplied with phosphorus and potassium before planting, annual applications of fertilizer may be limited to nitrogen primarily. On soils where leaching is not an important factor the young planting will respond to about 80 pounds of nitrogen applied annually. This amount may be gradually reduced to 50 pounds in an old field. Fertilizer mixtures such as a 5-4-4 or a 10-4-4 are commonly used in asparagus growing. These may be applied at the rates of 1,000 to 2,000 pounds per acre.

TIME OF APPLYING FERTILIZERS. Considerable difference of opinion prevails as to the proper time for applying fertilizers to asparagus. Much of the experimental data available indicate that the primary application of fertilizer should be made immediately after the cutting season. This tends to stimulate rapid and vigorous top growth necessary for a good crop the following year. The nitrogenous reserves are exhausted more readily than the carbohydrates of the crowns during harvesting. For this reason a response to readily available nitrogen applied early in the spring may also be expected.

METHOD OF APPLYING FERTILIZERS. Whether applied before or after harvesting, the fertilizer should be spread and disked into the soil. The early application and disking should be done before the spears begin growth, and should be shallow enough to prevent injury to the crowns.

LIMING AND MANURING. Asparagus does best on soils ranging from slightly acid to slightly alkaline (pH 6.5 to 7.5). If acid soils are used they should be limed to bring the reactions to pH 6.0 or 6.5.

Organic matter is important for improving the physical condition of the soil. Animal manure is a good source when it can be obtained. Even though manure may be used to supply fertility it should be supplemented with commercial fertilizers, especially in the early years of a planting. At the Maryland Experiment Station, a comparison of manure and chemical fertilizer on a fairly fertile loam soil showed that yields over a nine-year period were larger from the latter and were also much more profitable.

JOB 5.   CULTIVATING AND CARE

Cultivating

Asparagus should be cultivated to keep down weeds and grass and thus encourage good top growth. During the harvesting season, however, it is difficult to cultivate the beds without injuring the developing shoots. The spears are less brittle in the afternoon and cultivation is best done at this time. The weeding problem has been simplified by the use of chemicals. Recommendations are given in Chapter 9.

Disposing of Tops

The tops should be left standing in the field over winter and should be disked into the soil in early spring before any shoot development. The old tops protect the crowns over winter and add organic matter when incorporated into the soil.

Life of Asparagus Plantations

The life of an asparagus plantation depends upon natural conditions and upon the treatment received. Plantings are in existence which are said to have produced profitable yields for more than a hundred years. Commercial fields receiving average care remain profitable for 15 to 18 years, and yield their best crops at 5 to 10 years of age.

JOB 6. CONTROLLING DISEASES AND INSECTS

Asparagus Rust

This disease is caused by *Puccinia asparagi*. It injures the tops of the plant and limits the storage of reserve food in the crowns, thereby reducing the crop of the following season. Rust does not develop on the marketed product. It appears first as small reddish-yellow spots on the main stem and branches. The fungus produces spores in large numbers and these are disseminated by wind. The spots enlarge and become darker as the season advances, and the foliage turns brown and drops off, giving the plants a naked appearance.

Spraying and dusting are not usually effective enough to warrant their use. However, spraying the uncut plants in the spring with Zineb or sulfur may prevent the buildup of inoculum and thus reduce the severity of the disease. The use of a variety not highly susceptible to rust is recommended.

Asparagus Beetle

The asparagus beetle (*Crioceris asparagi*) is the most destructive insect attacking asparagus. It injures the spears during the harvest season and the full-grown tops later. The adult beetle overwinters in rubbish surrounding cultivated fields and emerges in time to feed upon the developing spears, causing them to become crooked and unsightly. Eggs are deposited on the spears and later both adults and larvae attack the fully developed plants, defoliating them in some instances and giving them a setback which may be reflected in reduced yields the following season.

The beetle does not thrive in hot weather. Although it causes considerable damage in certain cases, it has not proven as troublesome in the South as elsewhere. The most serious damage is that done to the marketable spears, and no remedy has been devised for this. The insect may be kept in check by dusting the mature plants with rotenone at 0.3 pounds, carbaryl at 1.0 pound, or malathion at 1.25 pounds per acre. Where rust is not a serious disease, a few of the early spears may be left to develop into mature plants to attract the emerging beetles. As the insects collect on these, they may be destroyed by dusting with DDT at the rate of 1.5 pounds per acre.

JOB 7. HARVESTING, HANDLING, AND MARKETING

Harvesting

It is perhaps best to delay harvesting until the bed is two years old, and to limit the cutting to not more than three or four weeks this first season.

The spears are cut when they have grown 5 to 8 inches above the surface of the ground. In cutting, the spears are severed just below the surface by means of an asparagus knife. They are collected in baskets and taken to the packing shed. Cutting is done preferably in the morning and as frequently as is necessary, which may be every day or only every two or three days, depending on the temperature and other growing conditions. Care should be exercised in cutting the asparagus in order to avoid injuring the younger spears. Tests in Massachusetts have shown that there is great variation in the quality and quantity of asparagus harvested from similar areas by different individuals, depending on the care used in cutting.

Grading, Bunching, and Packing

The returns from asparagus growing depend in a large measure upon proper grading, bunching, and packing. Usually No. 1 asparagus is shipped. The spears are first separated into three grades, Colossal, Fancy, and Choice, depending upon their diameter. The diameters of the spears included in each grade are as follows: Extra Colossal, ⅞ inch and over; Colossal, 1¹¹⁄₁₆ to ⅞ inch; Fancy, ½ to ¹¹⁄₁₆ inch (Fig. 14.2) ; and Choice, ¼ to ½ inch. Bunches of asparagus are normally 8½ inches long but in recent years 10-inch bunches also are shipped. Extra Colossal is always 10 inches long and the other grades may be of that length. All stalks should be straight, unblemished, and fresh.

In bunching, the required number of spears are placed with the tips even in a bunching machine, the bunch is clamped and tied firmly near each end with red or blue tape, or held together with colored rubber bands (Fig. 14.2) . The butts are then cut squarely with a large knife, leaving the bunch either 8½ or 10 inches in length. Twelve of the 2- to 2½-pound bunches are placed in a crate which has a pyramidal shape,

Fig. 14.2—Spears of asparagus bunched and held with rubber bands.

assuring a tight pack. Before packing, the bottom of the crate is lined with waxed paper and then with a layer of moist sphagnum moss, on which the bunches of asparagus are set with the butts down (Fig. 14.3). Unless kept at temperatures near the freezing point, the quality of asparagus deteriorates rapidly and the spears continue growing, thus causing loose bunches of ragged appearance. The packed crates should therefore be put into iced cars as promptly as possible.

On local markets, one-pound or smaller bunches may be preferred, or the asparagus may be sold without grading or bunching.

Fig. 14.3—Bunches of asparagus placed on damp peat moss in flat to keep them fresh.

USDA Photograph

Marketing

Much of the commercial asparagus crop is marketed through grower's associations and farmer's markets at shipping points. Strict regulations have been established in grades and packages in order to market a standardized product. Most asparagus is marketed fresh and shipped in refrigerator cars and trucks. Truck movement accounts for a large percentage of the total movement.

Considerable canned asparagus is exported from the United States to approximately 50 countries throughout the world. Increasing quantities ranging from an average of 1,223,400 cases during the 1955-1959 period to 2,075,000 valued at $15,100,000 in 1963 have been shipped. The bulk went to West Germany and other European countries, and sizable amounts were exported to Canada, South Africa, Venezuela, Mexico, and the Philippines.

Fig. 14.4—The bulk of asparagus is packed in crates, assembled at central shipping points, and moved to markets in iced refrigerator cars.

SELECTED REFERENCES

Anonymous, "Weed Control in Establishing Asparagus in Central Washington," Wash. Agr. Ext. Cir. 344, 1964.

Gorter, C. J., "Vegetative Propagation of *Asparagus officinalis* by Cuttings," *Jour. Hort. Sci.* 40: 177-79, 1965.

Hanna, G. C., "Asparagus Production in California," Calif. Agr. Ext. Cir. 91, 1950.

Judge, Jean F., "Fresh Asparagus," N. J. Agr. Ext. Ser. Leaflet 384, 1965.

Thompson, R. C., Doolittle, S. P., Davidson, L. L., and Mason, H. C., "Asparagus Culture," USDA Farmers' Bull. 1646, 1963.

CHAPTER 15

Beans (Snap and Lima)

Classification, Origin, and History

The snap or kidney bean (*Phaseolus vulgaris*) was grown by the Indians over a considerable part of both North and South America, and was introduced in Europe by early American settlers. The species includes field beans as well as varieties used in the green or immature stage. Snap beans have thick-walled pods that are free from strings (bast fibers) in the early stages of development.

The Lima bean (*Phaseolus limensis*) is a native of tropical America. It grows wild in Brazil, and its seeds have been found in Peruvian tombs at Pachacamac and Ancon. The name "Lima" probably comes from Lima, Peru, where large Lima beans were secured and imported to the United States.

Scope and Importance

The snap bean is one of the most extensively grown vegetables, both commercially and in home gardens. Beans for fresh market and processing constitute one of the leading vegetables, ranking fifth both in acreage and value among the 22 principal vegetables in 1965.

Harvested acreage of snap beans for fresh market declined from 184,100 in 1939 to approximately 103,000 acres in 1965. Total production also decreased, but farm value increased from $17,439,000 to $39,841,000. Snap bean acreage for processing rose from 54,170 in 1939 to an estimated 229,260 in 1965, and acre yields increased considerably. Crop value rose phenomenally from $4,051,000 in 1939 to almost $52,000,000 in 1965.

Lima beans are considerably less prominent, ranking 14th in acreage and 17th in value. The acreage for fresh market decreased from

227

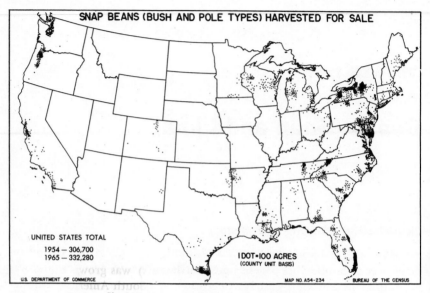

Fig. 15.1—Acreage and distribution of snap beans.

Fig. 15.2—Acreage and distribution of lima beans.

31,700 in 1939 to an estimated 13,100 in 1965. During this time, production dropped from 706,000 to 340,000 hundredweight but value increased
from $2,938,000 to $3,460,000. Acreage for processed Limas was 50,360 in
1939, rose to 115,000 by 1949 and then decreased to an estimated 82,870
acres in 1965. Acre yields rose considerably during this period and farm
value increased markedly from $1,987,000 to almost $17,000,000.

Figures 15.1 and 15.2 show the approximate geographical distribution of snap and Lima beans, which has changed considerably in recent
years. The acreage, production, and farm value of snap beans are listed
in Tables 15.1 and 15.2, while similar information for Lima beans is provided in Tables 15.3 and 15.4.

Table 15.1—Snap Beans for Fresh Market: Shipping Season and Estimated Commercial Acreage, Yield, Production, and Value in Leading States, 1965.

State	Season	Harvested Acreage	Yield per Acre, Cwt.	Production, 1,000 Cwt.	Price per Cwt.	Value, $1,000
Florida	Winter	15,500	37	574*	$11.80	6,289
Florida	Early spring	10,100	42	424*	11.30	4,509
Florida	Late fall	8,500	36	306	11.30	3,458
New York	Summer	8,400	42	353*	8.90	2,955
North Carolina	Summer	6,200	47	291*	8.00	2,080
South Carolina	Mid-spring	5,400	26	140	9.60	1,344
North Carolina	Late spring	4,500	35	158*	7.80	991
New Jersey	Late spring	3,800	40	152	9.30	1,414
Virginia	Early fall	3,300	40	132	9.10	1,201
Georgia	Mid-spring	3,200	25	80	10.00	800
Louisiana	Mid-spring	2,800	25	70	9.20	644
Ohio	Summer	2,600	45	117	9.50	1,112
Virginia	Late spring	2,300	30	69	8.00	552
Michigan	Summer	2,200	32	70	10.00	700
All states		103,020	39	3,974	10.42	39,841

*Includes some quantities not marketed and excluded in computing value.

Trends in Production Efficiency

Both snap and Lima beans can be produced at comparatively modest
costs. In 1959, snap beans required an average of 133 man-hours per acre
to grow and harvest, while the processed crop involved 91 man-hours.
Correspondingly, 120 man-hours were required for producing one acre
of Lima beans for the fresh market, while only 34 man-hours were required for growing the same acreage for processing. This difference was
due primarily to the use of harvesting machines for the processed crop.

Table 15.2—Snap Beans for Processing: Estimated Commercial Acreage, Yield, Production, and Value in Leading States, 1965.

State	Harvested Acreage	Yield per Acre, Tons	Production in Tons	Price per Ton	Value, $1,000
New York	50,800	1.8	91,400	$ 87.30	7,979
Wisconsin	36,300	2.3	83,500	73.30	6,121
Oregon	21,600	5.6	121,000	109.00	13,189
Maryland	13,700	1.8	24,700	99.40	2,455
Tennessee	12,800	2.0	25,600	112.00	2,867
Michigan	11,700	1.5	17,600	80.00	1,408
Pennsylvania	9,900	1.7	16,800	92.70	1,557
Florida	8,700	1.8	15,700	113.00	1,774
California	7,200	2.8	20,200 ·	133.00	2,687
Delaware	6,700	1.4	9,400	88.80	835
Texas	5,700	1.8	10,300	84.60	871
North Carolina	2,900	2.3	6,700	107.00	717
Washington	2,600	5.2	13,500	118.00	1,593
Colorado	2,300	2.4	5,500	82.70	455
Oklahoma	2,100	2.4	5,000	85.00	425
Virginia	1,900	1.3	2,500	101.00	252
Maine	1,600	2.1	3,400	90.00	306
South Carolina	700	1.2	840	109.00	92
Other states	30,060	2.1	62,880	99.50	6,255
All states	229,260	2.3	536,520	96.60	51,838
For freezing	49,480	2.3	112,320	106.40	11,948
For canning	179,780	2.4	424,200	94.00	39,890

Table 15.3—Lima Beans for Fresh Market: Shipping Season and Estimated Commercial Acreage, Yield, Production, and Value in Leading States, 1965.

State	Season	Harvested Acreage	Yield per Acre, Cwt.	Production, 1,000 Cwt.	Price per Cwt.	Value, $1,000
Georgia	Summer	3,500	24	84	$ 9.50	798
Alabama	Summer	3,200	24	77	11.40	878
South Carolina	Spring	1,900	22	42	9.50	399
North Carolina	Summer	1,400	30	42	9.50	399
New Jersey	Summer	1,200	34	41	10.40	426
Florida	Spring	900	28	25	11.50	288
Maryland	Summer	400	30	12	7.50	90
New York	Summer	350	35	12	9.80	118
Florida	Winter	250	20	5	12.80	64
All states		13,100	26	340	10.18	3,460

Table 15.4—Lima Beans for Processing: Estimated Commercial Acreage, Yield, Production, and Value in Leading States, 1965.

State	Harvested Acreage	Yield per Acre, Pounds (Shelled)	Production in Tons (Shelled)	Price per Ton	Value, $1,000
California	26,500	3,160	41,870	$199.00	8,332
Delaware	18,400	1,760	16,190	163.00	2,639
Wisconsin	4,800	1,970	4,730	144.00	681
Maryland	3,600	1,550	2,790	190.00	530
Washington	2,700	2,440	3,290	150.00	494
Michigan	1,700	1,850	1,570	102.00	160
Other states	25,170	1,942	24,440	159.70	3,903
All states	82,870	2,290	94,880	176.40	16,739
For freezing	57,720	2,462	71,060	184.30	13,099
For canning	25,150	1,894	23,820	152.80	3,640

The average acre yield of snap beans for fresh market increased from 29 to 36 hundredweight during the 1939-1959 period, during which time the output per man-hour rose 23 percent. The production of snap beans for processing rose from 36 to 45 hundredweight per acre as labor efficiency increased 79 percent.

The yield of Lima beans for fresh market did not increase during the 1939-1959 period, while yields for processed Limas almost doubled. Acre production, both for market and processing, rose somewhat between 1959 and 1965. The output per man-hour for fresh Lima beans decreased 18 percent during the 1939-1959 period while that for the processed crop increased by 210 percent (Table 1.4).

Climatic Requirements

Beans require a warm, frost-free climate, but the plants may drop their blossoms or pods during excessively hot or rainy weather. Varieties differ in sensitivity to weather conditions, and tests should be conducted to determine which ones are best suited for a given locality. Lima beans are especially sensitive to cold, water-soaked soil. When Lima beans are grown in the northern border sections, it is especially important to select warm soils that will hasten maturity. Beans thrive best on a mildly acid soil (pH 5.5 to 6.0). Sandy to clay loam and muck soils are used for growing beans, but good yields are seldom produced on very heavy soils.

JOB 1.   SELECTING VARIETIES AND SEED

Varieties

Both bush and pole varieties of beans are grown. Because of the cost of materials and labor, the pole types are limited to the home gardens

Table 15.5—Brief Description of Selected Varieties of Snap Beans.

Variety	Days to Maturity	Pod Cross Section	Pod Color	Seed Color	Principal Use	Resistance
			Bush Green Pod			
Bush Blue Lake	58	Round	Dark green	White	Canning, freezing, home	Bean virus 1, N.Y. 15
Contender	55	Round	Dark green	Buff, lightly modeled	Home market, shipping	Common bean mosaic, powdery mildew
Earligreen	55	Round	Medium	White	Canning	Common bean mosaic
Harvester	53	Round	Medium dark green	Pure white	Home garden, processing market	Rust, N.Y. 15, common virus
Processor	55	Round, oval	Medium green	Pure white	Canning, freezing	N.Y. 15, common virus
Resistant Asgrow Valentine	52	Oval	Medium green	Black	Market	N.Y. 15, common virus
Slenderwhite	56	Round	Medium dark green	Pure white	Canning, freezing	Common bean mosaic
Slimgreen	60	Round	Dark green	White	Canning, freezing, mech. harvesting	Common bean mosaic
Tendercrop	54	Round	Medium green	Purple mottled with buff	Home garden, freezing market	Pod mottle, N.Y. 15, common virus
Tenderette	52	Round	Deep green	White	Home garden, canning, freezing	
Tendergreen	53	Round	Dark green	Brownish purple mottled	Canning	Common bean mosaic
Trugreen	60	Round	Dark green	White	Canning, freezing, mech. harvesting	
Tenderwhite	58	Round	Medium dark green	Pure white	Home garden, freezing, canning	Common bean mosaic
Topcrop	52	Round	Medium green	Brown with buff splashing	Canning, freezing	Common bean mosaic
Wadex	60	Round	Dark green	Purple brown	Home garden, canning, freezing	Common bean mosaic, N.Y. 15, virus

(Continued)

Table 15.5—Brief Description of Selected Varieties of Snap Beans (Continued).

Variety	Days to Maturity	Pod Cross Section	Pod Color	Seed Color	Principal Use	Resistance
Bush Wax Pod						
Brittle Wax	57	Round	Yellow	White, black eye	Home garden, freezing, canning	
Earliwax	54	Round	Golden yellow	Pure white	Home garden, canning, freezing	Mosaic
Kinghorn Wax	54	Round	Golden yellow	Pure white	Canning, freezing, home garden	
Pure Gold Wax	60	Round	Golden yellow	White, brown eye	Canning, freezing, home garden	Common bean mosaic
Resistant Cherokee Wax	53	Oval	Bright yellow	Black	Home garden, shipping	Common bean mosaic, N.Y. 15
Pole Green Pod						
Blue Lake types	63-66	Round	Dark green	Pure white	Canning, freezing, home garden	Common bean mosaic
Kentucky Wonder	67	Round	Medium light green	Buff, brown stripes	Home garden	Some traces of rust
McCaslan	64	Flattened oval	Medium green	Ivory white	Home garden, market	
Romano	70	Flattened oval	Silvery	Tan	Market, freezing, home garden	

and also to the western United States and Florida, where high yields and prices offset the higher cost of production. The pole varieties require some means of support and produce later harvests over longer periods than the bush varieties. With the perfection of the mechanical bean harvester, the bush varieties with concentrated maturity and erect plants should replace pole beans for canning and freezing. In addition to low-cost production, processors are demanding round-podded, dark green beans with a minimum of fiber in the pods. Wax-podded varieties are discriminated against because they show mechanical injuries and disease spots very plainly. However, they do find a good market when they can be grown satisfactorily.

A wide choice of varieties of snap beans is available to the grower (Fig. 15.3). A selected list of these with brief description and principal

Fig. 15.3—Supergreen, a mosaic-resistant variety of snap beans.

USDA Photograph

use is shown in Table 15.5. Most of those listed are resistant to one or more diseases. The choice of variety for a particular locality may depend to a large extent upon its resistance to a disease prevalent in the area.

Lima bean varieties may be grouped as to dwarf or pole types and as to thin- and thick-seeded types. The dwarf types are used for processing and make up most of the Lima beans grown for market (Fig. 15.4). The climbing or pole varieties are grown mostly in home gardens.

Henderson Bush (thin-seeded) and Ford Hook (thick-seeded or potato) and selections from these are used for most of the acreage planted to bush Lima beans. Clark's Bush, Thaxter, and Early Thorogreen are similar to Henderson but have green cotyledons which are desired for processing. Ford Hook does not set pods well under unfavorable weather conditions and has been largely replaced by Ford Hook 242 and Concentrated Ford Hook. Nemagreen is a nematode-resistant baby Lima which may be expected to out-yield other varieties in nematode-infested soil.

Burpee's Best, a thick-seeded type, King of the Garden, and Carolina or Sieva are leading pole varieties.

Securing Seed

A number of serious bean diseases, such as anthracnose, are carried in the seed, and for this reason it is a great advantage to secure seed from relatively disease-free fields or sections. Low humidity and limited rainfall are unfavorable to the development of bean blight, anthracnose, and mosaic. Roguing seed fields is necessary to maintain a strain that is of high quality and true to type. The bean is usually a self-fertilized plant, but

Fig. 15.4—Triumph, a bush type of lima bean.

USDA Photograph

a certain amount of crossing may occur when two varieties are grown side by side, so that an occasional sport plant is to be expected. Seed injured in threshing germinates poorly. Most of the bean seed is produced in California and the Northwest.

JOB 2.   PREPARING THE SOIL

Soil Preferences

The bean is a universal crop in the United States, and can be grown on soils that range from sand to clay and peat. On sandy soils, beans mature in a shorter time than on the heavier soils. High moisture content and high nitrogen delay maturity. Most growers prefer a well-drained, fairly fertile loam soil containing considerable humus. Soils more acid than pH 5.5 should usually be limed, but overliming should be avoided.

Where soil-borne diseases are prevalent, beans should not be planted more than once or twice in a five-year rotation.

Preparing the Seed Bed

Bean cotyledons push up through the soil in germination, and need a well-prepared seedbed. A well-prepared, firm seedbed also saves cultivation costs after the crop is planted. Beans thrive after a cultivated crop, partly because of freedom from weeds. Sod land to be planted to beans is best plowed in the fall.

JOB 3.   FERTILIZING AND MANURING

Fertilizing

Beans may be placed in the group of vegetable crops least responsive to application of fertilizers. However, the crop does well on fertile soils. The application of fertilizer should be based upon known requirements of the soil. When this information is not available, a moderate amount of a complete fertilizer high in phosphorus may be applied. Excessive nitrogen should be avoided, since this element may increase vine growth at the expense of pod production.

Manuring

Soils of low humus content need a green-manure crop in the rotation. This should be plowed under at least one month before the beans are to be planted. Stable manure is usually high in nitrogen and can be used to best advantage on other crops.

JOB 4. PLANTING AND CULTIVATING

Planting

Most plantings of both Lima and snap beans are best made after the soil is warm and danger of frost is over. Earlier plantings are often made for early market and in home gardens. A fall crop is often grown in many sections of the South; and in Florida, most of the plantings are made during the fall and winter. Although beans quickly lose ability to germinate under warm, humid conditions, they should not be removed from dry storage and planted immediately, especially in cold and wet soils.

Pole varieties of snap beans and Lima beans are commonly planted in hills 3 to 4 feet apart each way. Five or six seeds are planted in each hill, and the plants are later thinned to three or four. In California, unsupported pole Limas are grown in drills. Garden varieties of the bush type are commonly spaced 2 to 4 inches apart in drills, with the closer spacings usually producing larger yields, but requiring more seed per acre. Gillis found that at the rate of six seeds per foot and with rows 3 feet apart, it would require 90 pounds of Stringless Green Pod seed to plant an acre. Ordinarily, about 50 pounds of snap bean seed of average size are planted to the acre. Large-seeded varieties would increase this amount, and small-seeded ones would decrease it. Tennessee Green Pod is a small-growing variety and can be spaced somewhat closer. Fertile soils and irrigation tend to produce larger plants, requiring more space. The average rate and method of planting different kinds of beans are given in Table 8.1.

Cultivating

It is not advisable to cultivate or to work among bean plants when the foliage is wet, because anthracnose and other fungus spores are easily disseminated in this way. Cultivation and hoeing, which are employed primarily to keep down and destroy weeds, should start when the bean plants first appear above ground, and should be shallow, especially as the plants approach maturity. Many of the feeding roots of beans are near the surface and are easily injured by deep cultivation. If beans are grown on a site relatively free of weeds, the number of cultivations for control may be reduced. The danger of injuring the roots and the cost of production will thus be decreased.

Supporting Vines

The dry climate in certain sections of California enables farmers to grow both pole and bush varieties without support. Staking or trellising is expensive, but necessary for pole varieties in humid regions, since pods touching or near the surface of the ground are usually injured. A common method of staking is to put an 8- or 9-foot pole at each hill and tie the tops of four stakes together. Such poles should be set before the beans are planted, or very soon thereafter.

JOB 5.   CONTROLLING DISEASES AND INSECTS

Diseases

Usually, Lima beans are injured less by diseases than are snap beans. General control measures include using disease-free seed, rotating crops, disposing of diseased bean refuse, using resistant varieties, and working the plants only when the foliage is dry.

ANTHRACNOSE. Caused by several strains of *Colletotrichum lindemuthianum*, this is a destructive fungus disease of snap and field beans grown in humid regions. Hot and dry weather is unfavorable for the development of anthracnose. The fungus overwinters in the seed and in bean refuse. The somewhat circular, dark, sunken spots are easily recognized on the pods and stems. Affected areas on the leaves become discolored and die. Most snap varieties show little resistance. The term "rust-proof," as used by seedsmen, refers to this disease, but anthracnose should not be confused with bean rust, which is caused by another organism discussed below. Use seed grown in regions where this disease does not occur, and spray or dust weekly with zineb, ziram, or ferbam.

BACTERIAL BLIGHT. Associated with *Xanthomonas phaseoli*, bacterial blight is common on snap beans in the central and eastern part of the United States. Diseased spots on the pods appear water-soaked, changing to a reddish brown, and infected seeds are yellowish or yellow-botched. The common bacterial blight, as well as similar blights on beans, may be controlled by using disease-free seed, by rotating beans with other crops, and by not cultivating the plants while they are wet.

RUST. Rust, caused by *Uromyces phaseoli typica*, is widely distributed over the eastern United States and also occurs in the coastal section along the Pacific coast. It is especially destructive on Kentucky Wonder. Lesions may appear on all aerial parts of the plant, but rust is most destructive on the leaves. The growing of resistant varieties such as Burpee's Stringless, Pencil Pod, Refugee, and Horticultural Pole, and the use of sulphur dusts and zineb and sulphur sprays are recommended as control measures.

DOWNY MILDEW. This disease, *Phytophthora phaseoli*, is a serious fungus disease along the eastern coast, especially on Lima beans. Control methods include crop rotation, use of well-drained fields, and spraying weekly with maneb or zineb.

COMMON BEAN MOSAIC. This disease causes mottling, curling, crinkling, and malformation of the leaves. Occasionally the pods are mottled, deformed, or rough. Diseased plants are often dwarfed and unproductive. The disease can be prevented by growing resistant varieties.

Insects

Bean insects cause widespread destruction of this crop, especially in home gardens, where satisfactory control measures are difficult to carry out. The rapid spread of the Mexican bean beetle has greatly increased control problems.

MEXICAN BEAN BEETLE. The Mexican bean beetle (*Epilachna varivestis*), believed to be a native of Mexico, has been present in the western United States since 1850, and has now spread over the eastern states. It prefers to feed on snap beans, field beans, and Lima beans, but beggarweed is a common food plant. The beetles usually appear before the beans start to blossom, and after feeding for a week or 10 days, they start to deposit their eggs. Reproduction is rapid, since the average female lays more than 400 eggs. The insect passes the winter as an adult. The young larvae are more easily killed than the adults. Turning under vines immediately after harvest removes the food supply, and helps in control.

Control measures should begin as soon as the beetles appear and the treatment should be repeated if control is not obtained. Malathion, methoxychlor, rotenone, diazinon, or carbaryl may be used (see Chapter 11).

BEAN LEAF BEETLE. The bean leaf beetle (*Cerotoma trifurcata*) is a small, dark yellow beetle with six black dots on the wing covers. It eats' large holes in the leaves, feeding from the underside (Fig. 15.5). The eggs are laid at the bases of the plants, and the grubs feed on the roots. Control can be had with DDT, rotenone or carbaryl.

Fig. 15.5—Injury by the bean leaf beetle.

ADULT BEAN WEEVIL. The adult bean weevil (*Acanthoscelides obtectus*) is a small, dull-colored beetle, and the larva is white. The bean weevil is chiefly a pest of dry beans, including bean seed. Infested seed should not be planted, as germination is poor and adults emerging from such seed may infect the next crop. The seed should be fumigated or treated with pyrethrins or premium-grade malathion. Treatment should be given early in the storage period before much injury has occurred.

JOB 6.   HARVESTING, HANDLING, AND MARKETING

Picking

Bush, as compared to pole varieties, mature over a relatively short time and may be harvested in only a few pickings. A concentrated set on erect plants is required for machine harvest. Snap beans are picked when the pods are nearly full size and the beans small, about one-fourth developed. Green-shell Limas are picked when the seeds are nearly full size and the pods are green. Less mature Limas bring a slightly higher price but yield less. Lima beans for canning are cut by a mowing machine and shelled by machinery.

Grading and Packing

Snap beans should be carefully sorted and graded for market. Lima beans handle and ship best in pods, but are often marketed after shelling. Both snap and green Lima beans need prompt refrigeration after harvesting; they also need refrigeration in transit all the way to retail stores in order to reduce the amount of soft rot. Hampers, bushel and half-bushel baskets, and crates are common packages.

Grade standards for green beans are sometimes revised, and the latest specifications can be obtained from the Consumer and Marketing Service of the U.S. Department of Agriculture.

Marketing

Immature beans wilt quickly after harvesting in hot weather and need cooling. A large part of the snap bean crop is shipped to northern markets during winter and early spring in refrigerated trucks. Volume buyers prefer fast, direct handling of beans from modern packing centers, which usually assure standard quality and established daily market prices for the various grades.

During the 1955-1959 period, an annual average of approximately 125,000 hundredweight of fresh beans were exported from the United States, mostly to Canada but some to Mexico and other countries. In 1963, exports approximated 185,000 hundredweight valued at $1,592,000. Canned beans are also being exported, primarily to western Europe with small quantities to more than 20 other countries. Almost 566,000 cases valued at $1,786,000 were shipped from the United States in 1963.

SELECTED REFERENCES

Aultman, D. A., "Herbicide Tests with Snap Beans," Miss. Agr. Exp. Sta. Farm Research 26: 7, March 1963.
Guyer, R. B. and Kramer, A., "Studies of the Factors Affecting the Quality of Green and Wax Beans," Md. Agr. Exp. Sta. Bull. A68, 1952.

Hills, W. A., *et al.*, "Bush Snap Bean Production on the Sandy Soils of Florida,"
Fla. Agr. Sta. Bull. 530, 1953.

Holland, A. H., *et al.*, "Production of Green Lima Beans for Freezing," Calif.
Agr. Ext. Cir. 430, 1953.

Lambeth, V. N., "Some Factors Influencing Pod Set and Yield of Lima Beans,"
Mo. Agr. Exp. Sta. Res. Bull. 466, 1950.

McMaster, G. M., *et al.*, "The Influence of Soil Moisture on Snap Bean Production," Idaho Agr. Exp. Sta. Bull. 435, 1965.

Moore, J. F. and Allmendinger, D. R., "Blue Lake Pole Beans in Western Washington," Wash. Exp. Sta. Bull. 548, 1954.

Seelig, R. A. and Roberts, E., "Green and Wax Snap Beans," United Fresh Fruit
and Vegetable Association, Washington, D.C., 1960.

Woodroof, J. G., Heaton, E. H., and Ellis, C., "Freezing Green Snap Beans," Ga.
Agr. Exp. Sta. Bull. 90, 1962.

Zanmeyer, W. J., "Snap Beans for Marketing, Canning, and Freezing," USDA
Farmers' Bull. 1915, 1954.

Zanmeyer, W. J. and Tomas, H. R., "Bean Diseases, How to Control Them,"
U.S. Agr. Handbook 225: 1-39, 1962.

CHAPTER 16

Cabbage

Classification, Origin, and History

Cabbage (*Brassica oleracea* var. *capitata*) is the most important member of the *Cruciferae* or mustard family. It is generally conceded that our present-day varieties of cabbage originated from the wild cabbage which is found growing along the chalky coasts of England and along the western and southern coasts of Europe. Cabbage has been used as a food crop since earliest antiquity. The ancient Greeks held it in high esteem, and their fables claim its origin from the father of their gods. The Egyptians are said to have worshiped cabbage. Today it still remains one of the leading vegetable crops of the world.

Scope and Importance

Cabbage is one of the most widely grown vegetables in the United States. It is grown in most home gardens, and in a large percentage of the market gardens and truck farms. It was one of the first crops to be grown in the South for northern shipments, and is today one of the most widely planted winter truck crops. Because of its wide range of climate and soil adaptability, its economical production, and its general use as a food crop, cabbage is always found on the American markets. Cabbage is widely known as a health food. It has a basic reaction and ranks high in its general food properties, particularly in vitamins B and C; and in minerals, being particularly rich in calcium.

The popularity of cabbage decreased somewhat in recent years in competition with other vegetables and foods. It ranked 11th in acreage and 13th in value among the 22 principal vegetables in 1965. Cabbage acreage for fresh market decreased from 159,180 in 1939 to approximately 119,000 acres in 1965. During this period, total production remained relatively constant, while farm value increased from $16,178,000 to about $54,000,000. Likewise, cabbage for sauerkraut declined from 19,710 acres in 1945 to approximately 12,400 in 1965, and farm value increased from $1,113,000 to approximately $3,000,000.

Fig. 16.1—Acreage and distribution of cabbage.

Figure 16.1 shows the approximate distribution of cabbage production, while Tables 16.1 and 16.2 present the acreage, production, and value of cabbage and sauerkraut by leading states.

While many of the southern states could begin shipping fall cabbage around October, it is usually not profitable to make shipments before January. Shipments are usually started from south Texas and south Florida, and as the spring advances, the shipping centers move north.

Trends in Production Efficiency

Cabbage production is comparatively expensive because of the cost of plants, fertilizers, pesticides, and the labor involved in cultivating and harvesting. About 104 and 56 man-hours per acre were required for the fresh market and processed crops, respectively. The average yield of cab-

Table 16.1—Cabbage for Fresh Market and Processing: Shipping Season and Estimated Commercial Acreage, Yield, Production, and Value in Leading States, 1965.

State	Season	Harvested Acreage	Yield per Acre, Cwt.	Production, 1,000 Cwt.	Price per Cwt.	Value, $1,000
Texas	Winter	19,400	145	2,813	$3.24	9,104
Florida	Winter	13,700	170	2,329*	3.05	6,969
New York:						
Long Island	Early fall	1,100	215	236	2.20	519
Upstate	Early fall	10,800	365	3,942*	1.25	4,674
Wisconsin	Early fall	6,200	295	1,829	1.03	1,881
California	Winter	5,000	200	1,000	2.30	2,300
Michigan	Early fall	4,700	175	822*	1.73	1,362
North Carolina	Late summer	3,800	180	684	1.86	1,273
California	Early spring	3,300	250	825	4.10	3,382
New Jersey	Early summer	3,300	200	660	2.40	1,584
Pennsylvania	Late summer	3,000	195	585	1.89	1,105
California	Late summer	2,800	220	616	2.15	1,324
All states		119,480	197	23,503	2.33	54,058

*Includes some quantities not marketed and excluded in computing value.

Table 16.2—Cabbage for Sauerkraut in Leading States, 1965.

State	Acreage	Yield per Acre, Tons	Production in Tons	Price per Ton	Value, $1,000
New York	4,100	21.0	86,100	$12.00	1,033
Wisconsin	3,600	17.2	61,900	13.20	817
Ohio	1,400	18.7	26,200	13.00	341
Other states	3,340	16.6	55,390	15.90	881
All states	12,440	18.5	229,590	13.40	3,072

bage for fresh market increased from 124 to 167 hundredweight per acre from 1939 to 1959 and continued to rise through 1965. The man-hour output rose 40 percent during 1939-1959. Yields of cabbage for kraut increased from 149 to 275 hundredweight and the man-hour output rose 210 percent during the same period (Table 1.4).

Climatic Requirements

Cabbage is a hardy cool-season crop and is at its best during a cool, moist period. It will, however, stand wide variations in temperature.

Plantings of cabbage are made in the South from July to April, during a period of extremes in weather.

Young cabbage plants of the Wakefield group, if well hardened, will stand temperature as low as 15° F. without serious damage. However, most varieties, particularly those of the Copenhagen type, will not stand temperatures below 20° F., and even at 20°, the plants must be well hardened.

JOB 1. SELECTING VARIETIES AND SEED

In selecting a variety, one must consider such factors as market demand, cold and disease resistance, season of the year to be planted, and resistance to premature seeding.

Types and Varieties

Small conical-headed varieties are grown early in the season. The Jersey Wakefield and the Charleston Wakefield are similar, but the heads of the latter are slightly larger, later, and less pointed. The earliest of the globe-headed varieties is Golden Acre, which belongs to the Copenhagen Market group. Midseason varieties include Globe and Marion Market (round-head types); and Wisconsin All Seasons and Flat Dutch, which have flat heads. The Hollander or Danish Ballhead type is grown in the North for winter storage. The outstanding characteristics of the principal varieties of cabbage are given in Table 16.3, and some are shown in Figure 16.2.

Securing Seed

Up until about 1915, most of the cabbage seed was imported from Europe, chiefly from Denmark and Holland. Since then many American seedsmen have been growing their own seed in the Puget Sound district, centering around Mount Vernon, Washington. Long Island, New York, is the oldest cabbage seed-producing district in the United States; but production in that area was discontinued in favor of the Puget Sound region. The ease with which members of the cabbage family cross makes it a difficult problem to maintain pure stock. For this reason, it is well to buy seed from seedsmen who are interested in cabbage seed production

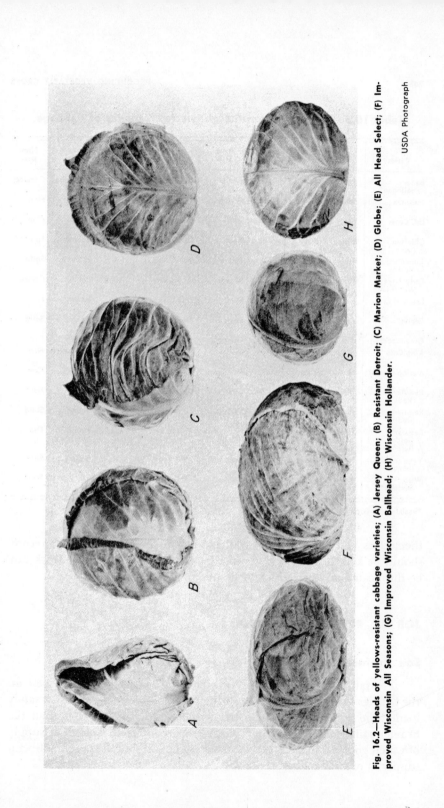

Fig. 16.2—Heads of yellows-resistant cabbage varieties; (A) Jersey Queen; (B) Resistant Detroit; (C) Marion Market; (D) Globe; (E) All Head Select; (F) Improved Wisconsin All Seasons; (G) Improved Wisconsin Ballhead; (H) Wisconsin Hollander.

Table 16.3—Chief Characteristics of Selected Varieties of Cabbage.

Variety	Chief Use	Season (Days)	Plant Size	Leaf Color	Wt. (Lbs.)	Shape	Firmness
Badger Ballhead*	Fresh Market	100	Medium	Grayish green	5	Flat globe	Compact
Bonanza	Market garden, shipping	73	Medium	Light green	4	Round	Firm
C-C Cross	Early market, shipping	61	Small	Blue green	2	Round	Firm
Chieftan (Savoy)	Home garden, market	88	Medium	Dark olive	5	Round	Firm
Copenhagen Market	Home market, shipping	68	Medium	Med. green	4½	Round	Solid
Early Jersey Wakefield*	Home garden, market	63	Small	Dark green	2½	Pointed	Compact
Emerald Cross	Home garden, market	63	Small	Blue green	3	Round	Firm
Globe*	Market, shipping, kraut	80	Large	Med. green	7	Round	Solid
Greenback*	Market, shipping	74	Compact	Dark green	7-7½	Round	Firm
King Cole	Market, early kraut	66	Medium	Med. green	5	Flat globe	Firm
Marion Market*	Market garden, kraut	79	Medium	Med. green	5½	Round	Firm
Red Acre (Red)	Market, home garden	74	Small	Deep red	5	Round	Hard
Red Danish (Red)	Pickling, cole-slaw	97	Medium	Purplish red	7	Round	Solid
Resistant Golden Acre*	Home, market, shipping	64	Med. small	Med. green	3½-4	Round	Firm
Vanguard II (Savoy)	Home, coleslaw, salads	72	Med. small	Med. green	4	Round	Firm
Wisc. All Seasons*	Kraut, storage	95	Large	Med. green	9	Flat globe	Solid

*Resistant to Fusarium wilt.

themselves and who maintain reliable stocks. In buying seed, a record should be kept of the stock number so the particular strain or stock can be duplicated another season if desired.

JOB 2. PREPARING THE SOIL

Soil Preferences

For fall, summer, and early winter plantings, cabbage does best on the heavier loam soils, while the spring crop does best on a sandy or sandy loam. The sandy soils drain better and naturally are warmer than the heavier soil types. While the cabbage crop requires an abundant supply of water, good drainage is very necessary. The soil should contain a liberal supply of organic matter.

Preparing the Seed Bed

A green-manure crop should be turned under at least a month in advance of planting. The land should be disked and the rows prepared a week or 10 days before planting. The disk cultivator is a good tool with which to prepare the rows as it pulverizes the soil thoroughly. Heavy soil should be sufficiently harrowed before planting.

JOB 3. FERTILIZING AND LIMING

Fertilizing

Cabbage belongs to the group of vegetable crops giving greatest response to soil fertility. Recommended amounts of nitrogen are given in Table 6.4, while phosphorus and potassium requirements are shown in Table 6.5. Part of the nitrogen on sandy soils may be applied as a side dressing, but phosphorus and potash are usually applied before or at the time of planting.

Liming

Cabbage grows best where the pH range is from 6.0 to 6.5. Where the soil is more acid than pH 5.5, an application of lime will be beneficial. Phosphorus, an important element, is most available between pH 5.5 and 6.5. The reaction should not be above this range except where clubroot is a serious problem. If crop rotation cannot be used to control the disease, soil reaction can be raised to neutral by applying hydrated lime.

JOB 4. PLANTING AND CULTIVATING

Growing Plants

Three distinct methods of plant growing are used.

PLANTING DIRECTLY IN THE FIELD. This method is adapted to areas favorable to germination and early plant growth. On sandy soils, irrigation is necessary to insure stands. On heavier soils, a stand can be obtained when the rainfall is well distributed. Before planting, the land should be well settled by rains or irrigation. The seed is drilled at the rate of three pounds per acre and given shallow covering, especially on heavy soils, the soil being firmed with a roller after planting. When the plants have grown to the usual transplanting size, some thinning is usually necessary, the plants that are removed being either sold or transplanted to other fields. The plants seeded directly in the field usually mature two or three weeks before transplanted plants of the same age.

PLANTING ON OPEN FIELD BEDS. In practicing this method, land is prepared in beds of convenient width, usually 5 to 6 feet, and the seed is drilled in rows 4 to 6 inches apart. Sometimes the seeds are sown broadcast over the bed, but the row system is recommended as it is more convenient to care for the plants properly. This method is used extensively in plant-producing areas around Charleston, South Carolina, and for late cabbage in the North. Seeding in the beds is usually done during fall—September and October—depending somewhat upon the locality.

PLANTING IN COLD FRAMES. This method of plant production is used extensively in the interior cabbage-producing areas such as the Crystal Springs area of Mississippi. Cautious growers along the Gulf and Atlantic coasts use this method along with the open field beds so that they will have reserve plants in case of a heavy freeze. The cold frames may be covered with glass sash, cloth or transparent polyethylene. Additional cover is needed to protect the plants against heavy freezes, and on warm days careful ventilation is necessary to prevent overheating. The cold frame not only protects the plants against unfavorable weather but enables them to develop in a shorter time. Plants to be transplanted where severe freezes may occur should be well hardened.

Setting Plants

Although transplanting is generally done with machinery, it may be done by hand where labor is not a problem or where only small plantings are made. When transplanting is done during late summer and early fall, only large, stocky plants should be used; and these should be watered and the soil firmed about the roots.

In the trucking areas from Virginia to Georgia, many of the plantings for the spring crop are set in the field in late fall and early winter. The plants make very little top growth during the winter, but as spring opens, they begin to grow and usually mature earlier than spring-set plants. In Texas and Florida, commercial plantings are made during fall and winter. In Alabama, Louisiana, and Mississippi, plants are seldom set in the field before January for the spring shipments. Plants for the early crop in the North are transplanted to the field as soon as hard freezes are over, while late cabbage is set out the latter half of June and in July.

The planting distances in the row are usually 12 to 18 inches for the Jersey and Copenhagen types, and 18 to 20 inches for domestic varieties such as the All Head Early and Flat Dutch. The width between the rows varies from 28 inches to 4 feet, depending upon the soil type, and methods of irrigation and drainage used. Closer planting tends to produce smaller heads but larger yields per acre.

Cultivating

Cabbage has an extensive shallow root system. Deep cultivation should not be used except when the soil becomes very hard and then only when the plants are small. After that, shallow cultivation should be practiced (Fig. 16.3). Fall and spring crops usually need three cultivations, while the winter crop requires less attention. Only when weeds are present should large plants be cultivated. Cultivation should be discontinued when the plants start to head. Broken leaves may result if plants are cultivated too early in the morning when they are turgid.

Premature Seeding

Investigations have shown that the single factor most closely associated with premature seeding is the size of the plants when exposed to the low temperature. Small plants having leaves about 1 to 1½ inches wide can stand low temperature for six months without going to seed. However, if the plants are large, having leaves 2 to 3 inches wide, many of them will shoot seed stalks if exposed to continuous cold weather, 40° to 50° F., for a period of 30 to 60 days. The longer the period of exposure, the higher will be the percentage of plants producing seed stalks. Some varieties and strains are more subject to premature seeding than others. The Copenhagen Market variety is more subject to bolting than the Jersey varieties. It is clearly evident that strains can be bred that are highly resistant to premature seeding. About the best control measures are to (1) use the best strains of seed available, (2) avoid setting plants too early in the field, and (3) prevent the stimulation of early plant growth. The plants should be relatively small during midwinter when there is continuous low temperature. It is not the freezing temperature that causes premature seeding, but a very low growing temperature that initiates seed-stalk formation.

Fig. 16.3—Well grown and cultivated field of cabbage.

USDA Photograph

JOB 5.   CONTROLLING DISEASES AND INSECTS

Diseases

The most important cabbage diseases the grower has to contend with are black rot, root knot, yellows, club root, and blackleg.

BLACK ROT. This disease, caused by *Xanthomonas campestris,* appears at any stage of plant growth. The disease is first indicated by yellowing of the leaves and a blackening of the veins. Later the plants show dwarfing and one-sided heads. If the disease attacks the plants early no heads will be formed. The organism is carried over on the seed and residues of infected plants. Soaking seed in water at 122° F. for 25 to 30 minutes will destroy the organism in as well as on the seed. The use of clean seed, crop rotation, and sanitation is recommended. Cruciferous plants should not be allowed to grow in the soil for at least three years.

ROOT KNOT. Root knot (*Meloidogyne sp.*) is a disease caused by a parasite eelworm which attacks the roots of the plants, producing irregularly shaped galls. These are sometimes confused with the galls produced by club root, which are located nearer the stem of the plant. Rotation with small grains, corn, velvet beans, some varieties of cowpeas, soybeans, and other crops immune to the nematodes is recommended. Soil fumigation is an effective but an expensive means of control, and may have to be limited to the seedbed. Methyl bromide, vapam, or chlorobromopropene may be used.

YELLOWS. Yellows, caused by *Fusarium oxysporum f. conglutinans,* while primarily a northern disease, does some damage to cabbage in the upper South. The plants turn yellow soon after transplanting, the leaves fall, and the plants die. If this trouble results, use yellows-resistant varieties which have been developed and are to be had on the market.

CLUB ROOT. Club root (*Plasmodiophora brassicae* Wor.) attacks the roots of cruciferous plants, causing characteristic swellings. The malformed roots are club-like in appearance. The disease may be controlled by avoiding infested areas, using crop rotation, keeping the soil alkaline (pH 7.2), and using PCNB at the time of transplanting.

BLACK LEG. This disease is caused by the fungus *Phoma lingam* Desmax. It attacks the stems of young plants, causing dark sunken areas. The entire plant wilts and the dead leaves adhere to the stem. Control is similar to that for black rot.

Insects

The most destructive insects to cabbage are various kinds of cabbage worms, particularly the green worm, the larvae of the cabbage butterfly, the diamond back, and cabbage looper. Plant lice and the harlequin bug are also serious pests.

CABBAGE WORMS. Cabbage worms, including the cabbage looper, can be controlled with DDT before the heads are formed and with rotenone afterwards (see Chapter 11). Control measures should begin as soon as evidence of feeding is observed.

CABBAGE APHID. The cabbage aphid (*Brevicoryne brassicae*) is a sucking insect. It has a waxy covering similar to the cabbage leaves. It is thereby protected from spray materials unless a detergent or sticker is used. Timeliness is very important in the control of aphids. The plants should be treated before the insect is established and before serious damage is done. Malathion, Diazinon, and nicotine sulphate are effective insecticides.

HARLEQUIN BUG. The harlequin bug (*Murgantia histrionica*) is mottled red, black, or yellow and about ⅖ inch long. Both the young and adult feed on cabbage, sucking juices and injecting poison into the plant. The adults can be controlled with DDT or naled.

JOB 6.   HARVESTING, HANDLING, AND MARKETING

Harvesting

Since both Texas and Florida have been making heavy shipments, there is not the rush to ship immature heads as in former years. The plant should be allowed to mature into a firm white head before harvesting. From two to three green wrapper leaves, unless worm-eaten, should be left attached, as new cabbage is wanted green and fresh. As the heads are cut, they are usually tossed to a man in a wagon or truck, and are hauled to the packing shed. Care should be taken not to bruise the head as this makes it unattractive.

Grading

The tendency is for better grading of cabbage as the market wants a firm, uniform head of high quality. The most desirable heads weigh between two and five pounds, the smaller ones being preferred. Prevailing grade and size standards and regulations can be obtained from the U.S. Department of Agriculture upon request.

Packing

In most sections, the cabbage is hauled from the field to a central packing house, while in some areas the crates are filled in the field or on the headlands. The heads should be arranged in orderly layers in the crates, with the stem ends to the outside. They should be packed firmly, but not tightly enough to cause bruising. The mesh bag and 1¾ bushel carton are standard containers for cabbage. In warm weather it is desirable to place crushed ice in or around the containers while in transit to prevent deterioration. In cool weather cabbage should be transported with vents open.

Storing

With the increase in production of winter cabbage, the acreage grown for storage in the North has markedly decreased. There is a definite consumer preference for the fresh green cabbage even though it is higher in price than the stored heads. Successful storage requires: (1) a good storage variety, (2) freedom from disease or injuries, (3) a temperature near 32° F., and (4) relatively high humidity. Well grown, solid heads of the Danish Ballhead variety keep best in storage.

Very little cabbage is stored in the South. To store spring cabbage for any length of time, it is necessary to place it in cold storage; and since the crop is bulky and the cold-storage rates are usually high, storage usually does not pay. However, if prices are low and expected prices high, cabbage can sometimes be stored to advantage.

Marketing

In some leading cabbage-growing areas produce agencies arrange for their own production and marketing. In most cases, however, volume buyers have a local agent or send a representative to buy on location. Some cabbage is shipped on consignment, but this method of marketing is limited. In many areas a portion of the crop is marketed through various types of cooperatives. This latter method is recommended only when the organization is large enough to maintain efficient management.

An average of approximately 650,000 hundredweight of cabbage was exported annually from the United States between 1955 and 1963, primarily to Canada, with small quantities to Mexico, Netherlands Antilles, the Bahamas, and other southern areas. In 1963 about 550,000 hundredweight value at $1,721,000 were exported.

SELECTED REFERENCES

Boswell, V. R., "Commercial Cabbage Culture," USDA Cir. 252, 1945.

Kohn, H. and Levitt, J., "Frost Hardiness Studies on Cabbage Grown Under Controlled Conditions," *Plant Physiol.* 40: 476-80, 1965.

Morrison, W. W., "Fresh Cabbage, From Grower to Retailer," USDA Marketing Bull. No. 21, 1962.

Oyer, E. B., "Growing Cabbage in New York," Cornell Agr. Ext. Bull. 1042, 1960.

Reid, W. J., Jr. and Cuthbert, F. P., Jr., "Control of Caterpillars," USDA Farmers' Bull. 2099, 1960.

Spangler, R. L., "Preparation of Cabbage for Market," USDA Farmers' Bull. 1423, 1956.

CHAPTER 17

Celery

Classification, Origin, and History

Celery (*Apium graveolens* var. *dulce*) belongs to the *Umbelliferae* family, which includes carrots, parsley, and parsnips. The native habitat of celery extends from Sweden to Egypt and Abyssinia, and in Asia from the Caucasus to India. It has also been found growing wild in California and New Zealand. Celery was first mentioned as a cultivated food plant in France in 1623.

Scope and Importance

Celery was once considered a luxury item, and was available for only a short period during the year. It is now produced in many sections of the country and is a popular salad throughout the year. Celery ranked 19th in acreage and 10th in value among the 22 principal vegetables in 1965.

Commercial celery acreage declined generally from 40,660 in 1939 to about 31,400 acres in 1965. Production rose from 10,198,000 to an estimated 14,293,000 hundredweight in this period. Farm value rose from $19,624,000 to $62,908,000 in 1945 and then declined to approximately $61,000,000 in 1965. California and Florida are the outstanding states in acreage, production, and value as shown in Table 17.1.

Trends in Production Efficiency

Celery is an expensive crop to produce, requiring heavy fertilization and extensive cultural practices. It requires more labor for planting, cultivating, and harvesting than any other vegetable—approximately 335 man-hours per acre. However, the average yield of celery increased from

251 to 415 hundredweight from 1939 to 1959 and continued to rise there-after. During the 1939-1959 period the output of celery per man-hour increased 82 percent (Table 1.4).

Table 17.1—Celery for Fresh Market and Processing: Shipping Season and Estimated Commercial Acreage, Yield, Production, and Value in Leading States, 1965.

State	Season	Harvested Acreage	Yield per Acre, Cwt.	Production, 1,000 Cwt.	Price per Cwt.	Value, $1,000
Florida	Winter	6,800	395	2,686*	$4.05	10,765
California	Late fall	5,600	520	2,912	4.50	13,104
Florida	Spring	4,800	415	1,992*	4.20	7,921
California	Winter	3,500	560	1,960	4.15	8,134
California	Spring	2,600	575	1,495	4.55	6,802
California	Early summer	2,100	535	1,124	4.30	4,833
New York	Late summer	2,000	380	760	4.40	3,344
Michigan	Early summer	1,200	390	486	4.01	1,875
Michigan	Early fall	800	350	280	3.80	1,065
All states		31,400	455	14,293	4.34	61,439

*Includes some quantities not marketed and excluded in computing value.

Climatic Requirements

Celery thrives best where the weather is relatively cool, especially at night, and where rainfall is well distributed or irrigation is used. Production is limited to the winter in Florida, and to fall, winter, and early spring in the rest of the South, except for especially favored localities. In California, fall, winter, and spring crops are produced, while in the North only summer and fall crops are grown.

JOB 1. SELECTING VARIETIES AND SEED

Varieties

Varieties of celery are generally classed as yellow or green. The former, which have been decreasing in importance, are earlier, less vigorous with thinner petioles, easier bleached, and inferior in both eating and keeping quality to the green varieties. Crossing has resulted in intermediate types, and strains showing differences in resistance to diseases, bolting to seed, and nutrient deficiencies are available. Some of the important yellow varieties are Cornell 19, Cornell 619, Michigan Improved Golden,

Fig. 17.1—Celery growing on muck soil with overhead irrigation.

USDA Photograph

Supreme Golden, Golden Plume, and Golden Self-blanching. The variety Utah and its several strains are used for most of the green celery. These include: Giant Pascal, Emerson Pascal, Summer Pascal, and Fordhook.

Securing Seed

Celery seed is expensive but its cost is only a minor item in the total cost of production. The quality of seed, on the other hand, may be a major factor affecting the value of the crop. The purchase of good seed of a desirable strain is therefore good economy. Since celery seed retains its viability for three or four years, it may be bought a year in advance and tested.

JOB 2. PREPARING THE SOIL

Soil Preferences

Because of the high nutrient and water requirements of celery, soil character is a determining factor in celery production. A fertile muck or sandy loam soil, which is loose and friable and has high waterholding capacity, is best. Celery prefers a moderately acid soil, approximating a pH of 6.0.

In the Great Lakes area, celery is grown primarily on mucks. In Florida sandy loams as well as mucks are used. In California celery is grown in delta regions where the soils are alluvial in character. With all types of soil adequate drainage must be provided.

Preparing the Soil

One of the determining factors of successful celery production is the preparation of the soil. The soil should be plowed deeply to increase its water-holding capacity, since celery, because of its shallow root system, suffers very readily from drought. Deep plowing should be followed by thorough pulverization. Usually numerous and thorough harrowings are sufficient.

Plowing should be done long enough before setting the plants to allow ample time for pulverization, the exact time depending on the crop previously grown. If a cover crop is used, it should be turned under in time to allow sufficient decomposition before the plants are set out, and the soil should be harrowed, raked, and smoothed, either by a roller or drag implement.

JOB 3.   FERTILIZING AND MANURING

Celery is a heavy feeder and a very poor forager. Therefore, large quantities of fertilizers are generally applied. When mineral soils are used for growing this crop, manure usually is applied in large quantities if available. In addition to the manure, it is advisable to supply some commercial fertilizer, especially some readily available nitrogen, such as ammonium nitrate, and also some phosphorus carrier, as superphosphate. In Florida, dependence is placed on commercial fertilizer and soil-improving crops.

Growers do not agree on the best kind of fertilizer for celery. The kind, amount, and method of applying fertilizer vary considerably from section to section and within a single producing area. On sandy soils in Florida where no marketable celery was produced without fertilizer, best results were obtained with a mixture containing approximately 6 percent nitrogen, 2 to 4 percent phosphoric acid, and 8 percent potash, used at the rate of 8,000 pounds per acre. In some areas in California there has been no response to applied phosphorus or potash, but good response to nitrogen. Muck and peat soils are usually deficient in potash and often low in phosphorus. Nitrogen may be limiting in these soils when they are cold and wet. The fertilizer recommendation for a given soil should provide a high level of fertility throughout the growing season.

JOB 4. PREPARING THE SEEDBED AND SOWING THE SEED

Celery seed is planted either in the open or under protection. It is seldom planted where the crop is to grow to maturity, because of the care necessary to get a stand of good plants.

Soaking seed prior to planting hastens germination and is practiced by growers in many sections, especially for the late crop. A common method is to moisten the seed in a receptacle and put it in a warm place for several days until the sprouts begin to appear. Another method used by some growers is to place the seed between folds of cloth, which are kept moist.

When the seed is sown in outdoor beds, and the plants are taken directly to the field, it is advisable to sow one-half pound for each acre to be planted. When the plants are grown in the greenhouse and transplanted prior to setting in the field, one-fourth pound of seed is sufficient for one acre planted in rows 3 feet apart.

Celery seed is planted shallow, not deeper than one-half inch. It should be covered with pulverized soil and sufficiently wet down.

In Florida, open seedbeds are prepared in the early part of July. After the ground has been thoroughly conditioned, the beds are made by digging shallow 2-foot trenches every 6 feet apart, leaving 4 feet for the slightly raised beds (Fig. 17.2). Seed is sown in drills across the beds, which are covered with burlap sacks until the seed sprouts. When the seedlings emerge, shade is provided by stretching light muslin over triangular supports placed on the beds 12 feet apart. These supports are held in place by three wires which also act as anchors for the muslin which is fastened to them with clothespins. On one side of the bed a fourth wire is stretched high enough that one side of the muslin may be raised to permit better aeration and hardening of the plants. Later, as the weather cools, these covers are removed entirely. Spraying begins as the leaves appear and continues at 7- to 10-day intervals until the plants mature, in order to control early and late blight.

Fig. 17.2—Celery plants grown for transplanting.

Plants seeded in the greenhouse or hotbed for the early crop are often transplanted after four or five weeks to flats or beds, spaced 1½ by 1½ or 2 by 2 inches. For a large portion of the acreage, however, the plants are transplanted from the seedbed directly to the field. In the coastal region of California where irrigation is available, some celery is seeded directly in the field.

JOB 5. SETTING AND APPLYING WATER

Setting Plants

The plant bed should be watered a few hours before taking up the plants to set in the field. It is desirable to set the plants when the soil is moist and the air rather humid.

Plants are generally removed from the beds and set in the field when they have attained a height of 3 to 4 inches and a crown diameter of ¼ to ⅜ inches. The plants should be set at the proper depth, not deep enough to cover the growing point, and the soil should be firmly pressed around the roots.

Planting distances and methods vary in different parts of the country. The distance between rows varies from 30 to 42 inches and the distance between plants in the row from 3 to 6 inches. Accordingly, 26,000 to 60,000 plants are required to set an acre

The rows should be straight to accommodate machine cultivation, dusting, or spraying. The use of gang transplanters insures a uniform distance between rows and reduces the cost of planting.

Irrigating

Celery is a moisture-loving plant, and unless the soil is naturally moist, the application of water is necessary. Three systems of irrigation are in general use: (1) the underground or subirrigation method, which is principally used in Florida; (2) the furrow or surface system, most common in California; and (3) the overhead-sprinkler system. The last mentioned is the most expensive to construct and operate, and it does not provide drainage during wet weather. The subirrigation system gives the grower almost complete control of the moisture supply, as it is used both for irrigation and drainage. Many muck and some sandy soils are ditched so the ditches can be filled for irrigation or used for drainage by reversing the pumps.

JOB 6. CULTIVATING AND BLANCHING

Cultivating

Good clean cultivation throughout the growing season is important, since weeds are troublesome on most soils used for growing celery. The celery plant grows slowly and is easily injured by weeds. Celery responded more to cultivation for the purpose of maintaining a soil mulch than any of the other crops grown in the cultivation experiment at Ithaca, New York. Celery roots do not have so much spread as most other vegetable roots, and it is thought that because of this, less moisture is intercepted by celery roots than by roots of cabbage, for example. In all cultivation the surface soil should be left as level as possible. Therefore, it is desirable to use small-tooth cultivators. Shallow cultivation is desirable at all times, especially near the plants, as many of the roots grow near the surface and within 6 to 12 inches of the row.

Blanching

The blanching of celery results in the loss of green coloring, reduces the strong flavor, and makes the leaf stalks crisp and tender. Blanching is accomplished by excluding the light from the leaf stalks while the plants are still growing. Several methods have been employed, including the use of paper, boards, and soil. Paper and boards are used almost exclusively for blanching celery in the South, since it is not safe to use soil when the weather is warm.

The demand for green celery has increased so that blanching is no longer a common practice. This change in consumer preference has been due to improved varieties and the association of the green color with vitamin A content.

JOB 7.   CONTROLLING DISEASES AND INSECTS

Diseases

Celery is subject to many diseases which, if not controlled, may cause serious losses. Some of these can be avoided by cultural practices and field sanitation, while others are controlled by spraying.

PINK ROT. Pink rot is caused by the fungus *Sclerotinia sclerotiorum*. It is one of the most destructive diseases of celery, especially during years when climatic conditions are favorable for the development of the fungus. Pink rot causes a damping off of young plants in the seedbed, a light pinkish rot of stalks in the field, and a watery soft rot in transit. It is prevalent in Florida and in northern celery-growing areas. Pink rot can be controlled partially by spraying with one of the fixed copper fungicides. Field sanitation and careful washing and packing are effective in preventing the disease in transit.

EARLY BLIGHT. Early blight, caused by *Cercospora apii*, first occurs in the seedbed. It causes great damage there and is transmitted to the field by the young seedlings. It appears first as small, circular, yellowish-brown spots on the leaves; these spots enlarge and eventually assume a grayish appearance. Early spraying with fixed coppers, maneb, or zineb is usually sufficient to control early blight, but it is profitable to continue spraying, in order to catch the late blight.

LATE BLIGHT. Late blight, *Septoria petroselini* var. *apii*, attacks the plants only in the cooler part of the growing season. It is very similar to early blight, being distinguished only by the smaller, more oval spots speckled with black dots, which occur on the petioles. It attacks all parts of the plant above the ground. The control is the same as for early blight. Emerson Pascal is fairly resistant to both early and late blight and is also highly resistant to fusarium yellows.

ROOT KNOT. (See Nematodes, Chapter 11.)

CRACKED STEM. This disease is very destructive in Florida, due to a deficiency of boron, and has caused considerable loss to celery growers in other regions. This disease first manifests itself by a brownish mottling of the leaf, usually appearing first along the margins. This mottling is accompanied by a brittleness of the petiole and is soon followed by the appearance of crosswise cracks in the outer layers of the petiole. The tissues surrounding the cracks turn brown. The roots also turn brown and the laterals die.

Results of experiments conducted in Florida indicate that an application of 10 pounds of borax to the acre is effective in preventing the development of cracked stem and in increasing the yield and quality of celery. Larger quantities of borax—even as little as 30 pounds to the acre—were found to be distinctly harmful.

BLACK HEART. Black heart often causes greater losses than any other disease. It is non-parasitic, being caused by a deficiency of calcium. It is particularly serious in regions where the irrigation water has a high content of sodium salts. The disease can be controlled by spraying the foliage at intervals with calcium chloride.

Premature Seeding or Bolting

Premature seeding as plants reach full development results in loss of a portion of the crop. In some seasons premature seeding is very serious in Florida and may result in almost total loss of a planting, but it seldom happens that all plantings are affected.

The temperature under which the plants are grown is a very important factor in premature seeding. If the temperature averages between 40° and 50° F. for two weeks or longer, or between 50° and 60° F. for a month or two while the plants are small, they are likely to develop seed stalks. After the plants have been subjected to the temperatures mentioned, any treatment that stimulates growth, such as applying nitrate of soda, tends to hasten seed stalk development. Contrary to a fairly common belief, freezing does not cause seeding, but rather tends to delay it. Likewise checking growth by other means, such as withholding water, delays seeding and may prevent it entirely. Relatively high temperatures (averaging 70° F.) may prevent seeding even after the plants have been subjected to the relatively low growing temperatures mentioned above.

Heredity is important in premature seeding. Some strains are much more subject to bolting than others, and it is possible to develop nonbolting strains. In fact, at least one such strain has been developed. So-called nonbolting strains require a longer exposure to relatively cool temperatures for seed stalk development than do bolting strains.

Insects

A large number of pests may attack celery. Among them are aphids, flea beetles, springtails, carrot rust fly, mole crickets, army worms, tarnish plant bug, wireworms, celery worm, celery leaf tier, celery looper, thrips, and spider mites.

Although any of these may cause serious losses, most of them seldom do. In many of the celery-growing regions the tarnish plant bug and the carrot rust fly are injurious pests. See Chapter 11 for control methods.

JOB 8.   HARVESTING, HANDLING, AND MARKETING

Harvesting

Celery may be harvested as soon as it attains proper size. Early celery often is harvested before the plants are full grown in order to take advantage of a high price. The celery plants are cut off below the surface of the ground with a sharp knife, with a spade, or with special large-scale implements. The trimmers follow the cutters, lift the stalk and strip off the outer leaves. During hot weather the celery should be taken from the field as soon as possible after it is removed from the row, as exposure to sun and wind causes plants to wilt. Harvesting machines are used in some localities. As the machine moves slowly through the field, the celery is harvested, trimmed, washed, and packed in crates. Figure 17.3 shows the "mule train" in operation.

Preparing for Harvest

After harvesting, celery stalks should be thoroughly cleaned by strip-

Fig. 17.3—Harvesting, grading, and packing celery in the field with portable equipment.

USDA Photograph

ping off damaged and discolored leaves and washed with fresh or chlorinated water to remove soil and trash. Washing may be done in the field when packed, but in large operations it is done in packing sheds, where it is inspected for grade (Fig. 17.4).

Packed crates of celery are sprayed with water at 33° F. and precooled in tanks for about 30 minutes. The crates are then passed down chutes or conveyed mechanically from the precooling room to refrigerator cars or trucks, which are usually "blower iced" in warm weather to prevent deterioration. Open ventilation is usually sufficient when transporting in cool weather.

If celery is shipped in the rough, leaves that are unwashed, discolored, and damaged should be removed. Packing is done in the field and the stalks are usually washed and repacked in terminal markets.

Although various types of crates are used in different areas, the 16-inch standard crate containing 30 to 36 stalks and weighing 55 to 60 pounds, is common. Information on celery grades and packaging can be

Fig. 17.4—Federal-state inspector examines celery during harvesting and packing.

USDA Photograph

obtained from the Consumer and Marketing Service, U.S. Department of Agriculture.

Storing

Celery may be stored for four or five weeks at 32° F. and at high relative humidity. Because the crop is available from producing areas most of the year, storage is seldom necessary. It can be used advantageously to prevent market gluts, and has to be done to prevent freezing during harvest. If the crop is to be shipped, the field heat should be removed as soon as feasible.

In the cooler sections, where celery is grown in late summer and fall, it may be kept for several weeks by trenching it in the field or garden.

Marketing

Celery marketing is very competitive, especially in California and Florida where large buyers vie on quality and price in order to meet the demands of retail stores, especially the supermarkets.

Most of the fresh celery is domestically consumed, but about 6 percent was exported in recent years. An annual average of approximately 900,000 hundredweight was shipped out of the country between 1955 and 1963. Most of this was exported to Canada, but some went to Panama, Saudi Arabia, Venezuela, Mexico, and several other countries.

SELECTED REFERENCES

Beattie, W. R., "Celery Growing," USDA Farmers' Bull. 1269, 1944.

Geraldson, C. M., "The Control of Blackheart of Celery," *Proc. Amer. Soc. Hort. Sci.* 63, 1954, pp. 353-58.

Seelig, R. A., "Celery," United Fresh Fruit and Vegetable Association, Washington, D.C., 1961.

Stewart, J. K. and Barger, W. R., "Effect of Precooling Method on the Quality of Crate-Packed and Prepacked Celery," *Proc. Amer. Soc. Hort. Sci.* 81: 347-53, 1962.

CHAPTER 18

Corn (Sweet)

Classification, Origin, and History

Sweet corn (*Zea Mays* var. *saccharata*) is a member of the grass family and a native of America. It is a comparatively modern vegetable crop. History records that the colonists began to grow the plant about 1780.

Scope and Importance

Sweet corn has become one of the most important vegetable crops, ranking second in acreage and fourth in value among the 22 principal vegetables in 1965. This crop is grown commercially in at least 25 states, and for local markets and home gardens throughout the country.

The acreage of sweet corn for fresh market increased sharply from 62,700 in 1939 to 215,100 in 1959 and fluctuated thereafter with an estimated acreage of 203,180 in 1965. The acreage of the processed crop increased from 251,160 to approximately 377,000 in 1965. Farm values of fresh market corn increased from $2,777,000 in 1939 to approximately $58,000,000 in 1965, while the crop for processing rose from $5,619,000 to about $36,000,000 during the corresponding 26-year period.

The approximate distribution of sweet corn production in the United States is shown in Figure 18.1 while the acreage, production, and value of corn for processing and fresh market are presented by leading states in Tables 18.1 and 18.2 respectively.

Trends in Production Efficiency

The growing and harvesting of sweet corn is highly mechanized, requiring considerably less labor than most vegetables. Between 1939 and

Fig. 18.1—Acreage and distribution of commercial sweet corn.

1959 the labor requirement for fresh market corn remained constant around 48 man-hours per acre, while that for the processed crop declined from 46 to 12 man-hours. The average acre yield of sweet corn for fresh market rose from 32 to 60 hundredweight between 1939 and 1959, while the output per man-hour increased 92 percent. Yields of sweet corn for processing rose from 53 to 76 hundredweight per acre during the same period, as the unit output per man-hour rose 434 percent (Table 1.4).

Climatic Requirements

Principal climatic factors are (1) temperature and (2) the moisture supply. The temperature has a marked effect on the growth of sweet corn. In general, the higher the temperature, between 40° and 90° F., the greater is the rate of growth and the shorter is the time necessary for the plant to attain a particular stage of maturity. Data presented in Table 18.3 obtained with Stowell's Evergreen grown at the Maryland Agricultural Experiment Station illustrate the effect of temperature.

Fairly uniform distribution of rainfall is necessary for good growth and high yields. If soil moisture is low when the weather is hot, the plant does not receive sufficient moisture for growth; the manufacture of food declines, and yields are low.

Table 18.1—Sweet Corn for Processing: Estimated Commercial Acreage, Yield, Production, and Value in Leading States, 1965.

State	Harvested Acreage	Yield per Acre, Tons	Production in Tons	Price per Ton	Value, $1,000
Minnesota	91,500	3.86	353,200	$21.70	7,664
Wisconsin	88,000	4.19	368,700	20.70	7,632
Illinois	48,500	4.23	205,200	23.60	4,843
Washington	30,400	5.20	158,100	24.80	3,921
Oregon	28,800	5.82	167,600	24.10	4,039
Maryland	28,700	3.22	92,400	23.10	2,134
Idaho	13,400	6.31	84,600	22.60	1,912
New York	13,100	4.05	53,100	24.00	1,274
Pennsylvania	9,200	2.58	23,700	21.80	917
Iowa	5,200	4.13	21,500	16.50	355
Delaware	3,200	3.39	10,800	23.90	258
Ohio	1,400	4.70	6,600	19.20	127
Maine	1,300	5.15	6,700	21.50	144
Other states	14,190	4.37	62,000	19.20	1,188
All states	376,890	4.28	1,614,200	22.30	36,008
For freezing	99,350	4.35	432,560	24.00	10,393
For canning	277,540	4.26	1,181,640	21.70	25,615

Table 18.2—Sweet Corn for Fresh Market: Shipping Season and Estimated Commercial Acreage, Yield, Production, and Value in Leading States, 1965.

State	Season	Harvested Acreage	Yield per Acre, Cwt.	Production, 1,000 Cwt.	Price per Cwt.	Value, $1,000
Florida	Early spring	34,800	80	2,784*	$5.10	13,964
Pennsylvania	Late summer	18,500	45	832	4.50	3,744
New York	Late summer	16,400	60	984	3.20	3,149
New Jersey	Early summer	15,000	80	1,200	3.10	3,720
Ohio	Late summer	13,500	85	1,148	3.20	3,674
Michigan	Late summer	12,500	70	875	3.35	2,931
Texas	Early spring	9,500	35	332	6.10	2,025
Massachusetts	Late summer	8,200	70	574	4.20	2,411
California	Early summer	7,900	70	553	4.50	2,488
Florida	Winter	7,800	60	468	8.10	3,791
Illinois	Late summer	6,400	70	448	2.15	963
Connecticut	Late summer	5,100	65	332	4.35	1,444
California	Late spring	5,000	80	400	5.70	2,280
North Carolina	Early summer	4,600	70	332	4.10	1,320
All states		203,180	66	13,473	4.32	57,940

*Includes some quantities not marketed and excluded in computing value.

Table 18.3—Calculated Rate of Sweet Corn Ripening for Mean Temperatures, 60° to 80° F.

Average of Daily Mean (Degrees F.)	Time Required to Pass from Pre-milk to Best Canning Stage* (Days)	Time Remained in Canning State (Days)
60	14.5	5.0
65	12.0	4.0
70	10.0	3.0
75	8.0	3.0
80	7.0	2.0
85	5.5	1.5

*The juice of the kernel is clear and watery at the pre-milk stage and milky at the canning stage. Data from Maryland Agricultural Experiment Station.

JOB 1. SELECTING VARIETIES AND SEED

Varieties

Most sweet corn varieties now used are hybrids, each resulting from the cross of two inbreds. The preference for hybrids is due primarily to their vigor, high yields, and uniformity. A few varieties in use are top crosses, with the seed parent an open-pollinated variety.

Varieties may be classified as early, medium, and late, with the time required for maturity varying from about 65 days for early varieties to 100 days for late ones. Among the popular early varieties are Sugar and Gold, Spring Gold, and Seneca 60; Duet, Gold Cup, Seneca Chief, and Wonderful are of medium maturity; and the late group includes such varieties as Illinois 11 × 14, Golden Queen, Golden Cross Bantam, Jubilee, and Victory Golden. These are among varieties described in Table 18.4.

Table 18.4—Brief Description of Selected Varieties of Sweet Corn.

Variety	Chief Use	Season (Days)	Stalk Height (In.)	Color	Ear Length (In.)	No. Rows	Quality
Barbacue	H,M	75	60	Yellow	8-9	10-14	Excellent
Cogent, Ill. No. 13*	P	94	84	White	7½	Irregular	Fine
Duet*	M	81	82	Yellow	7-9	14-16	Superior
Early Adams	H	84	72	White	7½	12-14	Fair
F-M Cross*	P,M	81	78	Bright Yellow	8½	14-16	Good
Gold Cup	M,F	80	78	Bright Yellow	7½	14-16	Excellent
Golden Beauty*	M,H	75	64	Yellow	6-8	12-14	Very good
Golden Cross Bantam	H,M,P	86	74	Yellow	7-9	12-14	Very good
Golden Queen	M,H	93	102	Yellow	8-9	14-16	Very high
Honey and Cream	H,M	78		Bi-color	6½-7½	12-14	Excellent
Illinois 11 × 14*	P	94	96	White	8	16-20	Excellent

(Continued)

Table 18.4—Brief Description of Selected Varieties of Sweet Corn
(Continued).

Variety	Chief Use	Season (Days)	Stalk Height (In.)	Color	Ear Length (In.)	No. Rows	Quality
Jubilee	P,M	87	90	Yellow	8½-9	18-20	Good
NK 199	P,H,M	84	93	Yellow	7½-8	18-20	Fine
Seneca Chief	H	81	67	Yellow	6-8	12	Excellent
Seneca 60	H,M	63	54	Yellow	7	10-12	Good
Silver Queen	H,M	92	90	White	8-9	14-16	Good
Spring Gold	H,M	67		Yellow	7	12-16	Fine
Sugar and Gold	H,M	57	44-50	Bi-colored	7-8	8	Extra high
Truckers Favorite	H	95	96	White	8½	12-16	Poor
Victory Golden	M	89	90	Yellow	8½	14-18	Excellent
Winter Garden*	M	88	78	Yellow	7¾-8	14-16	Fair
Wonderful	H,F	82		Yellow		12-16	Excellent

*Resistant to Stewart's wilt.

In the South, where the cornear worm is particularly severe, a resistant variety such as Aristogold or Trucker's Favorite is often used.

The variety should be productive and should yield high-quality ears which are relatively free from damage by the cornear worm. In addition, the kernels should be tender and sweet. Although tenderness of the pericarp (skin of the kernel) is an important varietal characteristic, it may also be associated with seed injury.

Securing Seed

If sweet corn is grown for either the fresh market or processing, it is desirable to harvest the entire crop at one picking. This requires uniform maturity, characteristic of good hybrids. Sizing of seed may also increase uniformity of maturity. In the home garden it is often desirable for the harvest to be spread over a period of several days, and thus it may be advantageous to use an open-pollinated variety.

The production of sweet corn seed not only requires carefully controlled pollination but careful handling as well. The tender pericarp of sweet corn is easily injured, and the endosperm because of its high sugar content dries slowly and may readily absorb moisture during storage. It is therefore important to secure seed from a concern equipped to produce and handle it.

JOB 2. PREPARING SOIL, FERTILIZING, AND MANURING

Preparing the Soil

Sweet corn is grown on a wide variety of soil types. Growers for the early market usually plant on well-drained, sandy loams, while those for the late market or for the cannery usually select silt or clay loams or well-drained bottom land.

Soil preparation consists of plowing and harrowing as needed. Usually the rows are 2½ to 4 feet apart. Fertilizer is applied in furrows and mixed with the soil or applied at the time of planting. If well-rotted manure is used, it should be applied broadcast on the plowed land and thoroughly disked into the soil. If coarse manure is used, it should be plowed under three or four weeks before planting time.

Fertilizing

Sweet corn is placed in Group II according to its nutrient requirements, and fertilizer recommendations are given in Tables 6.4 and 6.5. The kind and amount of fertilizer that should be applied depends on the fertility of soil used.

Tests with field corn have shown that commercial fertilizers applied in 1-inch bands slightly below and about 2 inches from the seed produce greater yields than fertilizer applied under the seed. Since the root system of sweet corn is similar to that of field corn, sweet corn should respond in much the same way as field corn. As is true of other vegetable crops, commercial fertilizer should never come in contact with the seed.

JOB 3. PLANTING

Treating Seed

Sweet corn seed is more susceptible than field corn seed to the rot-producing fungi in the soil. This is especially true if the seed is planted when the soil is cold and wet. Investigations have shown that treating the seed with Arasan effectively protects it against rot-producing fungi. Arasan can be purchased at most seed stores, and the directions should be followed closely.

Size of seed influences earliness and yield of sweet corn. Experiments at the Indiana Agricultural Experiment Station have shown that plants grown from large kernels tassel and produce ears about five days earlier than plants of the same variety grown from small kernels. This is particularly important from the standpoint of the market gardener and the canner.

Planting Dates

The seed for the early crop is usually planted just before or immediately after the average date of the last killing frost. However, market and home gardeners frequently take a chance on the frost. In this case, usually two or three plantings at intervals of 5 to 10 days are made.

The time required between planting and maturity depends primarily upon temperature and variety. The effective temperature may be calculated as heat units or degree days, the daily average above a predetermined base temperature. With a base temperature of 45° F., a day averaging 70° F. would accumulate 25 degree days. The number of heat units required for the development of a variety may be determined. These data together with the average accumulation of heat units per day during the growing season can be used to predict time of maturity. Early plantings usually require more days to mature than later ones. By taking the expected accumulation of heat units between harvesting intervals and allowing the same to accumulate between planting intervals, properly spaced harvests can be provided. These are essential for sweet corn grown for processing and may be important for supplying a particular market.

To secure a continuous supply of sweet corn throughout the growing season in the home garden, two systems may be used: (1) the same variety may be planted at intervals of 10 days or two weeks, or (2) early, midseason, and late varieties may be planted at the same time. In the South, the latter method is probably more advantageous than the former.

Whether different varieties or successive plantings are made, each should be planted in a block to insure pollination.

Planting Methods

Seed is planted by hand, or by hand-operated or power-drawn planters. Hand planting requires the making of furrows, and dropping the seeds in the furrow, while machine planters make the furrows and drop and cover the seed in one operation. Cheap and effective machines are on the market. In general, market gardeners or growers of small acreages use hand machines while canners or growers of large acreages use tractor-drawn machines.

Planting Rates

Sweet corn is planted in rows varying from 2½ to 4 feet apart, and spaced from 12 to 24 inches in the drill. The rate of seeding depends on (1) the time of planting, (2) the spacing, and (3) the variety. Ordinarily, the earlier the seed is planted or the colder the soil, the greater is the rate of seeding. As a rule, the true sweet corn varieties require a higher rate of seeding than field corn varieties. This is particularly true if the weather is cold and wet at the time seeding is made. Generally, 8 to 14 pounds of seed are required per acre.

JOB 4.   CULTIVATING

Cultivating

The primary purpose of cultivation is to control weeds, and a secondary purpose is to break the crust of self-crusting, usually heavy soils. In general, shallow cultivation should be practiced. To avoid the necessity of deep cultivation, weeds should be destroyed when they are small. When the weather is hot and dry, the moist soil should never be exposed to dry air, as the moisture evaporates and is lost to the plant.

Under average conditions, cultivation may be outlined as follows: (1) The first cultivation should be relatively deep to loosen the soil and to permit lateral root growth. (2) Succeeding cultivations should be relatively shallow. Scraper types of cultivators should be used rather than the toothed types, so that cultivations will not be too deep, injuring the feeding roots just beneath the surface. (3) Cultivation should stop when the main stem is about half grown, unless weeds are prevalent or the soil crusts badly after heavy rains.

JOB 5.   CONTROLLING DISEASES AND INSECTS

Diseases

The principal diseases are bacterial wilt and corn smut.

BACTERIAL WILT. Bacterial wilt, caused by *Bacterium stewartii*, develops inside the water-conducting tubes and produces wilting about the time the plants silk. The bacteria are carried over in the bodies of the corn flea beetles and in the seed. Cucumber beetles and flea beetles are known to spread the parasite from infected stalks to health noninfected stalks. The only reliable control measure is the use of resistant varieties, a number of which are now on the market. They should be tested on a small scale before they are planted extensively.

CORN SMUT. Corn smut, caused by the fungus *Ustilago maydis*, produces puffed-out membranous growths on the ears and stems. Inside these membranes are compact masses of black spores, which are liberated when the membranes break open. Control measures consist of (1) rotating crops and (2) practicing field sanitation. Manure containing diseased stalks should not be used on land planted to sweet corn. The development of resistant varieties appears to be a promising method of control.

HELMINTHOSPORIUM LEAF BLIGHT. Helminthosporium leaf blight is caused by a fungus, *Helminthosporium turcicum*, and results in large, linear water-soaked areas, which change to black or straw-yellow on drying. Control methods include a 3-year rotation, resistant varieties, and spraying with maneb or zineb when heavy damage occurs.

Insects

The principal insects are cornear worm, the Southern corn stalk borer, and the European corn borer.

CORNEAR WORM. The cornear worm *(Heliothis zea)* is destructive to a number of vegetables crops, but its damage is most severe on sweet corn and tomatoes. The cornear worm is the larva of a light grayish-brown moth (Fig. 18.2). The front wings are marked with dark irregular lines and there is a dark area near the top of the wing. The back wings are light in color.

In the fall the larvae burrow 2 to 6 inches into the soil to pupate. When spring comes, the moths emerge from the pupal cells and crawl up the tunnels made by the larvae in the fall. The eggs are laid singly on the corn silks. (If tomatoes are attacked, the eggs are deposited on the underside of the leaves.) After the larvae reach maturity, they drop to the ground and burrow in the soil, completing the cycle. This is repeated for each generation.

To control cornear worms on sweet corn in the whorl stage treat with carbaryl, or when silking treat the silks with DDT and mineral oil (see Chapter 11). Some varieties of sweet corn have been developed which are more resistant to the attacks of the cornear worm than others.

SOUTHERN CORN STALK BORER. The Southern corn stalk borer *(Diatraea crambidoides)* is the larva of a night-flying moth. The adult lays eggs on all parts of the plant. After the eggs hatch, the larvae bore into the stem. No chemical control measures are used, but crop refuse destruction is recommended, along with crop rotation and late fall and winter plowing.

EUROPEAN CORN BORER. The European corn borer *(Pyrausta nubilalis)* is also the larva of a night-flying moth. Eggs are laid on the leaves and the larvae bore through the stems, thus entering the ear from within. Control measures include using DDT, particularly in a granular form, carbaryl, and ryania.

Fig. 18.2—The cornear worm is destructive to corn, tomato, and other vegetables.

JOB 6.   HARVESTING AND GRADING

Harvesting

When the kernels are young and small, the juice is clear and watery, and the corn is said to be in the pre-milk stage. As they become larger, plumper, and older, the juice becomes milky, and this is known as the milk stage. In a relatively short time the kernels pass from the milk stage to the dough stage. At the pre-milk stage, the kernels are fairly sweet, but they are small and generally lack plumpness. At the milk stage they are also sweet, but they have attained full size and plumpness, while at the dough stage, most of the sugars have changed to starch. Obviously, ears should be harvested when the kernels are in the milk stage.

Experienced growers do not press the juice from the kernels to determine when they are in the milk stage. This would require partial stripping of the husks, which is objectionable. With many varieties growers have found that when the silks first become brown and the ears feel plump they are ready to be picked.

After the ears are picked, the sugars decrease and starch increases rapidly, and this change is directly proportional to the temperature. Table 18.5 presents data showing the effect of temperature on the loss in sugars of the Stowell's Evergreen variety. The higher the temperature the more rapid was the decrease in sugars and hence the more rapid was the lowering in quality.

Table 18.5—Loss of Sugar from Stowell's Evergreen Sweet Corn Stored for 24 Hours.

Temperature (Degrees F.)	Percent Sugars		
	Start of Storage	End of Storage	Less
32	5.91	5.43	0.48
50	5.83	4.83	1.00
68	6.17	4.59	1.58
86	5.34	2.65	2.69
104	6.72	3.64	3.08

Data from Appleman, C. O., and Arthur, J. M.: "Carbohydrate Metabolism in Sweet Corn in Storage at Different Temperatures," **Jour. Agr. Res.** 17: 137-152.

Corn should be picked in the early morning, and the ears should be kept in a cool place. Piling the ears or placing them in nonventilated crates increases the respiration rate and the loss of sugar. Because of the marked effect of temperature on loss of sugar, sweet corn to be canned should be processed immediately after picking. Equipment for rapid handling is illustrated in Figures 18.3 and 18.4.

Fig. 18.3—A portable machine used in harvesting and packing sweet corn in the field.

USDA Photograph

Grading and Shipping

Well-filled uniform ears of optimum maturity should be selected for best results. Poorly-filled, worm-eaten, overripe and undersized ears should be discarded. For long distance shipments, the ears are packed in 40 to 45 pound ventilated sacks or crates and adequately iced as shown in Figure 18.5. Much of the corn crop is shipped by trucks both on long and short hauls.

Marketing

It is evident from Table 18.5 that sweet corn must be marketed as

Fig. 18.4—Sweet corn being unloaded at the processing plant.

Photograph by E. K. Alban

soon after harvest as possible. Buyers insist on precooled corn especially for consumers in the more distant markets. There are opportunities for growers near urban areas to develop profitable local markets for high quality corn if it is properly handled.

General experiences indicate that the quality of sweet corn for market can be improved by (1) harvesting at optimum maturity, (2) picking early in the morning in ventilated crates, (3) cooling as soon as possible, (4) precooling to lower temperatures before shipping, (5) transporting under ideal refrigeration, (6) providing more adequate refrigeration facilities in the retail stores, and (7) shortening the marketing period in every practical way.

Because of the marked effect of temperature on the loss of sugar (Table 18.5), sweet corn for canning should be handled quickly under cool conditions if possible and processed immediately after picking.

An annual average of approximately 248,000 cases of canned corn was exported between 1955 and 1959, after which shipments declined.

Fig. 18.5—Crates of sweet corn in refrigerator car iced for shipping.

USDA Photograph

Most of this product went to Canada, the United Kingdom, Sweden, Hong Kong, and the Philippines, with small quantities to several other countries. Approximately 268,000 cases values at $1,101,000 were shipped from the United States in 1963.

SELECTED REFERENCES

Alban, E. K. and Scott, R. C., "Post-harvest Handling and Marketing of Garden Fresh Sweet Corn," Ohio Agr. Exp. Sta. Res. Cir. 23, 1954.

Anonymous, "Commercial Growing of Sweet Corn," USDA Farmers' Bull. 2042, 1961.

Dolan, D. D. and Christopher, E. P., "Plant Spacing of Sweet Corn," R. I. Agr. Exp. Sta. Bull. 316, 1952.

Hills, W. A., et al., "Sweet Corn Production on the Sandy Soils of the Florida Lower East Coast," Fla. Agr. Exp. Sta. Bull. 520, 1953.

Peterson, H. B. and Ballard, J. C., "Effect of Fertilizer and Moisture on the Growth and Yield of Sweet Corn," Utah Agr. Exp. Sta. Bull. 360, 1953.

Robert, Alice L., "Bacterial Wilt and Stewarts Leaf Blight of Corn," USDA Farmers' Bull. 2092, 1960.

Showalter, R. K., et al., "Long Distance Marketing of Fresh Sweet Corn," Fla. Agr. Exp. Sta. Bull. 638, 1961.

CHAPTER 19

Cucumbers

Classification, Origin, and History

The cucumber *(Cucumis sativus)* belongs to the same genus as the melon. It is probably a native of Asia and Africa and there is evidence that it has been cultivated in western Asia for at least 3,000 years. Cucumbers were known to the ancient Greeks and Romans, who introduced them into Europe. They have been grown in America since the earliest settlements.

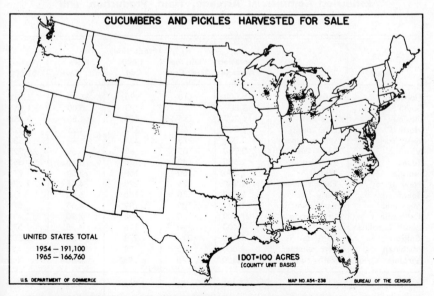

Fig. 19.1—Acreage and distribution of commercial cucumbers.

Scope and Importance

Cucumber production has increased over the years, and this crop now ranks 9th in acreage and 12th in value among the 22 principal vegetables in 1963.

The acreage for fresh market cucumbers increased from 45,600 in 1939 to an estimated 57,420 in 1965, with considerable fluctuations during this period. Farm value rose from $5,000,000 to approximately $28,000,000, and acre yields increased considerably between 1939 and 1965.

The acreage of pickling cucumbers rose from 55,710 in 1939 to approximately 109,000 in 1965, during which time there were large fluctuations in acreage. Farm value rose precipitously from $2,179,000 to about $32,500,000 during this period, while yields per acre more than doubled.

Figure 19.1 shows the approximate distribution of cucumber production, while the acreage, production, and farm value of cucumbers for fresh market and processing are listed by leading states in Tables 19.1 and 19.2 respectively.

Table 19.1—Cucumbers for Fresh Market: Shipping Season and Estimated Commercial Acreage, Yield, Production, and Value in Leading States, 1965.

State	Season	Harvested Acreage	Yield per Acre, Cwt.	Production, 1,000 Cwt.	Price per Cwt.	Value, $1,000
Florida	Early spring	9,000	110	990	$5.80	5,742
South Carolina	Late spring	7,800	50	390	5.00	1,950
Florida	Late fall	6,200	115	713	4.85	3,458
North Carolina	Late spring	5,200	60	312	4.25	1,326
New York	Late summer	3,000	75	225	6.80	1,530
Virginia	Early fall	2,900	65	188	6.50	1,222
Texas	Early spring	2,600	40	104	6.40	666
Florida	Winter	2,500	60	150	8.50	1,275
New Jersey	Early summer	2,200	125	275	4.65	1,279
Texas	Early fall	2,000	70	140	6.50	910
Maryland	Early summer	1,800	105	189	4.65	879
California	Late spring	1,400	220	308	7.90	2,433
South Carolina	Early fall	1,400	90	126	4.55	573
California	Early fall	1,300	210	273	5.80	1,583
Michigan	Late summer	1,300	75	98	5.70	559
Virginia	Early summer	1,300	75	98*	4.85	466
All states		57,420	86	4,965	5.65	28,040

*Includes some quantities not marketed and excluded in computing value.

Table 19.2—Cucumbers for (Pickles) Processing: Estimated Commercial Acreage, Yield, Production, and Value in Leading States, 1965.

State	Harvested Acreage	Yield per Acre, Tons	Production in Tons	Price per Ton	Value, $1,000
North Carolina	21,300	2.81	59,850	$73.60	4,405
Michigan	16,300	5.70	92,910*	92.40	7,325
Wisconsin	13,800	3.15	43,470	84.80	3,686
Texas	5,600	3.08	17,250	65.60	1,132
Delaware and Maryland	4,100	6.45	26,460	53.30	1,410
California	3,700	11.60	42,920	76.70	3,292
Virginia	3,000	3.50	10,500	85.10	894
Ohio	2,400	5.30	12,720	75.60	962
Washington	1,600	8.70	13,920	68.60	955
Indiana	1,200	5.50	6,600	69.00	455
Colorado	800	7.00	5,600	61.80	346
All states	109,340	4.07	444,870	75.50	32,558

*Includes some quantities not marketed and excluded in computing value.

Trends in Production Efficiency

Cucumbers require special planting, pest control, and cultural practices along with adequate fertilization, all of which involve considerable labor. Between 1939 and 1959 the labor involved in growing and harvesting fresh market cucumbers decreased on the average from 127 to 114 man-hours per acre, while that required for pickle production rose from 95 to 155 man-hours.

In 1965, however, two types of mechanical harvesters were available to growers. One was a "selective" and the other a "non-selective" or one-pick machine. These innovations promise to reduce drastically the labor input in harvesting pickles.

Average yields of fresh market cucumbers rose from 54 to 77 hundredweight during the 1939-1959 period, while output per man-hour rose 58 percent. Yields of cucumbers for processing increased from 29 to 67 hundredweight while man-hour production increased 47 percent during this period (Table 1.4).

Climatic Requirements

The cucumber is a warm-season crop, and young plants are seriously injured by frost. However, cucumbers can be grown anywhere in the United States because the crop matures in a relatively short season. Average daily temperatures of 65° to 75° F. are most favorable for growth, but heat is not so essential for cucumbers as it is for melons.

JOB 1.   SELECTING VARIETIES AND SEED

Varieties

Varieties should be selected which grow vigorously, yield well, resist disease, and have desirable market characteristics. The selection of variety will also depend upon the use for which the product is intended. Some varieties are best suited for slicing purposes and others are especially desirable for pickling. Table 19.3 gives a description of a selected list of the leading varieties.

Securing Seed

It is of the utmost importance to use good seed since the quality of the seed may be the margin of difference between success and failure of the crop. The difference in price between high- and low-quality seed is insignificant as compared with the difference in results. Seed should be purchased from seed houses which make a point of selling only the best.

Seed of F_1 hybrids usually costs more than 10 times as much as that of standard varieties. The grower must decide if the added vigor and uniformity obtained is worth the extra seed cost. It is recommended that hybrids be tried on a small scale in comparison with standard varieties to determine their value.

Most of the supply of cucumber seed is produced in California, Colorado, and Michigan, although some seed is produced locally in other cucumber-producing areas.

JOB 2.   PREPARING THE SEEDBED

Soil Preferences

Cucumbers can be grown on almost any good soil. A light, loamy, well-drained soil, which contains an abundance of organic matter and is fertile, is very desirable for early cucumbers. Although cucumbers are fairly tolerant to strongly acid soils, best results will be obtained if the soil reaction is kept between pH 5.5 and pH 6.8.

Preparing the Seedbed

The light soils used for cucumber production are relatively easy to prepare. However, the more thorough the preparation, the easier it will be to cultivate and work the crop. Plowing, disking, and harrowing are all necessary operations. The time of plowing and breaking will vary in the different regions according to the time of planting. For example, in North Carolina, where the planting dates are from March 25 to April 10, the land is broken during February or early March. In the South, cucumber land is frequently bedded up in order to facilitate drainage. The height of the beds will depend on the drainage situation. On the well-drained soils, the land is broken flat and the row-beds made by throwing together two or four furrows with a turn-plow and dragging the ridge down almost level. The rows are bedded up usually when the fertilizer is applied. The final dragging and harrowing are done just ahead of the planter. In more poorly drained soils, high beds are thrown up when the land is first broken and these beds are reworked and dragged down just before planting time.

In other sections the land is plowed, disked, and harrowed, and the seed is planted on the level or in slight furrows.

Fertilizing

The cucumber is a quick-growing crop, and must be well supplied with nutrients and moisture to keep it growing vigorously. As seen in Table 6.4, the crop requires from 30 to 45 pounds of nitrogen per acre. If the soil is subject to leaching, more should be supplied, part before planting and the remainder as a side dressing. On soils of medium fertility cucumbers require about 70 pounds of phosphorus and about 116 pounds of potassium per acre (Table 6.5). These nutrients should be worked into the soil before planting.

Manuring

Animal manures are an excellent source of soil organic matter and fertility. However, manure is now rather expensive and not readily available, so a combination of green-manure crops and commercial fertilizers is employed to meet the requirements of the crop. When a small amount of manure is available, it can be used to advantage by mixing with the soil under the row.

Summer soil-improvement crops of soybeans, cowpeas, or velvet beans are recommended. They should be turned under when they have reached

Table 19.3–A Brief Description of a Selected List of Cucumber Varieties.

Variety	Season (Days)	Fruit Shape	Fruit Size (Inches)	Fruit Color*	Fruit Spine**	Resistant to†
Slicing Type:						
Ashley	66	Ends sl. tapered	8 × 2½	DG	W	DM
Burpee Hybrid	60	Ends sl. tapered	8 × 2½	DG	W	M, DM
Challenger Hybrid	61	Slim, sl. tapered	8 × 2	DG	W	DM
FM Hybrid Ashley	66	Straight, tapered	8½ × 2¼	DG	W	DM
Palomar	64	Slightly tapered	8½ × 2¼	DG	W	DM, PM, A
Polaris	64	Rounded ends	7½ × 2¼	DG	W	M, S
Princess	60	Slim, sl. tapered	8 × 2	DG	W	M, DM
Saticoy Hybrid	63	Tapered to stem	7½ × 2½	DG		
Pickling Type:						
Ohio MR 17	56	Slender	6 × 2½	MG	B	PM, DM, A
Pixie	52	Blocky	5¾ × 2½	DG	W	S, M
Spartan Dawn	51	Blocky	6½ × 2½	MG	B	S, M
Wisconsin SMR 18	53	Blocky	—	MG	B	

*DG—dark green, MG—medium green.

**W—white, B—black.

†DM—downey mildew, PM—powdery mildew, M—mosaic, A—anthracnose, S—scab.

full growth but before they mature and become woody. For an early cucumber crop, rye is a practicable winter cover crop, and it should be turned under three or four weeks before planting time.

JOB 3.   PLANTING

Planting dates vary with climatic conditions. Cucumbers are easily injured by frost; consequently, field planting should be delayed until danger of frost is over. Some experienced growers make two or three different plantings, a week apart, the first about 10 days before the average date of the last killing frost. If the first planting is not killed by frost, it will give an extra early crop. If the first planting is killed, the grower still has one of the later plantings to fall back on.

Some cucumbers are still planted in hills but most commercial acreage is now planted in drill rows. When the hill method is used several seeds are planted in each hill and the plants are later thinned. The spacings vary from 4 by 5 feet up to 6 by 8 feet. In the row method the seeds are planted with a drill in a continuous row. The spacing between rows vary from 4 to 8 feet. Where the crop is grown in beds, the beds are usually 4 to 6 feet apart.

On land that has been previously bedded up, the beds are reworked at planting time and the seed planted in a row down the center of the bed. The depth of planting will vary with soil type and moisture conditions but will generally average about one-half inch. From two to four pounds of seed are required to sow an acre, depending on the space between the rows and the method used.

JOB 4.   CULTIVATING AND THINNING

Cultivating

Cultivation should be started as soon as the plants are up, and continued frequently enough to keep the weeds down and the soil loose. Early cultivations may be reasonably deep, but since the cucumber is a shallow-rooted plant, all cultivations after the plants begin to run should be shallow and not too close to the plant. Sometimes the vines are turned to permit later cultivation, but hand hoeing may be necessary to destroy weeds close to the plants.

Thinning

After the plants become well established and there is no more danger of loss of plants through insect injury, cucumbers are thinned by hand. Two or three plants per hill are left for plantings made by the hill system. Plants in rows are thinned to one per 1½ to 3 feet.

JOB 5.   CONTROLLING DISEASES AND INSECTS

Diseases

Downy mildew, bacterial wilt, anthracnose, root knot, angular leaf spot, mosaic, and scab are important diseases of cucumbers. The first four of these are discussed in Chapter 22. Resistance to downy mildew has been found and transferred into such commercial cucumber varieties as Palmetto, Santee, Ashley, Stono, and Palomar.

ANGULAR LEAF SPOT. Angular leaf spot *(Pseudomonas lachrymans)* is a bacterial disease carried over winter on the seed and in the soil. It causes small, angular water-soaked or tan-colored spots on the leaves and fruits. To control this disease, treat the seed for five minutes in a 1 to 1,000 solution of mercuric chloride (corrosive sublimate), wash thoroughly in water, and plant in uninfected soil. Spraying and dusting with copper fungicides will also help in control.

MOSAIC. Mosaic or "white pickle" is a virus disease found in many areas throughout the country and frequently causes heavy loss. It is characterized by a dwarfing of the plants; mottling, yellowing, and wrinkling of the leaves; and a warting and mottling of the fruits. Mosaic affects other cultivated plants such as muskmelons, squash, peppers, tomatoes, and celery. The organism also attacks several wild plants, including pokeweed, milkweed, catnip, and ground cherry. It overwinters on their roots or seeds, and is carried to cultivated crops in the spring by aphids and the striped cucumber beetle. It is also spread in the cucumber fields by pickers. Thorough eradication of wild host plants near the cucumber fields and strict control of insects are most important in the control of mosaic. Mosaic-resistant varieties have been developed for both slicing and pickling cucumbers. The leading resistant varieties are listed in Table 19.3.

SCAB. Scab is caused by a fungus *(Cladosporium cucumerinum)* which produces sunken, dark-brown spots on the fruits. In moist weather, the spots are covered with a greenish mold. A gummy substance oozes from the fruits. The leaves and stems may also be affected. The fungus also attacks muskmelons and pumpkins. The disease is found primarily in the north central and northeastern states, and is most damaging in cool, moist weather. The organism overwinters in old refuse and on the seed. The best control measures are fixed coppers, ziram, maneb, rotation, and use of disease-resistant varieties. In addition to the two resistant pickling varieties listed in Table 19.3, the slicing variety Highmoor is resistant.

Insects

The principal cucumber insects include aphids, twelve-spotted cucumber beetles, striped cucumber beetles, and spider mites. These insects and methods of control are described in Chapter 11.

Another insect, the pickle worm, feeds on flowers and leaf buds. It tunnels into the flowers, terminal buds, vines, and fruits. It is found in the southeastern part of the country and may be destructive as far north as New York, Michigan, and parts of Canada. Spraying or dusting with rotenone, lindane, or cryolite is recommended. Worms must be killed before they enter the fruits.

JOB 6. HARVESTING, HANDLING, AND MARKETING

Harvesting

Slicing or fresh market cucumbers must be fresh and crisp when received by the consumer. The market desires a medium-sized, well-formed, dark-green cucumber. This requires frequent picking and careful and prompt handling. They must be gathered often enough to prevent their becoming too large or overripe. No fruit should be allowed to ripen on the vines as further yield of the plant will be markedly decreased.

In normal seasons, the first picking can be made 60 to 65 days after planting. Normally, pickings may be made at two- to three-day intervals, but, during the height of the season, it may be necessary to harvest daily. Cucumbers usually are picked or cut from the vines, placed in baskets or hampers, and carried to the ends of the rows for packing, but labor-saving devices may also be used (Fig. 19.2).

Pickling cucumbers mature a few days earlier than slicing cucumbers. Frequency of picking will depend on the size desired by the pickling factory. Small-sized cucumbers are usually less profitable to the grower than larger ones. The increased price paid for the small sizes does not generally offset the lower yields obtained.

Harvesting machines for cucumbers are being developed and tested. Some of these machines show much promise for harvesting pickling cucumbers.

Fig. 19.2—Conveyer belts move harvested cucumbers to the sacking station.

USDA Photograph

Grading

Slicing cucumbers are usually sorted and graded by hand in the field or packing shed (Fig. 19.3). U.S. Fancy, U.S. No. 1, and U.S. No. 2 are the standard grades, but the U.S. Fancy grade is seldom used. Pickling cucumbers are sorted into various grades and sizes on belt grading machines at the pickling factory.

Packing

Sometimes cucumbers are packed in the field, although larger growers use packing sheds. A variety of packages is used, including bushel baskets, hampers, crates, and many kinds of boxes. Lug boxes and 12-quart baskets with handles have been used considerably in recent years, especially for fancy packs. The fruits should be well placed to minimize shifting within the package while in transit.

Waxing

Slicing cucumbers are usually waxed after grading and washing or

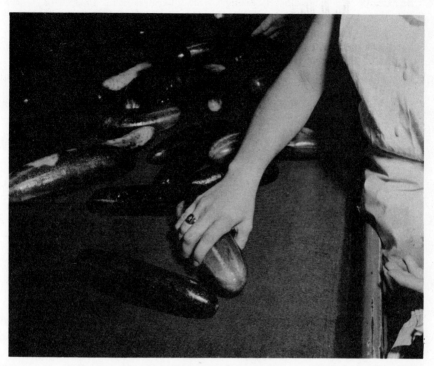

Fig. 19.3—Cucumbers sorted for size and grade on conveyer belt.

USDA Photograph

brushing. A number of different types of waxes with different methods of application are available. Waxing adds slightly to the cost of production, but is quite effective in preventing shrinkage and loss of freshness during shipping and marketing.

Marketing

Cucumbers are commonly shipped to distant markets under refrigeration. In recent years, however, a large part of the crop has been hauled to market by trucks, both with and without refrigeration, depending upon the distance and weather conditions. Competition among buyers and sellers is keen, especially when supplies are low.

SELECTED REFERENCES

Barnes, W. C., "Multiple Disease Resistant Cucumbers," *Proc. Amer. Soc. Hort. Sci.* 77: 417-23, 1961.

Beattie, W. R., "Cucumber Growing," USDA Farmers' Bull. 1563, 1942.

Callahan, J. W. and Crossman, B. D., "Economics of Pickling Cucumber Production in Massachusetts," Mass. Agr. Exp. Sta. Bull. 515, 1959.

Carew, J., Leiby, R. W., and Chupp, C., "Cucumbers," Cornell Agr. Ext. Bull. 917, 1954.

Hughes, G. R., et al., "Cucumber Production in North Carolina," N. C. Agr. Ext. Cir. 383, 1964.

Lambeth, V. N. and Cunningham, C. R., "Growing Cucumbers for Pickling," Mo. Agr. Ext. Cir. 608, 1952.

Whitaker, T. W. and Davis, G. N., Cucurbits. New York: Interscience Publishers Inc., 1962.

CHAPTER 20

Eggplants

Classification, Origin, and History

The eggplant (*Solanum melongena* var. *esculentum*), often referred to as the "Guinea squash," is a native of the tropics. It has been cultivated for many centuries in India, China, and Arabia and was probably introduced into Europe during the Moorish invasion of Spain.

Scope and Importance

The eggplant is grown commercially in only a few states, but it is produced for local markets and in home gardens in many areas. It is considered a minor vegetable commercially, being the least important of the vegetable crops for market. It ranks last both in acreage and value among the 22 principal vegetables in 1965.

Eggplant acreage declined from 4,650 in 1939 to 3,950 in 1965. During this time, total production increased from 343,000 to 593,000 hundredweight, and farm value rose from $694,000 to $3,301,000. Florida and New Jersey lead in eggplant production as shown in Table 20.1.

Trends in Production Efficiency

Because of special cultural practices and unusual labor requirements, eggplant production is expensive. This crop required 328 man-hours per acre for growing and harvesting in 1959, the highest for any vegetable except celery. The average yield of eggplants increased from 74 to 101 hundredweight per acre between 1939 and 1959, during which time the unit output per man-hour actually decreased 22 percent (Table 1.4). Yields per acre increased considerably in the 1961-1965 period.

Table 20.1—Eggplants for Fresh Market: Shipping Season and Estimated Commercial Acreage, Yield, Production, and Value in Leading States, 1965.

State	Season	Harvested Acreage	Yield per Acre, Cwt.	Production, 1,000 Cwt.	Price Per Cwt.	Value, $1,000
New Jersey	Summer	1,500	130	195	$5.40	1,053
Florida	Spring	1,000	150	150*	5.80	800
Florida	Fall	750	135	101	6.50	656
Florida	Winter	700	210	147*	5.70	792
All states		3,950	150	593	5.76	3,301

*Includes some quantities not marketed and excluded in computing value.

Climatic Requirements

The eggplant is a warm-season crop and thrives best at relatively high temperatures. Day temperatures of 80° to 90° F. and night tempera- tures of 70° to 80° F. are considered optimum. It is more susceptible to injury by low temperature than are tomatoes or peppers. It also has a high moisture requirement and responds well to irrigation during the periods of drought and high temperature.

JOB 1.   SELECTING VARIETIES AND SEED

Varieties

The principal varieties grown are Black Beauty and Fort Myers Market. Florida Market has resistance to Phomopsis fruit rot. The early hybrid variety, Black Magic, is adapted to regions with shorter growing seasons. Two other varieties used to a limited extent are Improved Long Purple and Florida High Bush. Most varieties reach maturity 85 to 90 days after transplanting, but Black Magic will mature in 72 days. A good plant type is shown in Fig. 20.1.

JOB 2.   PREPARING THE SOIL

Soil Preferences

For best development, the eggplant requires a well-drained, fertile, sandy-loam soil with a high organic content. In Florida, well-drained

Fig. 20.1—Eggplant showing good set of fruit.

hammock lands are preferable because of their fertility and moisture-holding capacity. In northern areas, a location with woods or windbreaks on the north and west sides is desirable because the young plants are susceptible to wind injury soon after being set in the field. The same care is needed in preparing the soil for eggplants as is required for other vegetable crops.

Fertilizing and Manuring

Soils low in humus should be planted to a green-manure crop the previous year, or if barnyard manure is available, it should be used at the rate of 15 to 20 tons per acre or as much as 30 tons on less fertile soils. Commercial fertilizer mixtures containing 5 to 6 percent nitrogen, 8 to 10 percent phosphorus, and 5 to 7 percent potassium are commonly used. They may be applied at the rate of 750 to 1,000 pounds per acre broadcast before working the soil for planting, plus an equal amount as a side dress three to four weeks after planting. The plant is a heavy feeder and occupies the ground for a long season, so one or two side dressings of nitrogen may be necessary. Applications of 20 to 25 pounds per acre should be used.

JOB 3.   GROWING PLANTS, PLANTING, AND CULTIVATING

Growing Plants

This is probably the most important and most difficult job in the whole procedure of eggplant culture. Temperature and moisture requirements are very exacting, and insect and disease control is also a problem. Eggplants are not readily transplanted to the field, particularly in periods of dry weather, unless the plants are stocky and a fair-sized clump of soil is attached to the roots when the plant is removed from the bed (Fig. 20.2).

It is usually desirable to transplant the seedlings, when about 4 to 5 inches high, into veneer bands or pots, or to space them at least 4 inches apart in the plant bed, so that the soil can be cut out in squares with a knife and a block of soil be lifted with the plant when it is transferred to the field.

Fig. 20.2—The stocky plant on right is preferable to the spindling plants grown in smaller containers.

In the far South, seeds are planted from June to August for the fall and early winter crop and in February and March for the spring crop. In more northern regions plants are started in greenhouses or hotbeds about 8 to 10 weeks before they are to be transplanted in the field. Care must be given not to check the growth of the seedlings.

Planting and Setting

Plants are usually set 2 to 3 feet apart in 3- to 4-foot rows. Small-growing varieties such as the New Hampshire can be set in 2½-foot rows and spaced from 1½ to 2 feet apart in the row. In general, eggplant should be transplanted into the field about 10 days later than the usual date for tomatoes. If plant protectors such as "hotcaps" are used the plants may be set about two weeks earlier than otherwise.

Cultivating

Frequent shallow cultivations should be given to eradicate weeds, and some hand hoeing may be necessary in weedy soil. Since the eggplant is a long-season crop, careful weed control before the plants become large is important.

JOB 4.   CONTROLLING DISEASES AND INSECTS

Diseases

The eggplant is very susceptible to serious injury in all stages of growth by a number of diseases which are widely distributed.

FRUIT ROT. Fruit rot, caused by the fungus *Phomopsis vexans*, is probably the most serious and widespread disease of eggplants. It occurs in the stems, leaves, and fruit. The fungus attacks the stems of the young plants at the soil line, often girdling the stem and causing the plant to break off, or at least to wilt and die. The fungus may attack the stems of older plants at any point, causing sunken, oval, dark-brown cankers. Leaf injury first appears as round, brown spots, the centers of which later turn gray. The fungus produces round or oval tan-colored areas on the fruit (Fig. 20.3). Frequently, these start near the calyx cap, causing the fruit to drop prematurely. To control this disease, use clean seed, as the fungus may be carried over in the seed; adopt a three- to four-year crop rotation; use resistant varieties such as Florida Market and Florida Beauty; and spray at intervals of 7 to 10 days with maneb, zineb, or ziram.

WILTS. Wilts, including *Verticillium, Fusarium,* and bacterial, are prevalent in the more important eggplant-producing areas. They cause wilting and yellowing of the foliage and finally kill part or all of the plant. They are especially insidious because the organisms causing the

Fig. 20.3—Eggplant fruit showing both round and oval fruit-rot lesions caused by Phomopsis.

diseases may live for several years in the soil. Seedbed and field sanitation and crop rotation are necessary if any of these diseases becomes established. Wilts cannot be controlled by spraying with fungicides because the disease-producing organisms are inside the conductive tissues of the plant. Methyl bromide and chloropicrin used as soil fumigants have shown some benefit in wilt control.

Insects

Important insects attacking eggplant in the different stages will be discussed briefly.

FLEA BEETLES. Flea beetles cause considerable damage in plant beds and fields if not controlled. Applications of DDT, endosulfan, carbaryl, or methoxychlor may be used for their control.

COLORADO POTATO BEETLES. Colorado potato beetles are often prevalent in areas where potatoes are grown. They can also be controlled by DDT, endosulfan, or carbaryl. (See Chapter 11.)

APHIDS AND LACE BUGS. Aphids and the lace bug can readily be controlled by nicotine sprays or dusts. They can also be controlled with endosulfan and malathion.

SPIDER MITES. Spider mites are small, reddish mites, which may become numerous on the under sides of the leaves and may be destructive in dry weather. They can be controlled with malathion or kelthane.

JOB 5. HARVESTING, HANDLING, AND MARKETING

Harvesting

The fruits when of marketable size are clipped from the plant, leaving the calyx or cap attached to the fruit. Very careful handling is essential because even slight bruising, will disfigure the fruit. Higher yields will be produced if fruits are harvested before they reach full size, provided they are well-colored and of good size. The fruits are edible from the time they are one-third grown until they are fully ripe.

Grading and Packing

If the fruits are harvested regularly at a definite size, there will be no need for grading except to discard all diseased, misshapen, or bruised fruit. The individual fruits are sometimes wrapped in paper or placed in small paper sacks before being packed in crates, bags, or baskets for shipment. The type and size of container varies from bushel and ⅝-bushel baskets to pepper and berry crates, but the 30-pound bushel basket, hamper, and crate are standard containers.

Marketing

Eggplants are sold for distant as well as for local markets. Attractive packaging and proper handling are necessary for maximum returns. Retail preference appears to be for small, uniform-sized fruits.

SELECTED REFERENCES

Boswell, V. R., "Growing Eggplant," USDA Leaflet 351, 1953.
Knapp, F. W., "Browning Enzymes of Eggplant," *Proc. Fla. St. Hort. Soc.* 74: 256-9, 1962.
Ramsey, G. B., Wiant, J. S., and McColloch, L. P., "Market Diseases of Tomatoes, Peppers, and Eggplants," USDA *Agr. Handbook 28*, 1952.

CHAPTER 21

Lettuce

Classification, Origin, and History

Lettuce (*Lactuca sativa*) belongs to the sunflower or *Compositae* family. It is closely related to the wild lettuce *L. serriola*—in fact, so closely related that the two species cross readily.

The three most commonly grown types in the United States are: (1) leaf or bunching type; (2) head lettuce, including both crisphead and butterhead varieties; and (3) cos or romaine type.

Lettuce is not new when compared with other vegetable crops. This is evident from historical references which relate that lettuce appeared at the royal tables of the Persian kings more than 550 years B.C.

Scope and Importance

Lettuce is the most important salad crop. It is grown commercially in at least 20 states and produced for local market and home use in areas throughout the country. Its production and consumption have increased markedly during the past 26 years. Lettuce ranked seventh in acreage and third in value among the 22 principal vegetables in 1965, and was exceeded in value only by potatoes and tomatoes.

Lettuce acreage increased from 169,670 in 1939 to approximately 216,000 in 1965, while acre yields rose from 101 to approximately 190 hundredweight during the 26-year period. Farm value increased substantially from $30,126,000 in 1939 to an estimated $189,760,000 in 1965.

Figure 21.1 shows the approximate geographical distribution of lettuce production; and the acreage, production, and value by leading states are presented in Table 21.1. California is by far the leading state in acreage, production, and value of lettuce.

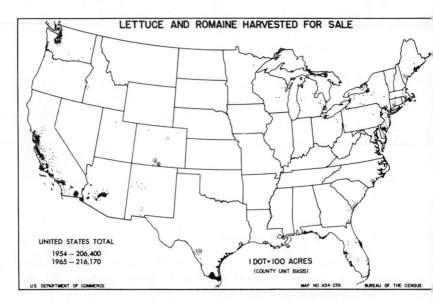

Fig. 21.1—Acreage and distribution of commercial lettuce production.

Table 21.1—Lettuce for Fresh Market: Shipping Season and Estimated Commercial Acreage, Yield, Production, and Value in Leading States, 1965.

State	Season	Harvested Acreage	Yield per Acre, Cwt.	Production, 1,000 Cwt.	Price Per Cwt.	Value, $1,000
California	Winter	46,700	180	8,406	$3.15	26,479
California	Early fall	27,000	185	4,995	4.75	23,726
California	Summer	25,700	290	7,453	3.55	26,458
Arizona, Yuma	Winter	19,500	165	3,218	3.75	12,068
Arizona	Late fall	19,200	170	3,264	4.85	15,830
Arizona	Early spring	17,300	210	3,633	7.40	26,884
California	Early spring	16,200	185	2,997	6.60	19,780
Texas	Winter	8,300	80	664	3.60	2,390
Colorado	Summer	6,100	200	1,220	4.10	5,002
New York	Summer	4,100	200	820	4.10	3,362
Florida	Winter	3,400	75	255	7.00	1,785
New Jersey	Late spring	3,300	170	561	7.90	4,432
Wisconsin	Summer	2,500	200	500	5.10	2,550
New Mexico	Early fall	2,400	220	528	4.90	2,587
Texas	Early fall	2,400	200	480	5.30	2,544
New Jersey	Early fall	2,100	160	336	4.80	1,613
All states		216,170	190	41,047	4.62	189,760

Trends in Production Efficiency

Special production and harvesting requirements categorize lettuce as a relatively expensive crop. Between 1939 and 1959, average labor requirements decreased from 141 to 115 man-hours per acre, and unit production increased 92 percent per man-hour. Correspondingly, acre yields increased from 101 to 159 hundredweight and reached 190 in 1965 (Table 1.4).

In 1965, a mechanical selective lettuce harvester was field tested and proven. Commercial production of the machine will enable growers to materially reduce the harvest labor input.[1]

Climatic Requirements

Lettuce thrives best at a relatively cool temperature. For that reason, it is grown principally as an early spring, fall, and winter crop in the South and Southwest. It is only in the most northern states, at high altitudes in the West, and near the coast in California, Oregon, and Washington that it can be grown as a summer crop. Ample sunlight, uniformly cool nights, and plenty of moisture in the soil are essential to well-developed, solid heads.

Control of soil moisture is important. Even where irrigation is practiced, the eastern grower does not have the control of soil moisture that western growers have. Sudden increases of soil moisture through heavy rains may cause rapid changes in the plant's growth rate. If such changes occur during heading, large, puffy heads may result.

High temperatures are conducive to early seedstalk development and inferior quality. Slow-bolting types have been bred that will help prevent premature seedstalk development.

JOB 1.   SELECTING VARIETIES AND SEED

Varieties

Most seedsmen list a large number of lettuce varieties and a larger number of variety names. It is too common a practice to give more than one name to the same variety. Although an effort has been made to standardize variety names, there is yet room for improvement.

---

[1]Garrett, R. E., Zahara, M., and Griffin, R. E., "Mechanical Harvest of Crisphead Lettuce," *Agricultural Engineering*, Vol. 45, No. 11, November, 1964, pp. 611-612.

There are about 150 distinct varieties, of which about 20 to 25 are of commercial importance. Several strains of the variety New York, and several Imperial varieties from the western states are marketed in the East as Iceberg or Western Iceberg lettuce. The true "Iceberg" variety has been in existence for many years and is distinctly different from varieties to which shoppers and produce dealers apply the name. Different types are shown in Figures 21.2, 21.3, and 21.4.

R. C. Thompson, of the U.S. Department of Agriculture, has described and classified the more important commercial varieties of lettuce as follows:

(1) Crisphead type: New York (Wonderful), New York No. 515, Imperial 44, Imperial 152, Imperial 456 (Cornell 456), Imperial 615, Imperial 847, Pennlake, and Great Lakes. A number of strains of Great Lakes exists, of which Nos. 407, 428, 6238, 97145, A36, and Premier are among the best.

(2) Butterhead type: Big Boston, White Boston, May King, Salamander (Black-Seeded Tennisball), and Wayahead. Only Big Boston and White Boston are grown to any extent commercially.

(3) Cos or romaine type: Paris White (White Cos, Paris White Cos), and Dark Green are the principal varieties. Paris White is the most popular of this high-quality lettuce.

(4) Leaf, or bunching type: Black-Seeded Simpson, Early Curled Simpson, Grand Rapids, Slobolt, and Salad Bowl. This type is not grown to any extent in the field, but is popular with home gardeners. Grand Rapids is used rather extensively as a winter greenhouse variety.

The bibb types are rapidly gaining in importance. Varieties include Bibb and Summer Bibb, a slow-bolting variety. Buttercrunch is larger than Summer Bibb and produces a head of loosely folded leaves of excellent quality.

Securing Seed

The importance of securing good seed cannot be overemphasized. The success or failure of the crop is determined to a large extent by the seed. Each grower, therefore, should be satisfied with none but the best. The seed supply should come only from a reliable seedsman, one who has established a reputation for his integrity and whose stocks have given good results in tests and in commercial plantings. The best seed may cost slightly more than an inferior grade, but this slight increase in cost is of minor importance when compared with the loss that may result from the use of inferior seed or a poorly adapted variety or strain.

Fig. 21.2—Black seeded Simpson variety of leaf lettuce.

Ferry Morse Seed Co.

JOB 2.   PREPARING THE SOIL

Soil Preferences

Lettuce is grown on a wide variety of soil types. The largest commercial acreages are on muck, sandy loam, and silt loam soils. A fertile sandy
loam is preferred for the early crop, while the later crops are grown most
extensively on mucks and loams.

Preparing the Seedbed

The preparation of the soil for planting and growing lettuce is much
the same as for growing other vegetables. The land should be thoroughly
prepared, both to assure germination of the small-sized seed and to give
the comparatively shallow roots of the lettuce plant a chance to develop
to best advantage.

Kinds of soil and climatic conditions govern somewhat the time for
plowing. The soil should be plowed as early as possible, but never when
it is too wet. Plowing should be deep wherever practicable. Preparation

Fig. 21.3—Great Lakes variety of head lettuce.

of the bed is usually completed by disking or harrowing with a spike-tooth harrow, then leveling with a plank drag or a Meeker harrow. On land that does not drain quickly beds are thrown up about 5 feet wide and dragged off flat.

JOB 3.   MANURING, FERTILIZING, AND LIMING

Since rapid growth is essential to crispness and high quality, there must be a liberal supply of readily available nutrients in the soil at all times.

Manuring

Where stable manure can be obtained at a reasonable price, heavy applications, 20 to 30 tons per acre, will give excellent results on mineral soils. It should be broadcast on the land at least four weeks before the time of planting. If stable manure is not available, humus can be supplied by growing green-manure crops such as cowpeas, soybeans, alfalfa, clover, and vetch.

Fig. 21.4—Planting of bibb lettuce.

Fertilizing

The commercial fertilizer used should be of high quality, analyzing about 4 to 5 percent nitrogen, 4 to 5 percent phosphorus, and 5 to 6 percent potassium. The rate of application may vary from 1,000 to 2,000 pounds per acre depending upon the fertility of the soil. The complete fertilizer should be applied when the soil is prepared. In addition to the complete fertilizer, a side dressing of a readily available form of nitrogen such as ammonium nitrate should be applied at the rate of 100 pounds or more per acre as soon as the plants start growth after they have been blocked and thinned. If a soil test has been made, Table 6.5 may be used as a guide for fertilizer application.

Liming

Experimental results indicate that lettuce does not thrive on a highly acid soil. A soil reaction between pH 5.5 and pH 7.0 is satisfactory. If the soil is more acid than pH 5.5, lime should be applied. Muck soils should be limed if they are more acid than pH 5.2.

JOB 4.   SEEDING AND TRANSPLANTING

Seeding and Growing Plants for Transplanting

A common practice for the extra early spring crops is to grow the plants under cloth or glass sash protection for transplanting to the field. The soil in the seedbed should be prepared carefully and should be made reasonably fertile by thoroughly mixing two to four pounds of a complete fertilizer per 100 square feet of soil.

One-fourth pound of good seed sown thinly on a well-prepared seedbed should produce enough strong, healthy plants to set an acre, but more seed is commonly used. Crowding the seedlings can be detrimental as it results in inferior plants and increases the danger from damping off and other diseases. The seed should be planted in an area covering at least 300 square feet. Very good results can be obtained by making the beds 12 feet wide and covering them with muslin or tobacco cloth stretched over a ridge pole supported on posts through the center of the bed. In the North most transplants are grown in sack-covered hotbeds or cold frames. For the winter or extra early spring crop it will take 8 to 10 weeks to produce plants large enough to be transplanted. Great care should be exercised in watering and ventilating the plant beds to prevent loss from damping off.

Planting in the Field

Early spring plants should be hardened and may be set as soon as hard freezes are over. When the plants are transplanted to the field, they should be lifted carefully from the soil and planted so that the tap roots are set straight in the soil. The plant should not be set deeper than it grew in the bed. All spindling and diseased plants should be discarded. The rows are spaced the same distance apart for plants as for seed sown directly in the field.

Commercially, most lettuce is grown from seed planted directly in the field with mechanical seeders. Seeding is usually at the rate of about two pounds per acre. Under good conditions adequate stands may be obtained with as little as one pound per acre. Lighter rates of seeding will save labor on thinning and blocking.

Systems of planting vary from one- to six-row beds. The most widely used method in the West is the two-row bed. The height of the bed varies with soil type and drainage.

Planting distances between rows vary, depending upon the systems of cultivation and irrigation used and the varieties grown. The smaller butterhead varieties can be grown closer than the crisphead types. Distances between rows in single-row systems should not be greater than 18 inches. In western irrigated areas where the two-row system is used, the spacing is generally 40 inches from center to center of the beds.

JOB 5. THINNING AND CULTIVATING

Blocking and Thinning

When the seed is sown directly in the field or when the plants are too thick in the plant bed, it will be necessary to do some hand thinning. In the field, the plants should first be blocked—usually 10 to 14 days after planting. All plants are removed from the row except small clusters, 10 to 16 inches apart. A few days later, as soon as the first true leaves are formed, the clusters are thinned to one plant. Frequently the more vigorous plants removed can be transplanted in areas where the stand may be poor. It is important that only one plant be left in a place.

The distance between plants in a row is determined by the variety, fertility of the soil, and size of plant desired. Small varieties should be spaced about 10 inches apart, while larger varieties like New York need a 12- to 16-inch spacing.

Thinning is the most laborious and expensive operation in the production of lettuce. In the large western areas, the blocking and thinning operation is often done under contract on an acre basis.

Cultivating

Shallow cultivation frequent enough to keep down weeds and to provide a light mulch is recommended. Lettuce plants have comparatively small root systems and most of the small roots are near the surface. For that reason, cultivation deeper than 2 or 3 inches will break off many roots and cause serious injury to the plants. Cultivator attachments which cut the weeds off just below the surface and leave a shallow mulch are usually more satisfactory than cultivator teeth or narrow shovels. If the soil is free of weeds and a mulch is present, nothing will be gained by additional cultivation until more weeds appear. It will be necessary to do some weeding between the plants in the row. This may be done effectively with the hands in loose soil or with a hand hoe.

JOB 6. CONTROLLING DISEASES AND INSECTS

General recommendations for both disease and insect control can be found in Chapter 11. The reader is also directed to his local agricultural experiment station or extension service for the latest recommendations for his area.

Diseases

TIP-BURN. One of the most prevalent and serious diseases of lettuce is tip-burn. The marginal tissues of the leaves turn brown and later die. The disease is nonparasitic and is most prevalent in hot weather. Plants making very rapid growth appear to be most susceptible to the disease. Factors which tend to check the rate of growth at maturity serve to reduce the amount of injury, but no satisfactory control has been found. Some progress has been made in breeding varieties with resistance to tip-burn.

LETTUCE DROP. Lettuce drop is the common name of a disease caused by *Sclerotinia libertiana* and *S. minor* fungi, which induce wilting and sudden collapse of the outer leaves. The organisms causing drop are widespread throughout the country and may attack many plants besides lettuce. Loss can occur in transit, in storage, and in the market, as well as in the field. Soil disinfection with formaldehyde solution is a satisfactory control on a small area. A gallon of formaldehyde solution (1 part of commercial formaldehyde in 100 parts of water) should be used to a square foot. Steam sterilization or treating the soil with PCNB or captan is also effective. No resistant varieties are available. Crop rotation is recommended.

BOTTOM ROT. A common fungus disease that is most prevalent during damp weather is bottom rot. It is caused by one of the organisms that commonly causes damping off (*Rhizoctonia solani*). The plants may be attacked at nearly all stages of growth, and the disease may be present throughout the growing season. Varieties that have a spreading habit of growth are most commonly infected, since the organism enters the plant through the lower leaves that are in contact with the soil. Rotation with nonsuscepible crops such as sweet corn and onions is a practical means of control. Treating the soil beneath the plants with PCNB has also proved effective, since it is quite specific for *Rhizoctonia*.

MOSAIC. Mosaic is a widespread virus disease characterized by a mottling of the leaves and stunting of the plants. The disease is spread by sucking insects such as aphids; therefore, a special effort should be made to control these insects. The initial infection in a field usually comes from infected seed. Some control can be obtained by roguing the infected plants.

DOWNY MILDEW. Downy mildew (*Bremia lactucae*) is characterized by a distinctly visible downy or velvety growth upon the affected surface. The disease is widespread, but is more common in western areas than in the East. It is most likely to develop in damp, foggy, moderately warm weather. Wild lettuce is a host for the organism that causes downy mildew. Eradication of this plant, therefore, is helpful in the control of the disease. Crop rotation also is recommended.

BIG VEIN. Big vein is a relatively new disease but is now known to be widespread in both eastern and western lettuce fields. It is a virus disease that is soil-borne. It is sometimes confused with mosaic, but the leaf symptoms are quite different. Rotation is partially effective as a control measure.

ASTER YELLOWS. A virus disease that has become very serious, especially in the northeastern states, is aster yellows. The virus is transferred from plant to plant by a species of leaf hoppers. Control of the insect vector is the only practical means of control.

Insects

Lettuce is frequently attacked by several kinds of insects. The main ones are cutworms, cabbage loopers, six-spotted leaf hoppers, wireworms, and aphids. Army worms and cornear worms will occasionally attack lettuce in its early stages of growth. DDT or malathion as applied for cabbage loopers (see Chapter 11) is effective in control. Chlordane is recommended for wireworms. The six-spotted leaf hoppers are best controlled with DDT, malathion, or carbaryl. DDT and toxaphane are effective on cutworms, while aphids are best controlled with nicotine, malathion, or diazinon.

JOB 7.   HARVESTING, HANDLING, AND MARKETING

Harvesting

Leaf lettuce is harvested for home use as soon as the leaves are large enough. For local market, the whole plant is harvested when it is well developed yet not so advanced that the leaves are tough and the flavor is bitter.

The home gardener sometimes harvests head lettuce before the heads become very firm. For market, however, the plants should be harvested when the heads become as hard as existing weather conditions will permit but before the seed stalk begins to develop. Immature heads are spongy and will not withstand the process of marketing.

Lettuce is usually cut with a sharp knife of convenient size. Head lettuce is commonly cut at or just below the surface of the ground, and all soiled and diseased leaves are removed before packing. Where lettuce drop is serious, the head should be cut above the leaves that come in contact with the soil. This will aid in preventing the spread of the disease spores throughout the package. The crop should never be cut when the heads are wet, as much breakage of the brittle leaves will occur in handling.

Grading and Packing

A marked change has taken place in the methods of harvesting and packing lettuce in the large producing areas of California, Arizona, and other sections. This change was brought about by the use of the vacuum cooling process. This process eliminated the need for direct icing and made it feasible to use corrugated paperboard cartons instead of wooden crates. This also moved the site for packing from the sheds to the field. Practically all of the lettuce crop from the Salinas, California, district is field-packed and vacuum cooled. Figures 21.5 and 21.6 show lettuce being harvested and packed in the field. The new paperboard cartons hold two dozen heads drypacked (Fig. 21.7). The cartons are mechanically placed in the precooling chambers. As much as half a carload can be handled at one time and the temperatures at the centers of the heads can be reduced to 34° F. in less than 30 minutes. The cooled cartons are placed in precooled refrigerator cars and trucks for shipment to market.

The old standard four- to six-dozen wooden lettuce crate is still used in some areas. The crates are lined with heavy waterproof paper. The heads are packed tightly in three layers with stem ends up. From 20 to 30 pounds of crushed ice are placed between the layers and on the top

Fig. 21.5—Harvesting and packing lettuce in the field. Lettuce in cartons is vacuum cooled for shipment.

USDA Photograph

layer of each crate before the lid is attached. The crates are placed in a precooled car as rapidly as possible. Crushed ice is also blown over the top of the load. The amount of ice used will vary with the temperature.

Packing and grading should be carefully done according to recognized standards. The U.S. Department of Agriculture has established specifications for standard grades, copies of which can be obtained from Washington or from state marketing agencies.

Storing

Lettuce may be kept in cold storage for a period of three to four

Fig. 21.6—Field packing van in operation.

USDA Photograph

weeks after harvest, if it is in good condition at the beginning of the storage period and is held at 32° F.

Marketing

Most of the lettuce grown in the principal producing areas of California and Arizona is shipped in refrigerator cars to market. However, increasing quantities are being moved by refrigerator trucks. The great year-round demand for lettuce requires expeditious handling under competitive conditions. Consumers demand good quality at reasonable prices.

Considerable quantities of United States lettuce ranging from approximately 1,400,000 to 1,600,000 hundredweight were exported annu-

Fig. 21.7—Carton of lettuce showing method of packing.

USDA Photograph

ally between 1955 and 1962. Practically all went to Canada, with small amounts to Mexico and the Caribbean Islands. Approximately 1,650,000 hundredweight valued at $7,578,000 were exported in 1963.

SELECTED REFERENCES

Chapogas, P. G. and Stokes, D. R., "Prepackaging Lettuce at Shipping Point," USDA, Marketing Res. Rep. 670, 1964.

Dewey, D. H., "Air Blast and Vacuum Cooling of Lettuce—Temperature and Moisture Changes," *Proc. Amer. Soc. Hort. Sci.* 56: 320-326, 1950.

Jones, M. B., "Performances of Head Lettuce Varieties Planted on Different Dates," N. M. Agr. Exp. Sta. Bull. 452, 1960.

Kasmire, R. F., "Sources of Information Related to the Handling, Transportation, and Marketing of Western Lettuce," Perishables Handling Supplement No. 1, Calif. Ext. Ser., 1964.

Knott, J. E. and Tavernetti, A. A., "Production of Head Lettuce in California," Calif. Agr. Ext. Cir. 128, 1944.

Thompson, R. C., "Head Lettuce Varieties and Culture," USDA Farmers' Bull. 1953, 1951.

Whitaker, T. W. and Ryder, E. J., "Lettuce and Its Production," USDA Agr. Handbook No. 221, 1962.

CHAPTER 22

Muskmelons (Cantaloups)

Classification, Origin, and History

The muskmelon (*Cucumis melo*) is frequently referred to as cantaloup in the South and by the trade. It is believed to have originated in India, was mentioned as being grown in Central America in 1516, and was reported in Virginia and New York in 1609 and 1629, respectively.

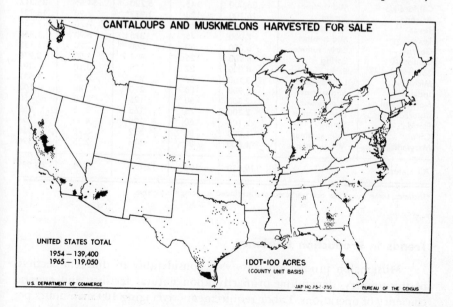

Fig. 22.1—Acreage and distribution of muskmelon (cantaloup) production.

Scope and Importance

Muskmelon popularity has increased in recent years. This vegetable, referred to as cantaloup in many parts of the country, ranked 12th in acreage and 8th in value among the 22 principal vegetables in 1965.

Muskmelon acreage, which was 133,800 in 1939, fluctuated downward to an estimated 119,000 in 1965. Total farm production rose from 9,439,000 in 1939 to an estimated 12,164,000 hundredweight in 1965. Farm value rose markedly from $12,909,000 to about $65,000,000 during this 26-year period.

Figure 22.1 shows the approximate distribution of muskmelon production while the acreage, production, and value are listed by states in Table 22.1.

Table 22.1—Muskmelons (Cantaloups) for Fresh Market: Shipping Season and Estimated Commercial Acreage, Yield, Production, and Value in Leading States, 1965.

State	Season	Harvested Acreage	Yield per Acre, Cwt.	Production, 1,000 Cwt.	Price per Cwt.	Value, $1,000
California	Mid-summer	36,000	145	5,220	$4.85	25,317
Arizona	Spring	16,100	120	1,932*	7.90	13,351
Texas	Spring	12,200	85	1,037	7.70	7,985
Texas	Mid-summer	7,000	45	315	5.90	1,858
Georgia	Early summer	6,000	60	360	3.20	1,152
California	Spring	4,900	125	612	6.50	3,978
South Carolina	Early summer	4,000	32	128	3.10	397
Michigan	Late summer	3,100	80	248	6.40	1,587
Indiana	Mid-summer	2,900	100	290	3.80	1,102
North Carolina	Mid-summer	2,500	50	125	3.60	450
Colorado	Late summer	2,200	75	165	3.95	652
Florida	Spring	2,100	60	126	4.50	567
Ohio	Late summer	1,900	80	152	5.70	866
Maryland	Mid-summer	1,800	80	144	2.75	396
All states		119,050	102	12,164	5.46	65,089

*Includes some quantities not marketed and excluded in computing value.

Trends in Production Efficiency

Muskmelon production costs vary considerably in different sections of the country, depending primarily upon natural fertility and general efficiency of operations. Labor requirements, averaging 109 man-hours per acre for growing and harvesting in 1959, are low compared with those of most vegetable crops. The acre yield of muskmelons increased from 61 to 104 hundredweight during the 1939-1959 period and unit production per man-hour rose 70 percent according to a 1964 report by the Economic Research Service, U.S. Department of Agriculture (Table 1.4).

Climatic Requirements

An ideal muskmelon climate includes a fairly long frost-free season with plenty of sunshine and heat, a dry atmosphere, and sufficient soil moisture. The Southwest is particularly suited to melon culture, but favorable natural conditions prevail in many other sections of the country, making it possible for skillful farmers to grow the crop advantageously for local markets. Ordinarily, 80 to 110 days of favorable growing weather are required between planting and first harvest.

JOB 1.   SELECTING VARIETIES AND SEED

In selecting muskmelon varieties, the grower should consider market preference, earliness, yield, disease and insect resistance, shipping quality, and other factors which influence profits. Muskmelons grown for shipment are mainly heavily netted, medium-size, nearly round specimens of both the green and salmon-fleshed varieties. This type is preferred because of its carrying quality, desirable size and shape, and superior quality when sufficiently ripened on the vine.

Varieties

Many varieties are grown for commercial and home use. A brief description of some of them is given in Table 22.2. Varieties used primarily for the home and local market are usually high in quality but are often not firm enough for shipment. Many of the older varieties are being replaced by similar ones resistant to one or more diseases. These should be considered in a region where a particular disease is prevalent.

Securing Seed

Since the cost of seed is a small item in production of muskmelons, it is important to obtain the very best quality available. Good seed should be pure, viable, free from pests, and true to name. Markets require melons of certain characteristics, and such fruit cannot be grown unless the seed planted came from melons having the desired qualities. A considerable amount of commercial seed is produced in the areas of production, yet large quantities come from the Rocky Ford area of Colorado, where climatic conditions and production methods are especially favorable for seed production. It is a good practice to secure seed only from a reliable distributor or producer.

JOB 2. PREPARING THE SOIL

Soil Preferences

Muskmelons are grown on a great variety of soil types, but they thrive best on a well-drained, sandy or silt loam soil. The soil should be fairly fertile, well supplied with organic matter, and free from nematodes and disease. A soil slightly acid or neutral is desirable.

Preparing the Seedbed

Seedbed preparation varies greatly in different regions. One essential everywhere, however, is thorough plowing, 5 to 9 inches deep, early enough in the spring to allow proper settling. It is very desirable to have the beds firm yet thoroughly broken.

In some sections, the beds are 5 to 8 feet wide with one row in a bed. In other areas, it is common practice to flat break the land and lay off narrow beds 18 to 24 inches wide and 5 to 7 feet apart. This elevates the plants for adequate drainage, and the interlying area can be worked toward the bed as the young plants develop. Where furrow irrigation is practiced, raised beds are essential. They are also used where heavy rains are expected and where drainage is inadequate.

JOB 3. FERTILIZING, MANURING, AND LIMING

Muskmelon plants grow rapidly and require an abundance of plant nutrients. Unless the soil is naturally fertile, commercial fertilizers or manure or both must be added for satisfactory production.

Fertilizing

Commercial fertilizers are almost indispensable in large producing areas because of the limited amount of animal manure. The amount,

Table 22.2—Brief Description of Selected Varieties of Muskmelons.

Variety	Use	Season (Days)	Size (Lbs.)	Fruit			Resistant to*
				Shape	Netting	Color (Flesh)	
Burpee Hybrid*	Market, home	82	4-4½	Oval	Heavy	Deep orange	
Casaba	Shipping	102	6	Round	None	White	
Crenshaw	Shipping	110	9	Acorn	None	Light orange	
Delicious 51	Market	86	3½	Round	Close	Bright orange	FW
Edisto	Market	95	4½	Oval	Heavy	Salmon	PM, ALS
Goldstar**	Market,	87	Medium	Oval	Thick	Dark orange	FW
Harper Hybrid**	Market	86	Medium	Round	Fine		FW
Harvest Queen	Market	95	3½	Oval, round	Coarse	Orange	FW
Hearts of Gold	Home, market	90	Medium	Oval	Medium	Deep orange	
Honey Dew	Market	88	6	Round	None	White	
Number 45 S J	Shipping	95	2½	Oval	Heavy	Salmon	PM
Saticoy Hybrid*	Shipping, Market	90	6½-5½	Oval	Fine	Orange	
Small Persian	Shipping	110	6	Round	Fine	Orange	
SR 91	Shipping	96	3½	Oval, round	Heavy	Salmon	SR
Supermarket**	Local market	84	Medium	Oval	Coarse	Orange	FW, DM

*FW—fusarium wilt; DM—downey mildew; PM—powder mildew; ALS—alternaria leaf spot; SR—sulfur res.

**Hybrid.

kind, time, and method of application vary considerably from state to state.

In several southern states, a complete fertilizer of a 1-2-1 ratio, analyzing approximately 4-8-4 or 5-10-5, is commonly applied a few days before planting. It is generally applied in a wide strip under the row, at the rate of 400 to 1,000 pounds per acre, rather than broadcast. In addition, when blooming starts, many commercial growers apply a side dressing of approximately 100 pounds of quick-acting, nitrogen-carrying fertilizer a foot from the plants. Tables 6.4 and 6.5 can be used as guides for rates of applying N, P, and K.

Manuring

Green manures produced by turning under cover crops have been found to increase materially the yields of subsequent muskmelon crops. Legume covers are preferable for the purpose, as nitrogen is added in addition to organic matter. Where winter crops are used, they should be turned under early enough to decay thoroughly before planting time.

For best results, the organic content should be maintained either by barnyard manure or soil-improving crops.

Liming

Muskmelons do not thrive on the medium or strongly acid soils. Investigations in Rhode Island and Virginia place the muskmelon with that group of vegetables which prefer soils ranging from slightly acid to neutral (pH 6 to pH 7). Tests in Arkansas, North Carolina, and other states have confirmed this classification. On very acid soils the plants make poor growth and the foliage becomes yellowish-green in color.

Soil acidity is generally corrected by applying some form of lime to the soil, calcium carbonate (ground limestone) being the most practical form to use. Hydrated lime acts more quickly but the cost is greater. The amounts of lime to apply on different types of soils are indicated in Table 6.2.

JOB 4.   PLANTING

Starting Plants

Seeds of the muskmelon do not germinate well at low temperatures, and the seedlings are very susceptible to freezing injury. Planting in the open should, therefore, be delayed until the soil becomes warm and there is no danger of frost. If early maturity is desired, plants may be started in greenhouses, hotbeds, or sash covered frames and shifted to the field when weather conditions become favorable. This method is suitable for comparatively small acreages and may be necessary in regions where the frost-free season is too short for maturing the crop in the field. Melons are difficult to transplant except when young. When started inside, they should be seeded in plant-growing containers so the plants can be shifted to the field without disturbing their roots. Seeding is usually done about 10 to 20 days before the plants are to be moved to the field.

Seeding in the Field

Seed is most commonly drilled in rows 5, 6, or 7 feet apart. Later the plants are thinned so as to stand 2½ to 4 feet apart in the row. With this method an economical use of labor and a good distribution of plants may be obtained. Seed may be planted in hills 4 to 6 feet apart and check-rowed so the field can be cultivated in both directions early in the season. Eight or ten seeds are planted by hand in each hill and covered from one-half to one inch deep. About two pounds of seed is required to plant an acre by drill or hill seeding.

Frost protectors are used in a limited way for starting muskmelons. The benefits resulting from desirable covers include (1) protection from unfavorable weather and pests, (2) higher germination and earlier emergence, (3) larger percentage of earlier melons, and (4) increase in total yield. The chief disadvantages of using protectors are (1) cost, (2) difficulty of properly applying, ventilating, and removing, and (3) inability to forecast the weather, which determines their value.

JOB 5. CULTIVATING AND THINNING

Cultivating

Cultivation of muskmelons should begin as soon as the young plants break ground. The muskmelon is a shallow-rooted plant, the roots often extending beyond the vines. Frequent shallow cultivations should be made until the vines interfere. In many sections where the muskmelons are drilled on narrow ridges, soil is worked toward the ridges at subsequent cultivations until the middle is finally broken out, thus leaving a wide, gently sloping bed. Where the hills are carefully checked, cultivation can be given in both directions by means of a weeder or any light cultivator. For the greater part, however, muskmelons are cultivated in one direction. Vine turning may be necessary during later cultivations. Cultivation after the vines cover a considerable portion of the ground is probably of little, if any, value, unless weed growth is heavy.

Irrigating

Muskmelon plants require an abundance of moisture during the period when the vines are developing most rapidly, and up to the time the melons are practically grown. Great care should be taken, however, to avoid overwatering just before and during the ripening period.

Where furrow irrigation is practiced, the melons are grown on beds and quick applications of water are applied in the furrows as needed. Careful study of soil conditions and weather prospects is necessary to irrigate successfully. This subject is discussed more fully in Chapter 10.

Thinning and Weeding

Two or more thinnings are necessary to reduce safely the final stand to the desired number of plants. To begin with, there are considerably more plants than needed. The first crowded plants are removed a few days after emergence, when the first true leaves develop. If the seed has been planted in hills, each hill is usually thinned to four or five well-distributed plants the first time. Where striped cucumber beetles or other injurious insects are troublesome, the final thinning is delayed until the plants are well established and have formed three or four true leaves. The number of thinnings required to obtain a desirable final stand varies from year to year, depending on the original stand, presence of pests, weather conditions, and local practices. Where the hill method is practiced, two plants are usually left in each hill. When the seed is drilled, single plants are left at intervals varying from 1 to 2 feet, depending on the distance between rows, fertility, and other factors.

Weeding is one of the most essential and costly operations in the production of good quality muskmelons. The cost of controlling annual weeds may be reduced by the use of herbicides. A granular application of three to six pounds of Alanap-3 made immediately after seeding or transplanting may be used. Sandy soils require a lower rate than loams. The herbicide is most effective when moisture levels and temperatures promote rapid germination of weed seed.

Training and Removing

In most sections, vines are trained parallel with the rows to permit closer cultivation. In addition, growers claim that increased shade protects the melons from extreme sunshine and heat.

Removing part of the melons from the vines will increase the size of the remaining fruit. This practice is not commonly followed, however, as melons will grow large enough without reducing their numbers.

JOB 6.   CONTROLLING DISEASES AND INSECTS

Diseases

Both the plant and the fruit of the muskmelon are susceptible to diseases, many of which can be prevented by planting on clean land, or reduced by seed treatment, spraying, and dusting.

BACTERIAL WILT. Caused by *Erwinia tracheiphila*, bacterial wilt is widely distributed, attacking muskmelons, cucumbers, squash, and pumpkins. The bacterial growth occupies some of the water vessels at the roots, stems, and leaves, and causes the plants to wilt and die. The bacteria causing this disease do not live in the soil but are carried over by the striped cucumber beetle, which spreads the disease from plant to plant. The best control measure for wilt is to treat for the cucumber beetles (see Chapter 11) as soon as the plants appear above the soil. On a small planting prompt removal and destruction of diseased plants are recommended as an aid in controlling the disease.

FUSARIUM WILT. Fusarium wilt, caused by *Fusarium Oxysporium* f. *Niveum*, turns vines yellow, resulting in wilt near fruiting time. A cross section of the stem shows the usual dark ring, characteristic of Fusarium. Control is accomplished with a three- to five-year rotation and planting of resistant varieties.

ANTHRACNOSE. Commonly called blight, anthracnose is caused by *Colletotrichum lagenarium* and may appear in epidemic form. The disease is more common on watermelons and cucumbers than on muskmelons. All parts of the plant above ground may be affected. Small yellowish or water-soaked areas develop on the leaves and fruit. The lesions on the fruit become dark, round, and sunken. This fungus is transmitted through the soil and by diseased plants and seed. It may be avoided or decreased by crop rotation, sanitation, and by planting treated seed. Field control can be achieved by spraying or dusting with ziram, maneb, or captan every seven days *after* runners have begun to form.

DOWNY MILDEW. Downy mildew, caused by *Pseudoperonospora cubensis*, attacks only the leaves during warm, damp weather. Thorough spraying with ziram or zineb at weekly or 10-day intervals is recommended.

ROOT KNOT (NEMATODES). Root knot, caused by the nematode *Meloidogyne* sp., attacks the roots. The galls produced on the roots by the eelworms check plant growth and prevent proper fruit maturity. Considerable damage is done by root knot on sandy soils, and the most practical control measure under field conditions consists of rotating with resistant plants. Nearly all cultivated grasses and cereals, such as corn, oats, wheat, rye, barley, and sorghum, are resistant, and if they are grown for approximately two seasons in heavily infested soil, the numbers of the parasite will be greatly reduced. Laredo soybeans, Brabham, Victor, and Monetta cowpeas, velvet beans, and peanuts also are resistant. When rotation is impractical, soil fumigants can be incorporated in the soil before planting with excellent results. However, soil fumigation is still quite costly.

Insects

Growers should be prepared to combat insects which attack all parts of the muskmelon at different stages of growth.

STRIPED AND SPOTTED CUCUMBER BEETLES. The striped and spotted cucumber beetles are very serious pests in many sections, destroying the young plants as soon as they come up. Methods for controlling these beetles are given in Chapter 11.

MELON APHID. The melon aphid (*Aphis gossypii*) or louse is a small, green, soft-bodied insect, which obtains its food by sucking plant juices. It can be controlled with malathion or diazinon.

It feeds on the underside of the leaf, causing it to curl, change color, and die. Muskmelon plants should be examined frequently so that an infestation of aphids can be detected early. If insecticides are applied promptly, they will be more effective and less damage will be done by the insect than if applications are delayed. Recommended control measures are given in Chapter 11.

Fig. 22.2—Muskmelons harvested and placed in crates for hauling to the packing shed.

PICKLE WORMS. Pickle worms (*Diaphania nitidalis*) frequently cause much damage in Georgia, the Carolinas, and other southern states. The adult is a large moth which emerges in the spring. It lays its eggs on the plant, and the young larvae bore into the fruit during the ripening season. Early planting and the use of bush squash, planted as a trap crop are preventive measures. In areas of serious damage, weekly applications of carbaryl and lindane are recommended.

JOB 7. HARVESTING, PACKING, AND MARKETING

Good production practices alone do not insure financial success. Much depends on the care and judgment exercised in harvesting, handling, and marketing the cantaloup crop (Fig. 22.2).

Harvesting

The length of time required to reach market, the variety, temperature at harvest time, and the method of shipment determine the stage of maturity at which melons must be harvested. Since edible quality depends on texture, flavor, and sweetness, the stage of maturity is a very important factor. The muskmelon does not increase in sugar after harvest but may improve in flavor and texture.

Proper maturity is difficult to ascertain, as color of skin, stem abscission, netting, and other familiar indications of maturity are not infallible in determining the degree of ripeness. A common guide used in determining the time of picking melons is the ease by which they can be removed from the vines. As a rule, the "full-slip" melon is one which has reached advanced maturity and can be easily removed. The stem separates from the melon, leaving a clean stem cavity. Melons pulled at this stage must be carefully handled and promptly shipped, either under refrigeration or to nearby markets. The "half-slip" melon is one which is less mature, requiring more pressure to detach. Upon removal, about one-half of the stem next to the melon remains attached. Most muskmelons which are shipped to distant markets are pulled at the "half-slip" stage. They should be ready for eating in 36 to 48 hours after reaching market, depending, of course, on shipping and weather conditions. Both the "full-slip" and "half-slip" melons are fully netted; and the background color has changed from a cucumber green to a mottled green and light yellow. In all cases, it is desirable for the melons to remain on the vines until they have reached the greatest degree of maturity which is consistent with the method of handling. Markets have made frequent complaints that many melons are picked too immature for best quality, thereby reducing the price and sale of the product.

Western growers now commonly ship the "cantaloup" varieties harvested at the early "full-slip" stage to eastern markets. These are quickly precooled and shipped under refrigeration.

The stem does not separate from the fruit of Honey Dew, Honey Ball, Crenshaw, Casaba, and Persian varieties at maturity. Maturity in these is determined by yellowing of the skin and a slight yielding of the blossom end when slightly pressed.

Grading

Melons are graded for uniformity in size and maturity. Although standard grades have been devised by the U.S. Department of Agriculture, specifications have been altered from time to time. Supply and price determine shipping grades to a large extent. Cracked, bruised, diseased, misshaped, soft, ripe, immature, and slick melons are discarded as culls. It usually pays to ship only the best quality melons of uniform size and maturity.

Packing

Although types of containers and methods of packing vary considerably, practices have been fairly well standardized in most commercial sections of the West. Crates are primarily used for shipping long distances. The 12-by-12-by-22⅛-inch standard crate is popular, but conditions frequently require the jumbo crate (13 by 13 by 23⅛ inches) or the pony crate (11 by 11 by 22⅛ inches). In addition, two sizes of flat crates are rather extensively used—the standard flat (4½ by 13½ by 22⅛ inches) and the jumbo flat (5 by 14½ by 22⅛ inches). Two sizes of flat crates are used for Honey Dew melons: 6¾ by 16 by 22⅛ inches, and 7¾ by 16 by 22⅛ inches.

The large markets recognize a pack consisting of 45 melons to a standard-sized crate. In this pack, the melons are 4 to 4½ inches in diameter. The 45-pack consists of three layers, each containing three rows of five melons each. The melons are placed end to end and completely fill the crate. Slightly larger melons are packed 36 to the standard crate, each of the three layers consisting of four melons in three rows. This size constitutes the bulk of the commercial crop in many sections. Melons exceeding 5 inches in diameter are usually packed 27 to a standard crate or 36 to a jumbo crate.

A large variety of crates are used in the East. A crate similar to the 32-quart berry crate is used to some extent in Virginia and other sections (Fig. 22.3). Hampers and baskets are used considerably for local markets and short hauls. In recent years, especially during periods of low prices, many muskmelons have been sold directly to truckers. The melons are loaded on the trucks in bulk or in various kinds of containers, both in the field and at packing sheds.

Marketing

Muskmelons and other melons have been increasing in importance in the American diet. The western melons are of good uniform quality and have contributed much to more orderly marketing of cantaloups. Consequently, melons of uniform quality are generally available. Hucksters who buy from any source at minimum prices may peddle melons of undependable quality.

SELECTED REFERENCES

Anonymous, "Muskmelons for the Garden," USDA Leaflet No. 509, 1962.

Fig. 22.3—Graded and sized muskmelons packed in crates for shipment.

USDA Photograph

Davis, G. N., *et al.*, "Production of Muskmelons in California," Calif. Agr. Ext. Cir. 429, 1953.

Doolittle, S. P., *et al.*, "Muskmelon Culture," USDA *Agr. Handbook No. 216*, 1961.

Gilbert, D. A. and Dedolph, R. R., "Quality Evaluation of Muskmelon Fruits," Mich. Agr. Exp. Sta., Quarterly Bull. 45: 589-94, 1963.

Lingle, J. C. and Wright, J. R., "Fertilizer Experiments with Cantaloupes," Calif. Agr. Exp. Sta. Bull. 807, 1964.

Lingle, J. C. and Wright, J. R., "The Yield, Fruit Quality, and Leaf Analysis of Cantaloupes as Affected by Nitrogen and Phosphate Fertilization," Uni. Calif. Veg. Crops Ser. 110, 1960.

Mitchell, C. E. and Huelsen, W. A., "Growing Melons in Illinois," Ill. Agr. Ext. Cir. 675, 1950.

Peirce, L. C. and Peterson, L. E., "Response of Muskmelons to Spacing, Seeding Date and Plant Container," *Proc. Amer. Soc. Hort. Sci.* 77: 432-9, 1961.

Stewart, J. K. and Ceponis, M. J., "Transit Temperatures and Quality of Cantaloupes," USDA Marketing Res. Rep. No. 554, 1962.

CHAPTER 23

Onions

Classification, Origin, and History

The onion (*Allium cepa*) belongs to the *Liliaceae* or lily family. There are about 300 widely scattered species in the genus *Allium*, and many of them have the characteristic onion flavor and odor. The onion has been used by man as far back as history records. The cultivated species are probably native to the general area of southwestern Asia. Early settlers introduced the onion to North America.

Scope and Importance

The onion, being used in many different ways, is a major vegetable in the American diet. Onions ranked 13th in acreage among the 22 principal vegetables in 1965, but the value of this crop was in 6th position.

Acreage of onions declined from 125,820 in 1939 to about 98,000 in 1965. Total production rose from 18,311,000 to approximately 28,000,000 hundredweight in this period, as farm value increased from $16,209,000 in 1939 to an estimated $85,305,000 in 1965.

Texas led the nation in acreage and value in 1965, followed by New York, California, Michigan, and Oregon. The approximate distribution of onion production in the United States is shown in Figure 23.1, while the acreage, production, and value in leading states are presented in Table 23.1.

Trends in Production Efficiency

The cost of growing onions varies greatly depending upon seed, fertilizers, cultural practices, irrigation, and extent of mechanization. In

Fig. 23.1—Acreage and distribution of onion production.

Table 23.1—Onions for Fresh Market and Processing: Shipping Season and Estimated Commercial Acreage, Yield, Production, and Value in Leading States, 1965.

State	Season	Harvested Acreage	Yield per Acre, Cwt.	Production, 1,000 Cwt.	Price per Cwt.	Value, $1,000
Texas	Early spring	23,100	130	3,003	$3.95	11,862
New York	Late summer	16,400	330	5,412	2.40	12,989
California	Late summer	11,400	350	3,990	2.43	9,701
Michigan	Late summer	7,500	360	2,700	2.00	5,400
Colorado	Late summer	6,500	275	1,788	3.20	5,722
Oregon						
Eastern	Late summer	3,300	525	1,732	2.21	3,822
Western	Late summer	2,200	410	902	2.15	1,939
Texas	Early summer	4,300	215	924	5.20	4,805
California	Late spring	3,600	330	1,188	6.00	7,128
Idaho	Late summer	3,300	535	1,766	2.21	3,898
New Jersey	Early summer	2,600	145	377	4.95	1,866
New Mexico	Early summer	2,200	330	726	5.50	3,993
Wisconsin	Late summer	1,900	295	561	2.30	1,290
Arizona	Late spring	1,500	475	712	5.50	3,916
All states		97,790	287	28,079	3.04	85,305

recent years, the labor involved in onion production experienced a marked decline, especially in preharvest labor requirements. On the average, 271 man-hours were used to grow and harvest an acre of onions in 1939, while only 139 man-hours were used for the whole operation in 1959. During this 20-year period, yields rose from 135 to 226 hundred-weight per acre while the unit output per man-hour increased 226 percent (Table 1.4).

Climatic Requirements

The onion is a cool-season plant that will grow well over a wide range of temperature. Onion seed will germinate best near 65° F., but will germinate satisfactorily between 45° to 85° F. The plant will grow best between 55° to 75° F. Best growth and quality are obtained if the temperature is cool during the early development and warm near maturity. A dry atmosphere at harvest is desirable to obtain satisfactory curing of the bulbs. The onion is fairly resistant to frost injury, but not immune. The root system is shallow, and to thrive well, the onion must receive a fairly adequate water supply. The crop responds well to irrigation in many areas. The bulbing of the onion is affected by the length of day and not by the age of the plant. The length of day required for bulbing varies with variety and ranges from 12 hours for very early types to 15 hours for late types.

JOB 1. SELECTING VARIETIES AND SEED

Rapid changes are being made in the varieties of onions. The new F_1 hybrids are replacing many of the older standard varieties throughout the country. Onion hybrids are being produced in all the major types; and the superior ones are more uniform and higher-yielding than the standard varieties.

Two dry bulb groups of onions are generally recognized in the United States. One, the American or domestic, includes many varieties; the other, referred to as the European or foreign, contains chiefly the Bermuda and Spanish types, all of which are grown more commonly in the South and in certain sections of the West and Southwest than in other regions. These two groups of onions are supplemented by the Egyptian, or top onions, and the multiplier, or potato onions, all of which are grown for green bunching. Onion varieties and hybrids vary in color, shape, flavor, and keeping quality as well as in time of maturity.

Table 23.2—Brief Description of Selected Varieties of Onions.

Variety	Season (Days)	Shape	Size	Color	Flesh	Remarks
Australian Brown	250	Globe	Medium	Brown	Firm	Late storage
Crystal White Wax	185	Very flat	Medium	White	Sweet	Bunching, South
Downing Yellow Globe	105	Globe	Medium	Deep amber	Firm	Storage, South
Early Harvest*	95	Globe	Medium	Yellow	Mild	Poor storage
Early Yellow Globe	100	Globe	Medium	Yellow	Med. soft	Early
Ebenezer (yellow)	105	Thick flat	Small	Yellow	Very firm	Sets
Ebenezer (white)	105	Thick flat	Small	White	Firm mild	Sets, bunching
Empire*	105	Tall globe	Medium	Yellow	Firm pungent	Long day, storage
Evergreen	70	Nonbulbing	Long stem	White	Tender	Green, bunching
Fiesta*	110	Deep globe	Large	Yel. brown	Firm pungent	Sweet Spanish type
F.M. Hybrid*	225	Flat top, basal taper	Med. large	Lt. yellow		California
Granex, Yellow*	165	Flat	Large	Yellow	Mild	Deep South
Granex, White*	175	Flat	Large	White	Mild	Deep South
Southport Red Globe	110	Tall globe	Medium	Red	Firm	Storage
Sweet Spanish hybrids*	100-130	Globe	Large	White-brown	Mild	Gen. purpose
Sweet Spanish strains	100-130	Globe	Med. large	White-brown	Mild	Gen. purpose

* Hybrid

In selecting a variety, consideration should be given to climate, market, and soil requirements, particularly to the first. Bermuda varieties are naturally more adapted to the extreme South than to other sections because normally they will mature in a shorter day, before the hot weather sets in. All the American types, as well as the Spanish varieties, will not mature in southwest Texas until late June, no matter how early the seed may have been sown the previous fall. Usually, only a small percentage of the crop will be marketable, since the atmospheric and soil temperatures during May and June are not conducive to normal growth.

Varieties

Yellow varieties of the American type make up about 75 percent of the bulb crop grown in the country. The most important varieties of this type are Early Yellow Globe, Australian Brown, Empire, Fiesta, and Downing Yellow Globe. The most popular variety grown from sets in this class is Ebenezer. White sets are usually White Ebenezer, and red sets are usually Red Wethersfield. White Portugal is grown from sets to produce green onions and is also good for pickling. Southport White Globe is a popular storage and processing onion. In addition to Red Wethersfield, Southport Red Globe is also a well-known red variety. Early Harvest and Empire are outstanding hybrids of the yellow globe class. Early Harvest is primarily for first-early harvest and direct shipping in main crop areas, where it matures from direct seeding at about the same time as standard varieties grown from sets. It is not intended for storage. Empire is about five days later. Fiesta, which is about five days later than Empire, is a very heavy-yielding hybrid of the sweet Spanish type with good storage qualities.

The sweet Spanish types require a long day length to bulb, as do the American types. There are a number of strains of both the white and yellow type. They are grown in Texas, California, and other areas of the West and Southwest. A number of strains and hybrids of the sweet Spanish type are available. Yellow Granex and white Granex are hybrids of the Bermuda type grown in the deep South. F_1M Hybrid is similar and grown primarily in California. (See Table 23.2 for characteristics of leading varieties.)

Leading varieties of green onions are Crystal White Wax and Evergreen. The latter is popular because it is hardy and overwinters in some areas. These types will not form bulbs. Any standard variety can be used as "green bunching" onions if harvested at the proper stage (Fig. 23.2). White varieties are most generally used.

Fig. 23.2—Green onions trimmed, washed, and bunched for market.

USDA Photograph

Over 90 percent of the onion seed used in the United States is produced in this country. Seed production is concentrated in the dry areas of the West. The leading states are Idaho, California, Oregon, and Colorado. The Canary Islands are heavy producers of Bermuda onion seed.

Regardless of the variety being grown, it pays to buy clean seed that has high germination and is true to type. Good seed is rarely cheap, but the product of good seed will usually repay the extra cost many times over.

JOB 2. PREPARING THE SOIL

Soil Preferences

Good onion land should be friable, fertile, well supplied with humus, and well drained. A heavy soil which will bake after rains or after irrigation is not desirable. Clay, alluvial, and sandy loams, as well as mucks, are often used for onions. Of the four types the last two are preferable, although they usually need more fertilizer. Muck soils are considered best for bulb onion production in the North.

Preparing the Land

The soil should be plowed to a depth of 6 to 8 inches, harrowed, and left in good tilth. The surface should be well worked and smooth; rough, lumpy ground is not suited to the planting of onion seeds, small plants, or dry sets. In irrigated sections, the land must also be leveled in order to irrigate properly. Muck soils are easily prepared as they have very good texture. They should be disked and harrowed or dragged smooth before planting.

JOB 3. FERTILIZING, LIMING, AND MANURING

Fertilizing

The onion, with its limited root system, responds to good fertilizer practices on almost any soil. Most nutrients are applied in the form of commercial fertilizer. In most areas, on mineral soils receiving no manure, 75 pounds each of nitrogen and potassium and 70 pounds of phosphorus should be sufficient. No potassium is used in western areas and Texas under irrigation. From 600 to 1,000 pounds of 6-6-0 are used and supplemented with additional nitrogen as a side dress. California growers use from 60 to 100 pounds of nitrogen per acre on early and intermediate crops but cut down to about 40 pounds on late crops. Phosphorus is also needed in California at the rate of about 25 pounds of phosphorus per acre.

Fertilizer requirements for muck soils vary considerably. Potassium is usually the most limiting element, but good increases in yield can usually be had by applying phosphorus. Even nitrogen under certain conditions will give a good response. This is especially true on poorly drained and strongly acid mucks. On old mucks in New York, the usual application is 1,000 pounds of a 5-5-12 fertilizer per acre. Michigan generally uses less nitrogen and more potassium at the usual rate of 1,000 pounds of 0-5-16. A deficiency of copper and manganese sometimes causes trouble with onions in certain muck areas. Copper deficiencies in New York have been corrected by making applications of 200 to 300 pounds of powdered copper sulfate per acre. As the treatment usually lasts several years, it may be reapplied only when needed. The application of 150 pounds per acre of manganese sulfate mixed with the fertilizer will be effective for the control of manganese deficiency in most areas.

Liming

The onion thrives best on slightly acid soils (pH 6.0 to pH 6.5), but it grows poorly on very acid soils. Very acid soils need a ton of hydrated lime or 1⅓ tons of finely ground limestone per acre per year until the acidity of the topsoil is sufficiently reduced. One-half ton of line should suffice on moderately acid soils. After the soil has reached the desired state, only occasional liming is necessary. Few, if any, of the soils used for onions in Texas require lime.

Manuring

Organic matter in the form of either barnyard or green manure should be added to the mineral soils at every opportunity, as it conserves soil moisture, improves the physical condition of the soil, and tends to retard the loss of available nutrients. If barnyard manures are available, they should be applied at the rate of 15 to 20 tons per acre. Even when well rotted, they should be added several weeks before planting. In Texas, growers are resorting more than formerly to green manures, such as cowpeas. Summer legumes alternate well with winter-grown onions and other vegetables. They shade the ground, reduce weed growth, and add an abundance of organic matter to the soil.

Manures are not needed on muck soils since they already have a high organic-matter content.

JOB 4. PLANTING

The most distinct methods of planting onions include (1) sowing seed directly in the field where the crop is to mature; (2) sowing in a seedbed from which the plants will be transplanted later to the field; and (3) planting sets. A grower may buy these sets, or grow them from seed himself. Most of the bulb onion crop, especially that for late market and storage, is direct-seeded. The transplanting method is used more commonly for early and intermediate varieties, especially in the Texas and California areas.

Seeding

Seed is generally sown with drills for the commercial crop. On large acreages gangs of four or more planters are used. The rate of seeding depends upon the purpose for which planting is done, and the distance between the rows. Where the bulb crop is to mature, four to six pounds per acre is a common rate for rows 12 to 18 inches apart. However, the rate may vary from 1 to 10 pounds; as in some sections very wide spacing is used, and in others, growers prefer to obtain a thick stand, so that there will be surplus plants to sell at thinning time. For the production of plants in southwest Texas, rates range from 20 to 30 pounds per acre, although experiments indicate 18 to 20 pounds as preferable. To produce dry sets, 60 to 80 or even 100 pounds of seed per acre are planted, depending on the soil fertility. The extremely crowded conditions cause the onions to mature when very small. Desirable sets are one-half to three-fourths inch in diameter.

Setting Plants

Only strong, healthy plants should be set. Medium or pencil-sized plants are the most dependable ones to use. The yield of small plants is undesirable, and when large plants are used there is more danger of splits, doubles, and seedstems in the mature crop, unless the plants are handled very carefully.

The practice of pruning the tops back to about half their length is not to be recommended, as experiments in Louisiana, California, and

Texas have indicated that this reduces yields and delays maturity to a certain extent. However, the unpruned plants are more difficult to handle. Plants are usually spaced 2 to 3 inches apart in the row, with the rows 14 to 16 inches apart.

The recent trend is away from transplanting toward direct seeding, as the labor requirement for transplanting is nearly 20 times that of direct seeding.

Planting Dry Sets

The operation of planting sets is very similar to that of planting seedlings. The chief difference is that the sets are dropped into a shallow furrow about 3 inches apart in the row, and then covered, permitting only the tips to show. Machines are available for this job, but the sets should be graded as to size to make efficient use of the machine. The quantity of sets needed for an acre varies with the size of the sets and the planting distances. The amount usually ranges between 15 and 30 bushels per acre.

Planting Time and Method

The time of planting will vary with the locality, type of onion, and method of propagation in use. In general, in the North, seed planted in place is sown as early as possible after the danger of severe frosts is over. Sets for dry bulbs and green onions are also planted as early as the soil can be prepared. In the far South onions are grown in the winter so seed, sets, or seedlings are planted in the fall or winter. The time will vary with local conditions. Seed for producing transplants is usually sown from 6 to 10 weeks before the time of transplanting.

Close spacing of the rows, 12 to 18 inches, is common in most irrigated sections, as well as in sections where rainfall is abundant. In some nonirrigated sections of Texas, onions are planted in rows 3 feet apart; these are frequently interplanted with cotton shortly before harvest.

JOB 5.   CULTIVATING AND IRRIGATING

Cultivating

Because of their slow growth, small stature, shallow roots, and lack of dense foliage, onions more than most vegetables cannot withstand the ill effects of weeds. In practically all sections, the onion crop is cultivated every week or two after the seedlings emerge or plants are set out. This operation is continued until several weeks before harvest. It not only helps to control weeds, but also loosens the soil after irrigations and rains. All cultivations except the very first ones should be very shallow, as many of the onion roots are close to the soil surface. Cultivating too deeply or too closely to the plants after the crop is well advanced may do more harm than good.

In narrow-row seedbeds, wheel hoes and small garden tractors are commonly used for cultivation and weeding.

Thinning and Weeding

Thinning is practiced only when the seed has been sown in the location where the crop is to mature. This is expensive and is not resorted to if it can be avoided. It is usually cheaper to control the stand as much as possible by a lower rate of seeding. In certain sections of south Texas, however, the practice of thinning often pays for itself because of the market farther north for plants that are removed.

Onions frequently require at least one good hand weeding. Sometimes this can be combined with the thinning operation, but more often it is an entirely separate job.

Chemical Weed Control

Expensive hand weeding in large plantings of onions has been virtually eliminated through the advent of chemical weed control (Fig. 23.3). A number of herbicides can be used to control weeds in onions at different stages of development. These chemicals are listed in Table 9.2.

Irrigating

In irrigated sections, where the success of the crop depends on proper irrigation methods, the time to apply water is important. Soil, both surface and subsoil, current weather conditions, and age of the crop need to be considered in deciding when to irrigate and how much water to apply. A seedbed is usually irrigated immediately after planting, and then just as frequently as is necessary to maintain a moist condition until emergence occurs. Normally one to three irrigations are necessary after the seedlings have emerged to insure steady growth. Sufficient water should be applied to moisten the soil thoroughly. Irrigation of onions in Texas is either by the furrow or by the flooding system.

The seedlings should be irrigated as soon as possible after transplanting. Between this irrigation and harvest time, irrigated onions in south

Fig. 23.3—Good weed control is essential for high yields of onions.

Ohio Exp. Sta. Photograph

Texas usually receive five to seven additional applications of water. At first, irrigations may be spaced as much as four to six weeks apart. For two to three weeks before harvest, when the onions are bulbing, irrigations may be as often as every week or 10 days, in order to prevent the soil baking around the bulbs, which causes them to be misshapen. Experiments in Texas have shown that overirrigation of onions should be avoided, since it may seriously reduce yields. When plants have started to mature, irrigation should cease and the soil allowed to dry out as much as possible.

JOB 6.   CONTROLLNG DISEASES AND INSECTS

General recommendations for disease and insect control can be found in Chapter 11. Specific recommendations should be obtained from the agricultural experiment station and extension service in your area.

Diseases

The onion is subject to a number of diseases, the most important of which are discussed here.

PINK ROOT. Pink root is caused by the soil-borne fungi, *Pyrenochaeta terrestis* and *Fusarium sp.*, that may infect onion plants of any age. Since the disease, especially in the early stages, is confined to the roots and bulb plate, it may go unnoticed for some time. Roots turn pinkish in color, then shrivel and die; yields are thereby considerably reduced. Every precaution should be taken to use disease-free land for the seedbed and the transplanted seedlings or to purchase plants free from the disease. If disease-free seedlings are grown on disease-free land, there is no danger of pink root. In addition to this precaution, it is well to combine rotation and proper fertilization and cultural practices, in order to produce fairly rapid and steady growth. Varieties and hybrids are being produced with resistance to pink root.

NECK ROT. Neck rot (*Botrytis sp.*) is a rather serious disease in all sections. Infection occurs at the neck or in the wounds on the bulbs during or following harvest. The disease can be recognized by the grayish mold on the surface of the infected area. Losses may occur in the field, and bulbs often decay while in storage or in transit. Stands in certain sections of Virginia were reduced as much as 80 percent on one occasion. Control measures for neck rot include proper curing and storing. Bulbs that are well dried, especially at the neck, are less likely to succumb to the disease than those that are not well cured. Dry at 90° to 120° F. for two to three days and then store at 32° F. Temperatures in storage should be kept as near 32° F. as possible, and there should be adequate ventilation to maintain a dry atmosphere. The disease can be reduced in the field by planting only healthy sets.

ONION SMUT. Onion smut (*Urocytis cepulae*) is usually the most destructive disease on northern-grown onions. High soil temperatures are unfavorable for its growth, hence it is not generally a problem in the South on onions grown in warm weather. The disease is caused by a soil-borne fungus. Infection occurs only in seedlings before the first leaf has made full growth. Onion sets, being largely resistant, are used in some areas where smut is severe. Pelleting seed with a fungicide such as Arasan and a methocel sticker is the most effective method of control. The Beltsville Bunching and Nebuka type bunching onions have good resistance to smut.

DOWNY MILDEW. Downy mildew (*Peronospora destructor*) is a common disease of onions and is especially destructive in onion seed crops. The disease is favored by cool, wet weather. Resistance to the disease is found in the Calred variety. Six to ten applications of a zineb fungicide spray at approximately weekly intervals is recommended for control.

Other diseases of limited importance are black mold, leaf mold, smudge, yellow dwarf, and white rot.

Insects

Onion thrips and onion maggots are the only important widespread onion insect pests.

ONION THRIPS. Onion thrips are similar to other thrips such as the bean thrips, and can be controlled by two or three applications of malathion or diazinon spray or dust. Dieldrin, toxaphene, and DDT can be used. Rotenone can be used on dry onions only.

ONION MAGGOTS. The onion maggot is a larva of a small fly that lays its eggs near the base of the plant. The small maggots kill the plant by burrowing into the stem and bulb. Control is best obtained by spraying with malathion or diazinon.

Other insects that cause damage in certain areas are wireworms and leaf miners.

JOB 7. HARVESTING, HANDLING, AND MARKETING

Harvesting

Onions may be harvested either as green-bunch onions or as mature bulbs. An onion is suitable for green bunching from the time it has reached pencil size until it begins to bulb. Such immature onions are commonly harvested in home and market gardens. In the large onion-growing sections, the crop is harvested almost entirely at the mature stage. Harvesting may begin when the tops start to fall over (Fig. 23.4). The exact time of harvest varies with environmental conditions. In the West and South it should begin during warm weather when approximately 25 percent of the tops are down. Under cooler weather conditions harvesting is usually delayed until over 50 percent are down. In the East it does not usually begin until most of the tops are down.

Fig. 23.4—Matured onions harvested and placed in windrows for drying.

USDA Photograph

A small onion plow is frequently used to loosen the bulbs. In muck soils bulbs are easily pulled by hand without lifting. In irrigated sections water may be used to soften the ground a day or two before harvesting. The pulled onions are thrown into windrows with the bulbs being shaded by the tops to minimize sunscald. In many cases harvesting is now done by machines that lift and top the bulbs and then sack or place the cleaned bulbs in crates. Some onions are also handled in bulk.

A period of curing usually follows the pulling (Fig. 23.5). In the South and West, curing is usually accomplished in a few days, but in the North the curing period may take three or four weeks depending upon climatic conditions. In Texas, onions are often pulled, clipped, and shipped the same day. Care should be taken to avoid sunscalding caused by curing too long in direct sunlight.

Tops are usually removed after they are well dried down. The tops may be cut by hand with shears, or by a topping machine. One-half to one inch of the top is usually left on the bulb to prevent entrance of disease organisms.

Yields in all sections vary greatly depending on conditions, but in general range between 100 and well over 1,000 sacks (50-pound) per acre.

Fig. 23.5—Windrowed onions being cleaned, topped, and bagged.

The average yield in the United States is around 550 sacks and a good yield is around 700 sacks per acre.

In the Chicago area onion sets that were planted in April are harvested in mid-July. Most sets are harvested when the tops are yellow and falling over unless a harvesting machine is used. The roots are cut with a blade attachment that runs beneath the row. The sets are then pulled by hand and the tops are removed by twisting them off. Preliminary screening is done in the field to remove soil. The sets are placed in shallow crates, which are stacked in the fields to permit curing. After six to eight weeks, when the tops are dry, they are nipped off, and the sets are placed in storage.

Grading

After the tops have been removed, the onions are cleaned and graded. Onion grades depend somewhat on the variety involved, Bermuda and domestic onions all being classified on slightly different bases. These grades change slightly from time to time, and it is well to obtain periodically the latest rulings direct from the U.S. Department of Agriculture or from local state marketing agencies.

Packing

In nearly all sections 50-pound open-mesh bags have practically replaced all other containers. Onions are also packed by some growers in smaller mesh bags of 3- to 10-pound sizes for direct use in the retail trade.

Storing

Varieties vary considerably in their storage characteristics. Bermuda onions are notoriously poor keepers and are rarely stored for any length of time. The late maturing American or domestic types are generally much better adapted to storage. However, marked varietal differences do exist even within this group.

Unless the onions have been carefully handled and properly cured and are free from disease, storage is likely to lead to disappointment and loss instead of gain. Under any storage conditions handling, repacking, and skrinkage are unavoidable. Cold storage at slightly above 32° F. with a dry atmosphere and adequate ventilation is the only method which will normally give satisfaction. Even then bulbs must be cured properly and free from disease. Actual freezing must be avoided.

The chemical maleic hydrazide has been found effective in the inhibition of sprouting. The most satisfactory treatment has been a spray application of two pounds of maleic hydrazide on the plants when 50 percent of the tops are down. Timing of the spray is very important, as an application too early may result in puffy bulbs while one that is too late will give little sprout inhibition. The use of ionizing irradiation is also being explored as a possible way to inhibit sprouting.

Marketing

The problem of marketing is a very specialized one. In the South and West the average grower disposes of his crop at or soon after harvest.

Dealers, jobbers, shippers, and others are usually on hand at harvest time to buy onions for cash provided they pass the Federal-state inspection satisfactorily. In the large onion-producing sections, Federal or state agencies publish daily reports of the number of cars being sold, the range of prices, and the general conditions of the market.

Between 1955 and 1959, the United States exported an average of 1,500,000 hundredweight of onions. Exports declined thereafter until 1963, when about 1,300,000 hundredweight valued at $5,988,000 were shipped. Canada was the major recipient, with substantial quantities going to the United Kingdom, Jamaica, Panama, Mexico, Trinidad, the Netherlands Antilles, and small amounts to approximately 25 other countries.

SELECTED REFERENCES

Binkley, A. M., *et al.*, "Onion Production in Colorado," Colo. Agr. Ext. Bull. 414A, 1951.

Davis, G. N., "Onion Production in California," Calif. Agr. Exp. Sta. Cir. 357. 1943.

Huchinson, J. E., *et al.*, "Onions in Texas," Texas Agr. Ext. Bull. 220, 1953.

Isenberg, F. M. and Ang, J. K., "Northern-Grown Onions," Cornell Ext. Bull. 1116, 1963.

Jones, H. A., *et al.*, "Growing the Transplant Onion Crop," USDA Farmers' Bull. No. 1956, 1957.

Walker, J. C. and Larson, R. H., "Onion Diseases and Their Control," USDA *Agr. Handbook 208*, 1961.

CHAPTER 24

Peas

Classification, Origin, and History

The garden pea (*Pisum sativum*) is a cool-season, hardy, annual, tendril-climbing plant, belonging to the *Leguminosae* family. It is grown primarily for edible green seeds, although one kind is grown in Europe for the edible pods, as are snap beans. In the South, peas are generally referred to as English peas. The pea originated in Europe and Asia, and the plant was commonly grown in the gardens of the ancient Romans and Greeks.

Scope and Importance

Green peas for fresh market are grown commercially in only a few states, but the processed crop is grown in the eastern, middle-western, and far-western regions of the country. This vegetable is also popular for local markets and home gardens in many areas and is considered an important crop. Of the 22 principal vegetables, peas ranked third in acreage and ninth in value in 1965.

The popularity of green peas for fresh market has decreased markedly during the past 26 years, primarily because of expensive harvest labor and the availability of canned and frozen peas. Although yields have risen substantially, harvested acreage declined from 102,390 in 1939 to about 4,500 in 1965. Farm value decreased from $10,805,000 to approximately $1,838,000 during this period.

The loss in fresh market peas has been offset by green peas for processing, the acreage of which increased from 248,030 in 1939 to about 442,000 acreas in 1965. Total production increased from 195,260 tons of shelled peas to more than 514,000 during this 26-year period. Value of the processed crop rose from $9,217,000 in 1939 and approximated $60,000,000 in 1965.

The approximate distribution of green pea production is shown in Figure 24.1, while acreage, production, and value for fresh market and processing by leading states are listed in Tables 24.1 and 24.2 respectively.

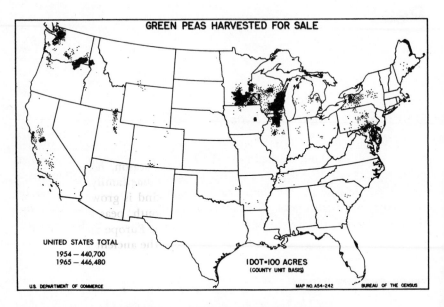

Fig. 24.1—Acreage and distribution of pea production.

Table 24.1—Green Peas for Fresh Market: Shipping Season and Estimated Commercial Acreage, Yield, Production, and Value in Leading States, 1965.

State	Season	Harvested Acreage	Yield per Acre, Cwt.	Production, 1,000 Cwt.	Price per Cwt.	Value, $1,000
California	Early spring	2,100	40	84	$10.70	899
California	Early fall	1,000	35	35	12.00	420
Colorado	Summer	850	30	26	9.90	238
New York	Summer	600	40	24	11.70	281
All states		4,550	37	169	11.01	1,838

Table 24.2—Green Peas for Processing: Estimated Commercial Acreage, Yield, Production, and Value in Leading States, 1965.

State	Harvested Acreage	Yield per Acre, Pounds (Shelled)	Production in Tons (Shelled)	Price per Ton	Value, $1,000
Wisconsin	124,700	2,540	158,370	$ 95.60	15,140
Washington	88,200	3,170	139,800	101.00	14,120
Minnesota	56,900	2,470	70,270	104.00	7,308
Oregon	56,400	2,750	77,550	88.00	6,824
Idaho	14,000	2,310	16,170	88.30	1,428
California	11,700	3,260	19,070	124.00	2,365
Maryland	9,000	3,310	14,900	120.00	1,788
Delaware	7,800	2,390	9,320	116.00	1,081
New York	7,600	2,990	11,360	106.00	1,204
Pennsylvania	5,600	2,750	7,700	131.00	1,009
Michigan	5,300	2,380	6,310	95.20	601
Indiana	1,300	1,750	1,140	91.40	104
Other states	53,430	2,674	71,430	101.00	7,216
All states	441,930	2,731	603,390	99.70	60,188
For freezing	159,520	2,926	233,410	99.40	23,209
For canning	282,410	2,620	369,980	99.90	36,979

Trends in Production Efficiency

Green peas are comparatively inexpensive to produce since costs for seed, fertilizer, and labor are modest. In 1959, peas for fresh market required an average of 128 man-hours per acre for growing and harvesting while the processed crop involved only 11 man-hours, the lowest labor requirement for any crop.

The yield of green peas for fresh market increased from 28 to 37 hundredweight per acre between 1939 and 1959, and unit production per man-hour rose 53 percent. Acre yields of green peas for canning and freezing increased from 16 to 27 hundredweight during this period while output per man-hour rose 275 percent (Table 1.4).

Climatic Requirements

The pea is a cool-season crop and thrives best when the weather is cool and when ample moisture is available. The young plants will tolerate considerable cold and light frosts, but the flowers and green pods are often injured by heavy frost. If the crop is planted late, maturity takes place when the temperatures are too high for optimum growth and yields.

Therefore, it is important to plant late enough to avoid freezes, yet early enough to mature the crop before hot weather.

JOB 1.   SELECTING VARIETIES AND SEED

Varieties

Varieties of garden peas may be divided into two types, smooth-seeded and wrinkled-seeded. The former are hardy but low in quality. Seeds of varieties also vary in size, skin toughness, and color. The smaller-seeded varieties have been preferred for canning because the small seeds were associated with sweetness and tenderness. A pea with a tough skin will hold its shape during processing. A dark green color is essential for freezing. Varieties range in size from small dwarf to tall climbing plants. The dwarf types tend to be earlier and produce pods over a shorter period of time. This is desirable when the plants are harvested at one time for processing, but would not be advantageous for the home gardener desiring a succession of harvests.

Fig. 24.2—The Little Marvel variety of peas approaching maturity.

Table 24.3—Characteristics of Selected Varieties of Peas.

Variety	Chief Use	Days to Maturity	Plant Height in Inches	Pod Color	Pea Size	Resistant to Wilt
Alderman	Home freezing	75	60	Dark green	Large	+
Early Perfection	Canning	65	30	Med. green	Small	+
Eureka	Canning	68	30	Light green	Medium	+
Freezonian	Freezing	63	35	Dark green	Small	+
Perfected Freezer 60	Freezing	69	30	Dark green	Large	+
Little Marvel	Home garden	64	18	Dark green	Medium	+
Perfection	Canning	70	30	Med. green	Medium	
Pride	Canning	64	30	Med. green	Medium	+
Progress No. 9	Home garden	60	20	Dark green	Large	
Stratagem	Freezing	78	28	Dark green	Large	
Thomas-Laxton WR	Market freezing	62	36	Dark green	Large	+
Wando	Gen. purpose	66	26	Dark green	Small	+
Wasatch	Canning	64	28	Light green	Med. large	+
Wisconsin Early Sweet	Canning	60	30	Light green	Small	+

A brief description and the chief use of some of the leading varieties of peas are given in Table 24.3. The list includes varieties suitable for the home and market gardens, for canning, and for freezing. Although the time required for maturity varies primarily with temperature, relative values are given. For example, under the same weather conditions, Progress No. 9 would require 60 days to edible maturity, while Perfection would require 70 days.

Securing Seed

Since it is impossible to definitely identify varieties of peas by the seed alone, growers should procure their seed from reliable sources. The seed should be from the crop of the previous year. Most seed-producing areas are in the semi-arid West and on the Pacific Coast, where diseases are less of a problem than elsewhere. Experiences of growers indicate that it is essential to secure seed from such sections.

JOB 2.   PREPARING THE SEEDBED

Soil Preferences

Peas are grown on a variety of soils. The sandy loams with clay subsoil are generally preferred for earliness. Ample drainage is essential, especially in sections where heavy rainfall occurs during the early part of the growing season. If well drained, some of the heavier soils, such as the clays and loams, produce higher yields than do the more porous, sandy soils, but maturity is later.

Regardless of the soil type, humus or organic matter is very essential in the satisfactory production of peas. Experiences indicate that soils which have previously been improved by applications of barnyard manure or by growing and turning under cover crops are best for growing fine crops of peas. Studies at the Maryland Agricultural Experiment Station indicate that soil organic matter was the factor most positively correlated with plant growth, yield, and nodule formulation.

The garden pea, like most legumes, prefers a slightly acid soil, but will not tolerate excess soil acidity. The crop should be grown in a soil with a pH range of 5.5 to 6.5. While lime is very desirable for strongly acid soils, it should be remembered that liming will not solve other production problems, and that the use of excess quantities of lime would be very undesirable. On some soils that are limed too heavily, peas and other vegetable crops fail to grow and become chlorotic because of lack of available manganese. Some of the southeastern sandy soils are deficient in magnesium, and, on such soils, a magnesium limestone should be used.

Preparing the Soil

Very close attention should be given to the matter of soil preparation because poor growth and low yields often are traceable to lack of thorough soil preparation. During the fall months, the soil should be thoroughly disked to cut up and incorporate any cover crop or other plant residues and hasten their decomposition. The land should later be plowed deeply; and just before preparing the beds for planting, further disking or harrowing should be done. Poor soil preparation results in uneven germination and the peas do not mature uniformly. This is particularly disadvantageous for processing.

Fertilizing

Peas are less responsive to fertility than are most of the other vegetable crops. Even so, in most sections some commercial fertilizer is essential. On some very rich, fertile virgin soils, only a maintenance application of fertilizer may be needed, while in some of the less fertile sections, growers use 800 to 1,000 pounds per acre of a high-grade fertilizer. The fertilizer is usually applied to the side and slightly below the seed or thoroughly mixed with the soil before planting, in order to prevent the fertilizer from seriously interfering with germination.

Certain coastal plains soils of the Atlantic seaboard are quite generally deficient in magnesium and manganese. Where these elements are deficient and the soil also needs liming, basic slag is an excellent material to use, because it contains these two minor elements in addition to calcium. It also contains iron oxide, which is helpful on some of the very light sandy soils of the area. A very cheap source of magnesium is dolomitic (or magnesium) limestone. Unless deficiencies in magnesium and manganese have been corrected with basic slag or magnesium limestone, a special fertilizer containing the necessary minor elements should be applied.

Inoculating

The garden pea, as other legumes, requires inoculation with specific legume bacteria. The nodule-forming bacterium is the same for garden peas, vetch, and Austrian peas. Where the soil has not been inoculated in previous years by growing one or more of these crops, the seed should be artificially inoculated. In some demonstrations, yields have been increased 50 to 100 percent by inoculation, while in others on soils containing the inoculum no increase in yields was obtained.

JOB 3. PLANTING AND CULTIVATING

All varieties should be planted as early as the season will permit. Planting made later than the earliest practicable dates usually mature in less time but invariably produce lower yields, apparently on account of high temperatures.

Most of the peas for processing are planted with grain drills in rows 7 inches apart. From three and one-half to five bushels of seed are required per acre, depending upon the size of seed planted. For the home and most market gardens, peas are planted in rows. When they are planted in single rows, the distance between rows varies from 2 to 3 feet; when double rows are used the beds are about 4 feet apart, the two rows on each bed being 8 to 12 inches apart. About two bushels of seed are required per acre. The usual depth of planting is 1 to 2 inches depending upon the type of soil and moisture content.

Cultivating

Peas are cultivated only where the rows are far enough apart for cultivation. Since the pea develops rapidly, no great amount of cultivation is necessary. The cultivations should be shallow to avoid destroying too many of the fibrous roots, and only frequent enough to destroy weeds.

Staking

With few exceptions, no support is given the vines in the commercial pea sections. Cane or small stakes, set at intervals in the row, and overlapping near the top, are generally used by home gardeners. Wire netting supported by stakes between double rows or to the side of single rows is sometimes employed. Inexpensive twine also is used, three to five parallel lines being fastened to laths or small stakes spaced 6 to 10 feet apart along the rows.

JOB 4. CONTROLLING DISEASES AND INSECTS

Diseases

The most important pea diseases found are: (1) root rots, (2) Fusarium wilt, (3) Aschochyta blight, (4) mosaic, (5) bacterial blight, (6) downy mildew, and (7) powdery mildew. From a practical standpoint, the only feasible control measures are: (1) use of disease-free seed, (2) seed treatment, (3) use of resistant varieties, and (4) crop rotation. Bacterial blight and Aschochyta blight are seed-borne diseases; the wilts also are seed-borne to a slight extent. For the control of these seed-borne diseases, disease-free seed should be obtained from the semi-arid West and Pacific Coast states when available. The wilt organisms are reported to live almost indefinitely in the soil, and the only satisfactory control, therefore, is the use of resistant varieties. There is no definite control for the root rots, but good soil drainage, crop rotation, and seed treatment with chloranil or thiram are recommended.

Insects

The following insects attack peas: (1) pea aphid, (2) thrips, (3) spider mites, (4) seed corn maggot, and (5) pea weevil. The pea aphid (*Macrosiphum pisi*) is the worst pest in some sections. It can be controlled with malathion or nicotine sulphate (see Chapter 11). Treatments should be applied when the aphids are first observed and before serious damage is done. Except where the pea aphid is bad, insect control in peas has not generally been found economical.

The only control for nematodes is to practice a rotation and to avoid growing susceptible crops on the land.

JOB 5. HARVESTING, HANDLING, AND MARKETING

Harvesting

Peas for processing are harvested with a mowing machine. The plants are usually hauled to a vining station where the peas are shelled by machinery. Some viners are self-propelled and harvest or pick up the plants from windrows in the field. Rapid handling is essential to prevent loss of quality after harvesting, especially during high temperatures.

Green peas for the fresh market are harvested entirely by hand. Two or three pickings are usually necessary. The vines should be handled carefully if the yield and quality of the later pickings are not to be impaired.

In some sections the peas are picked and placed directly into the container in which they are to be shipped, while in other sections field crates or picking containers are used. Common labor is employed to do the harvesting, but it is desirable to have a competent foreman or supervisor in charge.

Often too little attention is given to harvesting peas at the proper stage of growth for a product of highest quality. The pods should be picked when fully green and well developed, and before the peas start hardening. It has been shown that quality depends primarily upon tenderness and sugar content. As the peas increase in size during maturity the percent of sugar decreases while starch and proteins increase. The seed coats as well as the cotyledons become tougher. Maturity is measured by the sizes of peas in a sample and by tenderness determined with a tenderometer.

Grading

As the peas come from the field to a central packing shed, they are placed in a grading machine which has a blower attachment to remove the trash. Laborers standing along each side of the belt pick out defective and exceptionally small pods as the peas pass by. The machine used for this purpose is similar to the one used for grading snap beans and cucumbers.

Packing and Loading the Car

Peas are packed for market in baskets and bushel hampers, but during the past decade the flat crate has been in general use. Since peas are rather perishable and heat easily, a shallow or flat container is desirable. The container should be well filled, since a slack pack detracts materially from the package and is often the cause of poor sales.

The field heat should be removed from fresh peas as soon as possible after harvest. This can be done by immersing in cold water. After wetting, however, the pods must be kept refrigerated and shipped to market in a refrigerated car or truck. Salability can be maintained for about two weeks at 32° to 40° F.

Marketing

Peas are marketed in a manner similar to that for other vegetable crops, the method depending upon the prevailing practice in the particular section. Where the production is controlled by an organization, it is desirable to use central packing houses not only to standardize the product but also to aid in marketing. In many instances the peas are packed on the farm by the individual growers and brought to the local market, which may be an auction or cash-truck buyers' market. In some instances the peas are handled by dealers or shippers who load and sell them to cash buyers or ship on consignment, depending upon the market conditions. Much of the crop is transported to market in refrigerated trucks.

The United States exported declining quantities of canned green peas to Canada, the Philippines, West Indies, Kuwait, Hong Kong, and several other countries during the past several years. The 1956-1959 average annual export of 325,000 cases decreased to approximately 200,000 valued at $975,000 in 1963.

SELECTED REFERENCES

Brindley, F. A., et al., "The Pea Weevil and Methods for Its Control," USDA Farmers' Bull. 1971, 1952.

Dudley, J. E., Jr. and Bronson, T. E., "The Pea Aphid on Peas and Methods for Its Control," USDA Farmers' Bull. 1945, 1952.

Harter, L. L., et al., "Pea Diseases and Their Control," USDA Farmers' Bull. 1735, 1957.

Murphy, H. J. and Terman, G. L., "Fertilizer, Liming, and Seeding Practices for Processing Peas in Maine," Me. Agr. Exp. Sta. Bull. 496, 1952.

CHAPTER 25

Peppers

Classification, Origin, and History

The peppers (*Capsicum annuum* and *C. frutescens*) belong to the *Solanaceae* or nightshade family, and are therefore closely related to egg-plant, potato, tomato, and tobacco. Virtually all varieties of the commonly cultivated pepper belong to the species, *C. annuum*. Tabasco is the only variety of *C. frutescens* grown commercially in the United States.

The native home of the peppers is thought to be tropical America, where they have always been very popular. After the discovery of America, peppers were rapidly disseminated over Europe. The garden pepper is unrelated to the vine that produces black pepper, *Piper nigrum*.

Scope and Importance

The popularity of green peppers has increased markedly over the past 25 years. Although peppers ranked only 16th both in acreage and value among the 22 principal vegetables in 1965, they are widely consumed.

Peppers are grown commercially in more than a dozen states and for local markets and home use in many others. Pimento peppers for canning are produced almost exclusively in Georgia, paprika peppers are grown primarily in small areas in California and Arizona, and chili peppers are produced mainly in southern California and New Mexico. The main crop, sweet peppers for the fresh market, are grown over a wide area, primarily in the eastern half of the United States.

The acreage of peppers for fresh market and processing doubled from 22,800 acres in 1939 to almost 48,000 in 1965. Total production in-

creased substantially, while farm value rose from $4,881,000 to about
$37,000,000 between 1939 and 1965.

The acreage, production, and value of peppers produced in the leading states are shown in Table 25.1.

**Table 25.1—Green Peppers for Fresh Market and Processing: Shipping
Season and Estimated Commercial Acreage, Yield, Production, and
Value in Leading States, 1965.**

State	Season	Harvested Acreage	Yield per Acre, Cwt.	Production, 1,000 Cwt.	Price per Cwt.	Value, $1,000
New Jersey	Late summer	7,900	70	553	$ 7.40	4,092
Florida	Winter	7,000	105	735*	9.08	6,191
North Carolina	Early summer	6,700	40	268*	8.30	1,868
Florida	Spring	6,200	90	558	13.96	7,787
California	Late summer	4,500	165	742	7.99	5,928
Texas	Fall	3,600	100	360	11.20	4,032
Virginia	Fall	1,900	35	66	7.03	464
Florida	Fall	1,400	75	105	13.50	1,418
Ohio	Late summer	1,400	90	126	7.30	920
Michigan	Late summer	1,400	75	105	5.96	626
Louisiana	Early summer	1,300	38	49	12.20	598
Texas	Spring	1,200	100	120	14.00	1,680
All states		47,650	84	3,987	9.55	37,175

* Includes some quantities not marketed and excluded in computing value.

Trends in Production Efficiency

Green peppers are comparatively expensive to produce because of
fertilizer, cultural, and labor requirements. The great amount of hand
work in growing and harvesting involves approximately 200 man-hours
per acre, and this figure has not changed materially for many years. Average production of peppers increased from 62 to 71 hundredweight per
acre during the 1939-1959 period, while the unit production per man-
hour rose only 6 percent (Table 1.4).

Climatic Requirements

Peppers have very much the same climatic requirements as the eggplant and tomato, although pepper plants may withstand lower temperatures. They thrive best in a relatively warm climate where the growing
season is long and where there is little danger of frosts. The pepper is

apparently more drought-resistant than either the tomato or eggplant; nevertheless, best yields are contingent upon an ample supply of well-distributed rainfall and a mean temperature at blossom-setting time ranging from 65° to 80° F.

Irrigation is necessary in some pepper-growing sections of the West and Southwest, and it is used to some extent in other areas.

JOB 1. SELECTING VARIETIES AND SEED

Varieties

Of the several groups of peppers grown, there are two general classes: (1) those which produce mild or sweet fruits called sweet peppers, and (2) those which bear pungent or hot fruits better known as hot peppers. Generally the sweet varieties are harvested at the mature green stage,

Table 25.2—Important Characteristics of a Selected List of Leading Varieties of Peppers.

Variety	Use	Season* (Days)	Flavor	Fruit Shape	
				Length (Inches)	Di- ameter
Allbig	Home and market	62	Sweet	4-5	3-4
Anaheim Chili	Home, canning, market, and drying	80	Hot	6-8	1½
California Wonder	Home, shipping, market, and canning	74	Sweet	4½	3½-4
Early Calwonder	Market and shipping	68	Sweet	4	3½
Cuban	Home, market	62	Sweet	6	2
Delaware Belle	Home and market	65	Sweet	4	3½
Florida Giant	Home, market, and shipping	75	Sweet	4½	3½-4
Hungarian Yellow Wax .	Home, market and canning	65	Hot	6	1½
Italian El	Market and shipping	65	Sweet	4	2
Lincoln Belle	Home and market	70	Sweet	4½	3½
Long Red Cayenne	Home, market, canning and drying	70	Hot	4½-5	½
Neapolitan	Market, shipping	62	Sweet	4	2
Ruby King	Home, and market	70	Sweet	4½-5	3
Sunnybrook	Home and market	73	Sweet	2½	2¾
Tabasco	Canning and drying	95	Hot	1	¾
World Beater	Home, market, and shipping	70	Sweet	4-4½	3-3½
Yolo Wonder	Market and shipping	74	Sweet	4	3-3½

*Days from transplanting until marketing stage.

while the hot varieties are harvested when at the mature red stage, except for the wax types which are picked when yellow. Table 25.2 gives the important characteristics of a selected list of the leading varieties.

Securing Seed

Growers should make a special effort to obtain the best seed available of varieties that are well adapted to their particular region. Proper seed production is a specialized business, and, as a rule, growers should not attempt to raise their own seed.

JOB 2.   PREPARING THE SOIL

Soil Preferences

A sandy loam which holds moisture fairly well and which has a liberal supply of organic matter is the ideal soil for the growing of bell peppers. For canning peppers, a soil with some clay is preferable, as the color of the fruits seems to develop better than on lighter soils. Soils conducive to earliness are especially desirable in regions where the growing season is limited by killing frosts. The pepper is not especially sensitive to soil acidity, having an optimum pH range between 5.5 and 7.0. Strongly acid soils should be limed to bring the pH within this range.

Breaking and Conditioning

Land to be planted to peppers in the spring should be broken deeply during the previous late fall or early winter. If green-manure or cover crops are used, they may be plowed under in the early winter or early spring. In the spring the surface should be disked and well harrowed.

Fertilizing and Manuring

To produce high yields of peppers on soils low in fertility, manures and commercial fertilizer will be needed. Barnyard manure, compost, or green manure at the rate of 10 to 15 tons per acre should be applied annually.

The fertilization of peppers is similar to that of tomatoes. However, peppers seem to require a little more nitrogen and potassium. On light sandy soils, 750 to 1,000 pounds per acre of a 5-8-8 or 5-10-10 fertilizer should be worked into the soil before transplanting. A top dressing of nitrogen fertilizer is needed at the time of fruit setting to prevent a check in the growth of the plants. About 100 pounds of ammonium nitrate or its equivalent should be used. For sandy soils an additional 50 pounds of muriate or sulfate of potash should be added to the nitrogen top dress.

On heavier soils of fair to good fertility, less fertilizer is required. Five hundred to 600 pounds per acre of a fertilizer containing 4 to 5 percent nitrogen, 6 to 8 percent phosphorus, and 6 to 8 percent potassium should be applied before transplanting. A nitrogen top dressing should be used at about the same rate as listed above, after first fruit set.

JOB 3. PLANTING AND CULTIVATING

Growing the Plants

Seed should be treated with a protective fungicide before planting. If hotbeds are employed, the seed should be sown six to eight weeks before the plants are to be set in the field. In most areas, the seed is planted about a month before the average date of the last spring frost. A soil temperature of 70° to 75° F. before emergence of the seedlings, and a soil temperature between 65° and 70° F. after emergence should be maintained. After emergence, the plants should be kept at about 75° F. during the day and 65° F. during the night. Watering should be carefully done during bright, warm mornings if possible. Excessive moisture lowers soil temperature and encourages damping off. To encourage moderate hardening, increased ventilation should be given as the plants approach the transplanting stage.

Large acreages of peppers for shipping, canning, or drying are grown with plants produced in open beds. The seed is sown thinly and the plants are undisturbed until they are ready to be pulled for transplanting in the field. Seed is sown at the rate of about 20 seeds per foot in rows 6 inches apart. Plants are generally thinned to a spacing of about 12 to 15 plants per foot.

Setting the Plants in the Field

It is the usual practice to set plants, 4 to 8 inches tall, in rows 3 to 3½ feet apart with the plants spaced 1½ to 2½ feet apart in the row. Good yields, however, are obtained in some sections with closer spacings. The plants are set either by transplanting machines or by hand, the former method being much faster and just as efficient. In either case, care must be taken to see that the plants are properly placed and that the soil is firmed about the roots. Plants set by machine are usually smaller in size than those set by hand (Fig. 25.1).

Transplanting machines should be equipped with a watering device that will supply about a cup of water or starter solution per plant. A starter is frequently dissolved in the transplanting water. A mixture of one and one-half pounds of monopotassium phosphate and one and one-half pounds of diammonium phosphate in 50 gallons of water is recommended. Commercial preparations of these soluble chemicals are available under various trade names.

Fig. 25.1—Transplanting pepper plants in the field.

Photograph by E. C. Wittmeyer

A homemade mixture of five pounds of commercial fertilizer analyzing about 5 percent nitrogen, 8 to 10 percent phosphorus, and 5 percent potassium in 50 gallons of water is also effective when plants are set by hand. This mixture would contain an insoluble residue not suitable for a transplanter.

Cultivating

As soon as the young plants have become established in the soil, they should receive shallow cultivation only often enough to control the weeds. Deep cultivation invariably results in root pruning as well as a drying out of the soil, both of which cause a severe check in plant growth.

JOB 4.   CONTROLLING DISEASES AND INSECTS

Diseases

The pepper is subject to diseases which may become very destructive under certain conditions, especially where a large acreage is grown without proper rotation. Seed treatment, crop rotation, and seedbed sterilization are general control measures that should be followed in the production of peppers. Many of the diseases that attack peppers are the same as those which attack the tomatoes, and the control methods are similar. For specific control measures, refer to Chapter 11. For methods applicable under local conditions, help may be obtained from agricultural experiment stations and extension services.

Very often damping off is destructive to young seedlings, causing the stems to decay near the soil line. Usually it can be kept under control by planting treated seeds in rows 4 to 6 inches apart and stirring the surface soil soon after each rain in order to keep it loose and dry. In rainy weather, other means of control, such as maneb, thiram, and captan sprays, are sometimes necessary.

BACTERIAL SPOT. Associated with *Xanthomonas vesicatoria*, bacterial spot causes small, dark-brown, wart-like spots on the leaves and fruits. During damp weather the disease spreads rapidly and may cause almost complete defoliation of the plants. The spots in the fruits allow the entrance of molds and other decay organisms. The same disease is common on the tomato. Seed treatment, seedbed sanitation, and crop rotation are the recommnded control methods. Fixed copper sprays also aid in control.

SOUTHERN BLIGHT. Southern blight, associated with *Sclerotium rolfsii*, is often one of the most destructive pepper diseases in the South. The plants are attacked near the soil line, and during dry periods the roots are destroyed. The plants turn yellow and wilt gradually. A carefully planned rotation is the only means of control which can be recommended. Peppers should never be planted after soybeans or cowpeas, but cotton, corn, and small grains are almost immune and are good crops to precede peppers.

BLOSSOM-END ROT. Blossom-end rot (physiological) causes spots to appear near the tips of the fruits during dry periods before the plants have established a large root system. The early crop is most seriously affected. The spots usually become infected with *Alternaria* and other fungi which may decay the entire fruit. The plants should be set deeply in well-prepared soil. The roots should not be disturbed after fruiting begins.

ANTHRACNOSE. Caused by *Gloeosporium piperatum*, anthracnose frequently causes serious spotting of both green and ripe peppers. The fungus lives on and within the seed coat, and that within the seed coat cannot be killed by seed treatment. Seeds should be saved from disease-free fruits and treated to destroy any spores that may adhere to them. Spraying in the field and seedbed with captan, zineb, or maneb also helps hold down this disease.

RIPE ROT. Associated with *Colletotrichum capsici*, ripe rot is one of the most serious diseases of the pimiento pepper, destroying the fruit after it has ripened. Like the anthracnose fungus, it penetrates the seed coat and is not controlled by seed treatment. It also lives from season to season in the field. Careful seed selection from disease-free fields and crop rotation are necessary for control.

Other diseases causing economic loss are blue mold or downy mildew, *cercospora* leaf spot, *phytophthora* blight, fusarium wilt, bacterial soft rot, and virus diseases. Varieties such as Yolo Wonder, Rutgers World Beater No. 13, and Burlington have high resistance to tobacco mosaic virus, but are susceptible to cucumber mosaic and tobacco etch virus. Curly top, another virus disease, causes damage in the West and Southwest. The root knot nematode also causes losses, chiefly in southern regions. Pepper fruits are susceptible to sunscald when exposed to direct sunlight. Partial defoliation of plants by bacterial spot or *cercospora* leaf spot increases the danger of sunscald to the fruit.

Insects

There are a number of important insect pests of peppers in the United States.

PEPPER WEEVIL. The pepper weevil (*Anthonomus eugenii*) is closely related to the cotton boll weevil but is much smaller. Grubs feed in blossoms and in the core of young pods, causing the fruits to drop prematurely. This pest is established in most pepper growing regions. In the western states, it breeds during the winter on black nightshade, *Solanum nigrum*, and it is essential that this weed be eradicated around pepper fields. The remains of the pepper crop should also be disposed of after harvest. Treating with DDT on a 10-day schedule is usually an effective control.

PEPPER MAGGOT. The pepper maggot (*Zonosemata electa*) is the larva of a species of fruit fly. Eggs are laid through the wall of the pod and the maggots feed on the core, causing it to rot. The maggot is very injurious in New Jersey, and it is known to occur in northern Florida and also may appear in other pepper-growing sections. Horse nettle is a native host plant, and the eggplant also is sometimes infested. Picking of peppers while they are green prevents great injury by the pepper maggot, though the cores may already be infested. Dusting or spraying with malathion has been proven effective. The dusts should be applied two days after flies appear in the field, and the treatment should be repeated at five-day intervals as long as any flies can be found.

Aphids, cutworms, flea beetles, hornworms, and leaf miners may also cause economic loss. The methods of control for these insects on peppers are generally the same as for their treatment on other crops.

JOB 5. HARVESTING, HANDLING, AND MARKETING

Harvesting

The time to harvest bell peppers should be determined largely by the size of the fruit and its stage of maturity. For market, they are picked as soon as they reach approximately full size and become firm, but before they begin to turn red or yellow, as the respective colors may be when ripe (Fig. 25.2). Green peppers are picked in baskets and hauled to central packing sheds for grading. Yields ranging from 2 to 5 tons per acre may be expected on the most fertile soils, though greater yields have been reported. Mechanized harvesting of green peppers is shown in Figure 25.3.

Practically all of the pimientos grown are canned in the red or ripe stage. They are harvested either in cotton-picking sacks or in baskets, and are hauled in bags to the cannery, where they are run through grading machines and then processed. Yields of 2 to 4 tons of pimientos per acre are considered average.

Pepper yields are at times unusually low because of the dropping of the young buds, blossoms, and immature fruits. Growers have attributed this almost complete shedding to various conditions, but results of controlled experiments at Ithaca, New York, justify the conclusion that hot dry weather is the condition that causes most of the difficulty. The soil fertility also is important.

Fig. 25.2—Liberty Bell variety of green pepper.

USDA Photograph

Fig. 25.3—Green peppers conveyed to bags in the field.

Photograph by E. C. Wittmeyer

Grading and Packing

Bell peppers after reaching the packing shed are graded either by hand or by machinery. Various kinds of containers are used for shipment to market. In some sections of the South, the crop is packed for shipment in specially constructed one and one-half-bushel crates, which are easier to handle and ship than the standard one-bushel hamper, which is still used to some extent.

Peppers are sold commercially in four grades: U.S. Fancy, U.S. No. 1, U.S. No. 2, and Unclassified. The current grade specifications may be secured from the U.S. Department of Agriculture.

Marketing

The green bell pepper is a perishable crop, and should be sold as soon after it is picked as possible. The crop is moved short distances from the packing plant by unrefrigerated trucks but is shipped to large terminal markets in refrigerated freight cars and trucks. Buyers for large produce companies or dealers make it their business to visit the intensive vegetable-growing sections of the South and West and purchase most of the peppers in season, f.o.b., the growers' shipping points. Some of the growers, however, sell their crop through certain local vegetable associations and a few sell on consignment, the later method usually being the last resort.

SELECTED REFERENCES

Boswell, V. R., et al., "Pepper Production," USDA Agr. Res. Ser., Agriculture Information Bull. No. 276, 1964.

Boswell, V. R., et al., "Pepper Production, Disease and Insect Control," USDA Farmers' Bull. 2051, 1959.

Cochran, H. L., "Some Factors Influencing Growth and Fruit-setting in the Pepper," Cornell Univ. Agr. Exp. Sta. Memoirs 190, 1936.

Dempsey, A. H. and Brantley, B. B., "Pimiento Production in Georgia," Ga. Agr. Exp. Sta. Bull. 277, 1953.

Ozaki, H. Y., "Effect of Spacing, Fertilizer and Variety upon Pepper Yields," Proc. Fla. St. Hort. Soc. 74: 178-80, 1962.

Sneed, Ruth, "Chile (Peppers)," N. M. Agr. Ext. Ser. Cir. 309, 1960.

CHAPTER 26

Potatoes

Classification, Origin, and History

The potato (*Solanum tuberosum*) belongs to the family *Solanaceae* and is a close relative of the tomato, eggplant, pepper, tobacco, and the wild nightshade. The potato and Indian corn are the New World's greatest contributions to the food supply of mankind. Peru is thought to be the place of origin of the potato; some authorities, however, believe that it was also native to parts of Mexico. When and how it reached the United States is not known.

Potatoes had little significance as a food crop in this country prior to the influx of Presbyterian immigrants from Ireland in 1718. The crop gained its greatest impetus in America, however, immediately after 1846, the year that blight destroyed the potato crop in Ireland and caused a famine.

The reliance of the Irish people on the potato as a food crop and their influence on its extended culture and use in this country were no doubt responsible for this product being called the Irish potato rather than the Peru or South American potato. The word Irish as a prefix to the word potato has a very definite meaning in the rural South, where the single word potato is often understood to mean sweet potato. In the North, the reverse is true.

Scope and Importance

Three centuries ago the potato was scarcely known as a food crop in either Europe or America. Today, however, its culture encircles the globe in both temperate zones and it stands out as the most important food crop in the world.

Potatoes are by far the most important of the vegetables in terms of quantities produced and consumed. They are grown commercially and for home use throughout the United States and lead all vegetables in acreage and value. The importance of this basic food crop has declined relatively over the years, but it remains the principal vegetable. Figure 26.2 compares the importance of potatoes with sweet potatoes.

Potato acreage decreased from 2,813,000 in 1939 to approximately 1,403,400 in 1965, while yields almost tripled during this time. Total production increased from 205,423,000 in 1939 to 195,776,000 in 1951, and increased steadily to about 289,000,000 hundredweight in 1965. Farm value rose from $236,839,000 in 1939 to an estimated $666,980,000 in 1965.

Figure 26.1 shows the approximate distribution of potato production in the United States. Idaho, Maine, and California are the outstanding states in acreage, production, and value as shown in Table 26.1.

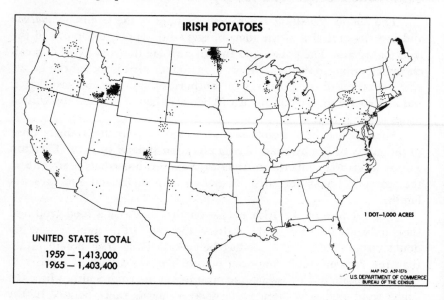

Fig. 26.1—Acreage and distribution of potato production.

Trends in Production Efficiency

The potato is an expensive crop to produce. Seed, fertilizers, cultural and pest control practices, and labor vary considerably in different regions, but average costs are high. With improved mechanization, fertilization, and other practices, potato yields have increased rapidly during the last 30 years. Average man-hour requirements decreased from 69 to

Table 26.1—Potatoes: Estimated Commercial Acreage, Yield, Production, and Value in Leading States, 1965.

State	Harvested Acreage	Yield per Acre, Cwt.	Production, 1,000 Cwt.	Price per Cwt.	Value, $1,000
Idaho	282,000	219	61,695	$1.66	102,737
Maine	148,000	238	35,244	1.40	49,314
California	106,900	299	31,979	4.05	126,964
North Dakota	105,000	145	15,225	1.40	21,315
Minnesota	94,200	142	13,368	1.61	21,374
New York	77,000	252	19,425	2.35	45,946
Wisconsin	58,500	203	11,865	2.59	30,769
Michigan	50,400	188	9,494	2.16	20,477
Washington	50,000	331	16,560	1.42	23,243
Colorado	47,800	232	11,071	1.79	19,735
Pennsylvania	38,000	198	7,534	2.72	20,467
Virginia	28,200	112	3,167	4.70	14,527
Texas	22,000	131	2,890	4.98	14,439
North Carolina	21,300	132	2,802	5.40	14,662
Alabama	21,100	109	2,310	4.85	11,166
New Jersey	16,600	250	4,150	2.62	10,873
Ohio	13,500	191	2,578	2.70	6,957
Arizona	11,000	210	2,310	4.18	9,656
Nebraska	10,900	193	2,106	1.55	3,283
All states	1,403,400	206	288,927	2.34	666,980

50 hours per acre between 1939 and 1959, and yields rose phenomenally from 73 to 184 hundredweight and are still increasing. Unit production of potatoes per man-hour increased 250 percent between 1939 and 1959 (Table 1.4), and higher labor efficiency is anticipated as more areas complete the shift to mechanical harvesting.

The late or main crop, which comprises about 80 percent of the total production in the United States, is produced primarily in the northern tier of states from Maine to North Dakota and Idaho.

Climatic Requirements

The potato requires a cool growing season with an abundant and well-distributed rainfall. Since the seed pieces will usually sprout at temperatures ranging from 40° to 50° F., it is the common practice to plant early potatoes five or six weeks before the last spring frost is expected. It requires about this length of time for the eyes to sprout and the young plants to push through about 2 to 3 inches of soil, the usual depth of planting. There is, of course, some risk of the young plants being injured by frost, although the increased yields and prices obtained from early planting warrant taking this risk. Late plantings in the South have to be started during very hot and often dry weather, and seldom produce satisfactory crops. The late crop is usually restricted to regions with mild summers.

Growers prepared to irrigate are most certain of success. Irrigation is decidedly important for growing late potatoes, and it helps to assure the early crops, which mature during periods of uncertain rainfall. In dry areas irrigation is absolutely essential.

JOB 1.   SELECTING VARIETIES AND SEED

Varieties

A large number of varieties of potatoes are available. These differ in time of maturity, yield, appearance, cooking and marketing qualities, and resistance to various insects and diseases. If other characteristics are equal, a resistant variety should be chosen. A variety may be well adapted to one region but not to another. For this reason a new variety should be first tried on a small scale only. A number of varieties and their characteristics are given in Table 26.2.

Securing Seed

It is desirable to purchase certified seed when possible. Most states growing seed potatoes commercially have associations which send out inspectors to inspect both field and storage bins of potatoes before giving a certificate of inspection to show that the seed stock is standard in type and free of serious diseases. Field inspection of the plants is the only way known to identify some of the virus diseases, such as mosaic, which are carried in the tubers. This is discussed under the disease section (Job 6) of this chapter.

The second or fall crop of potatoes grown in the mountainous sections of North Carolina, Georgia, and Tennessee, on the eastern shores of Virginia and Maryland, and in sections of Oklahoma and Arkansas are held over winter and used for seed purposes in the following spring. This seed stock does not mature a crop quite so early as seed from the North, but the yields are generally satisfactory.

More recently, seed potatoes have been saved from the early or main crop of the mountainous sections of Georgia, North Carolina, and Tennessee to be shipped to south Florida for the production of winter crops. The crop matures early enough to provide the necessary rest period of the seed prior to planting.

Table 26.2—Brief Description of Selected Potato Varieties.

Variety	Season	Flower Color	Resistant to	Shape	Color	Eyes
					Tubers	
Cherokee	Med. early	White	Late blight, common scab	Roundish	Creamy white	Medium
Chippewa	Midseason	Lavender	Mild mosaic	Long-oval flat	White	Shallow
Early Gem	Early	White	Common scab	Long-elliptical	Light russet	Shallow
Irish Cobbler	Early	Lilac	Wart, mild mosaic	Roundish	Creamy	Medium
Katahdin	Late	Lavender	Mild mosaic, brown rot, net necrosis, wart	Oval	White	Shallow
Kennebec	Late	White	Mild mosaic, late blight, net necrosis	Elliptical	Creamy buff	Shallow
Norland	105 days	Purple		Oblong, thick	Red	Shallow
Red Lasoda	Early	Lavender	Common scab	Long-elliptical	Red	Medium
Red Pontiac	Late	Lavender	Common scab	Oval-round	Dark red	Medium
Russet Burbank	Late	White		Long, roundish	Russet	Shallow
Russet Rural	Late	Violet	Common scab	Oblong, flat	Russet	Shallow
Russet Sebago	Late	Lavender, dark	Common scab	Oval-round	Russet	Shallow
Sebago	Late	Lavender, dark	Yellow dwarf	Oval-round	White	Shallow
Superior	Med. early		Common scab	Round	White	Shallow
White Rose	Midseason	White		Long, flattened	White, smooth	Medium

JOB 2.   PREPARING THE SOIL

Soil Preferences

The potato must have a fertile soil for even moderate yields. If drainage is good, heavy clay soils can be made to produce potatoes by adding large quantities of organic matter, or very porous sandy soils can be used by adding heavy applications of commercial fertilizers.

Preparing the Soil

The land should be broken deeply and then harrowed just before planting in the early spring. Where the land is very flat, it should be thrown up into high beds and a ditch provided along the ends of the rows for taking off the drainage water.

JOB 3.   FERTILIZING AND MANURING

Fertilizing

Nitrogen, phosphorus, and potassium are required in a fertilizer mixture for practically all the soil types used for growing potatoes. There may be exceptions in the case of some of the muck soils containing a high percentage of available nitrogen.

The potato belongs to the group of vegetable crops having the highest fertilizer requirement. The amount of fertilizer that can be applied profitably depends not only upon soil type and fertility but also upon environmental conditions affecting yields. Tables 6.4 and 6.5 can be used as guides for fertilizer recommendations. It may be noted that more nitrogen is recommended for the early than for the late crop. This element is usually less available early in the season and potatoes need to develop rapidly. For this reason fertilizer placement often gives increased yields, especially if less than optimum amounts are applied. Best results are obtained when the fertilizer is applied about 2 inches to the side and slightly below the seed piece. Injury and reduced yields result when the fertilizer and seed piece are placed together.

Manuring

Animal manures should be used where available. Summer cover crops turned under in the fall are good soil-improvement crops for potatoes to follow in the spring. Winter cover crops are not well suited because the potatoes are planted before the crop has time to make any appreciable amount of spring growth.

JOB 4. PLANTING

Treating Seed

Whether certified or common seed stock is used, the potatoes should be disinfected before they are cut for planting. Either one pint of commercial formaldehyde solution mixed with 30 gallons of water, or four ounces of corrosive sublimate dissolved in 30 gallons of water may be used.

The solutions should be handled in wooden vessels. The potatoes should be soaked in either solution from 45 minutes to 1½ hours and spread immediately after being removed in order for the surfaces to dry. They are then ready to be cut and planted.

Planting Rate

From 9 to 50 bushels of seed potatoes are required to plant an acre. The heavier rate of seeding should be employed on the most fertile soils, and under ideal climatic conditions.

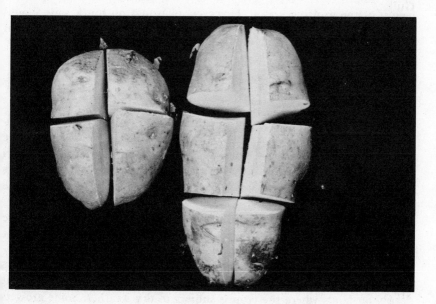

Fig. 26.2—Blocky seed pieces with one or more well placed eyes are desirable.

A medium-sized tuber is cut into four to six pieces, each piece containing one or more eyes (Fig. 26.2). Very small pieces containing only one eye frequently produce weak plants. If the pieces are cut too large, a large amount will be required to plant a given area, thus increasing the cost of seed.

There are mechanical devices for cutting potatoes for planting, but if the work can be done by hand, there will be a greater certainty of each piece containing one or more eyes. Potatoes should be planted soon after cutting, or the cut pieces should be cured by keeping them in an atmosphere of high humidity (85 percent or higher) and at a temperature of 60° to 65° F. If the cut seed is to be kept more than a week, curing is desirable. The tubers should not be cut immediately after removal from low-temperature storage.

Planting Time

In most sections early potatoes should be planted about five or six weeks before the last spring frost is expected or when the soil temperature reaches 40° F. In the milder sections of the South, as in Florida and in the Gulf Coast sections of Texas, the main planting of early potatoes is done in late fall or early winter. The date of a late planting depends upon the length of the growing season. However, plantings on muck soils should be made early enough that the plants will shade the soil before hot weather. High temperatures prevent tuber set as shown in Figure 26.3.

Planting Methods

The grower has a choice of one- or two-row planters, which will enable him to plant rather large areas in a comparatively short time, or he may drop the seed pieces by hand. The usual custom is to space the rows from 32 to 36 inches apart and drop the seed pieces from 12 to 15 inches apart in the row. Close spacing on good land well supplied with moisture tends to increase yields.

The seed pieces should usually be planted 2 to 3 inches deep. On the flat lands where drainage is difficult, the potatoes are planted only about 2 inches below the general level of the land and ridges are thrown up over the rows, covering the seed pieces about 2 inches more. Since the tubers are formed on the plant above the planted seed piece, it is well to plant deeply on lands where the crop is subject to dry weather. Some growers follow the plan of throwing up high ridges over the rows after planting,

Fig. 26.3—The potato may fail to produce tubers at high soil temperatures.

covering the seed pieces 5 to 6 inches deep. Then just before the young plants emerge a spike-tooth harrow is run over the land, killing the first crop of small weeds and breaking the crust of the soil to assist the plants in coming through.

JOB 5. CULTIVATING AND SPRAYING

Cultivating

If the land has been deeply broken and well harrowed before the potatoes are planted, the cultivation of the crop is a rather simple task. Sufficient shallow cultivations should be given to keep down weeds. At the same time, the soil should be gradually worked to the plants as they increase in height. If the soil becomes compact after planting, it may be necessary to give one deep cultivation soon after the plants come up. Following this, however, deep cultivation should be avoided to prevent serious injury to the roots.

By the time the plants bloom freely and begin to form tubers, beds or ridges in which the potatoes form should be completed and the crop cultivated no more.

Spraying and Dusting

Foliage diseases of the potato are most effectively controlled by keeping the plants covered with a fungicide. Spraying or dusting should begin when the plants are 4 to 6 inches tall and should be repeated at regular intervals throughout the growing season. Bordeaux mixture was formerly used almost exclusively, but it is now being replaced by newer fungicides such as Zineb, Maneb, or Nabam. These give effective control of the early and late blights and are less toxic to the plants.

In the spray schedule an insecticide such as DDT should be included to control insects prevalent at the time of application. See Chapter 11 for specific recommendations for controlling insects and diseases.

JOB 6.   CONTROLLING DISEASES AND INSECTS

Diseases

The potato is subject to a great variety of fungus, bacterial, and virus diseases, requiring a variety of control methods. Some of these diseases cause serious losses wherever the potato is grown, while others are more localized. Many of the most important diseases are seed-borne. Therefore, the importance of disease-free seed and seed treatment is being recognized by growers everywhere. Crop rotation is necessary to prevent increasing destructiveness of organisms that live over in soil and on old decaying vines and tubers, and spraying or dusting is necessary for control of insects and leaf diseases.

EARLY BLIGHT. Caused by *Alternaria solani*, early blight appears as large grayish-brown spots, usually showing concentric light and darker markings on the leaves. As the spots enlarge, they coalesce and finally involve the entire leaf.

This disease is most common in the South when a rainy period occurs during May or June. It is often confused with tip-burn, which becomes serious during dry, hot weather immediately following a period of excessive moisture. Together they cause heavy reduction of the crop nearly every year, sometimes as much as 50 percent. Loss from early blight can be reduced by spraying or dusting with Zineb or Maneb to kill this fungus.

LATE BLIGHT. Associated with *Phytophthora infestans*, late blight is usually considered the most serious leaf disease of the potato. Ordinarily it is not important in the South, but flourishes in the cool, wet weather common in the North. Control is accomplished by planting disease-free tubers, partly-resistant varieties, and spraying with fixed copper, Maneb, or Zineb.

MOSAIC. Mosaic is a virus disease, appearing as a mottling of the leaves with paler areas interspersed between darker ones, and accompanied by more or less crinkling. The loss of chlorophyll causes reduced elaboration of starch and consequent reduction of the tuber yield. The disease is carried from year to year in seed tubers. In the field, it is spread by insects, principally the potato aphid, which carries the juice from infected to healthy plants. Control consists in the use of properly certified seed.

LEAF ROLL. Leaf roll is a virus disease in which the affected plants are of a paler green color, more upright in habit, with the lower leaflets rolled upward. The yield is more seriously reduced than by mosaic. The means of transmission and methods of control are the same as for mosaic.

SCAB. Scab, resulting from attacks of *Streptomyces scabies*, is recognized by most potato growers by the characteristic pitting of the tubers. Badly pitted tubers are unsalable. The fungus lives in the diseased spots on the surface of healthy tubers, and in the soil. It grows best in slightly alkaline, neutral, and slightly acid soil, and may survive for several seasons unless the soil reaction is below pH 5.2. Varietal resistance offers a promising means of control. New introductions with resistance include Menominee, Ontario, Cayuga, Seneca, and Cherokee.

RING ROT. Ring rot is caused by the bacterium (*Corynebacterium sepedonicum*) and is extremely infectious. It affects the plants as well as the tubers. The lower leaves of an infected stem first turn yellow. Other leaves begin to roll and wilt, and the stem soon dies. Tubers are infected at the stem end, and the organism follows the vascular area.

The bacteria causing ring rot are spread by diseased seed, handling, and storage equipment. Use only disease-free seed and thoroughly disinfect anything used in handling diseased tubers.

BLACKLEG. Blackleg is a bacterial disease caused by *Erwina astroseptica*. Diseased plants assume a yellowish-green color, the stem is blackened below the soil line, the soft parts and the old seed piece decay, and with continued moist conditions the new tubers may decay in place. Tubers may also rot in storage or in transit. The bacteria may be carried either within or on the surface of the potato. When infected tubers are planted, the bacteria may enter the sprouts. The bacteria also live in the soil. Control methods include the use of disease-free seed stock, seed treatment, and crop rotation.

BLACK SCURF. Caused by *Pellicularia filamentosa*, black scurf consists of irregular, scurfy, blackish patches (sclerotia) on the surface of the potato. When such infected tubers are planted, the fungus often attacks the sprouts, killing them before they emerge from the soil or causing wilting and death at a later date. Infected tubers should not be used for seed. Large sclerotia are difficult to kill by the most thorough seed treatment, and thus it is not too satisfactory. PCNB disked into the top 4 to 6 inches of severely infected soils has given some control. Disease-free seed is still the most effective method.

Insects

More than 25 species of insects have been found injurious to the potato, but most of these are seldom seriously destructive over any great area (Fig. 26.4).

COLORADO POTATO BEETLES. Colorado potato beetles (*Leptinotarsa 10-lineata*) are thick-bodied yellow beetles about three-eights inch long, with dark-brown stripes on the wing covers. The young are red and soft-bodied, and cling to the edges of the leaves. Yellow eggs stand in close

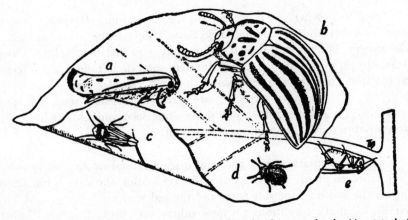

Fig. 26.4—Important potato insects: (a) tuber moth; (b) Colorado potato beetle; (c) potato leaf hopper; (d) potato flea beetle; (e) potato aphid.

groups on the under sides of the leaves. Adults and young eat irregular holes in the leaves and branches, beginning to feed as soon as plants are up.

The beetle is the best-known and most destructive enemy of potatoes in the United States. Since its spread eastward from its native home in the Rocky Mountains, it has now occupied all the potato-growing regions. The potato is its favorite food plant; it also feeds freely on tomato, eggplant, and horse nettle.

POTATO FLEA BEETLES. Potato flea beetles in the adult stage are about one-sixteenth inch long, black, and oval in outline. They jump quickly when disturbed and disappear from sight. The adults chew the leaves, causing shot-holes, while the larvae feed on the roots and tubers. The overwintering adults will attack young potato plants early in the spring. If control measures are used at this time, later damage may be reduced.

POTATO LEAF HOPPERS. Potato leaf hoppers (*Empoasca fabae*) are small, green, active-jumping, streamlined insects which suck juice from the under side of the leaves, causing the tips to turn brown and the edges to curl upward.

The leaf hopper is the worst pest of potatoes in the north central states and it occurs over the East and South, except in the southern parts of Florida and Texas. Its feeding brings about the condition called hopper-burn. Beans, alfalfa, and apple trees also suffer from this insect, and many other herbaceous and woody plants serve as hosts.

POTATO APHIDS. Potato aphids or plant lice of four different kinds feed on the potato plant. They cause damage by sucking juices from the foliage and by spreading virus diseases.

POTATO TUBERWORMS. Potato tuberworms (*Gnorimoschema operculella*) are pinkish-white caterpillars, approximately one-quarter inch long. They mine the leaves and stems and burrow into the tubers. Late potatoes and those in storage are more frequently attacked than the early crop. The tuberworm has been of importance in practically every state. Hot, dry weather in the field and the accumulation of potatoes in storage encourage this pest.

In Maryland, infestation of potatoes by the tuberworm was prevented by hilling the tubers 6 to 8 inches deep about 40 days after planting. Tubers, after being dug, should not be left on the ground overnight, and should not be covered with potato vines. Eggs are laid by moths on exposed tubers, during the late afternoon and night.

OTHER PESTS. In addition to these specific pests, several general feeders sometimes become destructive to potatoes. They include blister beetles, white grubs, wireworms, plant bugs, nematodes, and the vegetable weevil. The general treatment of these is discussed in Chapter 11.

JOB 7. HARVESTING, GRADING, STORING, AND MARKETING

Potatoes of the early crop seldom reach full maturity on account of dry warm weather, early blight, tip-burn, and other conditions which interfere with normal growth. Consequently, the plants usually begin to die down before the crop is mature even though good culture has been given and a spray schedule followed. As this stage approaches, harvesting is in order. Some growers harvest even earlier if the price for early or new potatoes is high. On the other hand, harvesting is delayed when prices are low.

Although the harvesting time for late potatoes is determined primarily by maturity of the crop, other considerations such as market prospects, availability of help, and weather conditions, may be influencing factors. The vines should mature and die before harvest so the skins of the tubers will set and thus decrease the likelihood of skinning and bruising. Also, if the vines are not dead, there is a chance spores of late blight will be transferred from the vines to the tubers, where they may later produce rot in storage. Especially now, with more effective methods of pest control, the vines live longer and it is often necessary to kill them before harvesting. This can be done by machines that have a beating action on the plants, but this is costly. Dinitro compounds and ammonium sulphate can be applied with regular spray equipment and a good kill obtained in 4 to 10 days.

Harvesting and Grading

Potatoes should be handled as gently as practicable from the harvesting machine to the retail store. They are dug by a variety of machines ranging from one-row, horse-drawn potato diggers to elaborate two-row, mechanical harvesters (Fig. 26.5). In any case, the potatoes should be removed from the soil economically with the least possible movement and

Fig. 26.5—Two-row harvester delivering potatoes to truck.

Photograph by E. C. Wittmeyer

injury to the tubers. Modern potato harvesters convey potatoes to low-level trailers in order to minimize movement and bruising. To decrease handling, supplemental grading and bagging equipment is attached to or operates in conjunction with mechanical harvesters in many instances.

Early potatoes are sensitive to the sun and wind and may be easily damaged by handling in the field and packing shed. They are frequently washed in chlorinated water for cleaning and disinfecting. Early potatoes should be harvested, graded, and packed as expeditiously as feasible, and shipped under refrigeration when the weather is warm.

The U.S. Department of Agriculture has developed detailed specifications and tolerances which are generally understood by growers and packers and demanded by the trade.

Storing

Most of the main crop of potatoes cannot be marketed immediately after harvesting and must be placed in storage. At first the tubers should be held at 55° to 60° F. with high relative humidity and good ventilation for two to three weeks. These conditions favor the healing of cuts and bruises. The temperature may then be lowered to 38° to 40° F. At this range the tubers will not sprout in storage. Where low temperatures are not available, sprouting of table stock may be reduced by the use of a sprout inhibitor. Maleic hydrazide at the rate of three pounds per acre applied to the plants a few weeks before harvesting is effective. Temperatures below this range, to some extent, favor the accumulation of sugars, making potatoes unsuitable for chips. This condition can be overcome by storing the tubers for about two weeks at 60° to 70° F.

Marketing

Potato growers usually sell through cooperatives or central packing sheds as volume buyers want a uniform quality pack in dependable quantities. Most of the larger producing districts attract competitive buyers from large markets who purchase potatoes at the assembling and shipping points. Attractive packaging promotes sales. Potatoes are sold by the hundredweight usually in 100-pound bags but other types of packages are used also. Some early potatoes from California, Florida, and Alabama, for example, are being packed in 50-pound mesh or "open window" bags. Regardless of the source or type of container, most buyers and consumers demand high quality potatoes.

The United States exported an average of 3,265,000 hundredweight of fresh potatoes annually during the past 10 years, while exports of dehydrated potato products increased greatly. In 1963 about 3,260,000 hundredweight of fresh potatoes valued at $7,207,000 were shipped primarily to Canada with small irregular quantities going to Mexico, Venezuela, Panama, Argentina, and more than 20 other countries.

SELECTED REFERENCES

Dudley, J. E., Jr., et al., "Control of Potato Insects," USDA Farmers' Bull. 2040, 1952.

Dykstra, T. P., "Potato Diseases and Their Control," USDA Farmers' Bull. 1881, 1948.

Edmundson, W. C., *et al.*, "Potato Production in the Western States," USDA Farmers' Bull. 2034, 1951.

Houghland, G. V. C., *et al.*, "Potato Production in the Northeastern and North Central States," USDA Farmers' Bull. 1958, 1954.

Humphrey, E., "Steps That Can Be Taken to Reduce Mechanical Damage to Potatoes at Harvest Time," Idaho Agr. Exp. Sta. Bull. 278, 1950.

Kehr, A. E., Akeley, R. V., and Houghland, V. C., "Commercial Potato Production," USDA *Agr. Handbook 267*, 1964.

Kunkel, R., *et al.*, "Results With Potato Vine Killers in Colorado," Colo. Agr. Exp. Sta. Tech. Bull. 46, 1952.

LeClerg, E. L., "Potato Production in the Southern States," USDA Farmers' Bull. 1904, 1942.

Ohms, R. E., "Producing the Idaho Potato," Idaho Agr. Ext. Ser. Bull. 367, 1962.

Pawski, L. and Findlen, H., "Handling and Shipping Potatoes to Processing Plants in Pallet Boxes and Burlap Bags," USDA Marketing Res. Rep. No. 495, 1961.

Schoenemann, J. A., "Growing Wisconsin Potatoes," Wisc. Agr. Ext. Cir. 440, 1953.

Seelig, R. A., "Potatoes," United Fresh Fruit and Vegetable Association, Washington, D.C., 1959.

Simmons, W. M., "An Economic Study of the Potato Industry," USDA Agri. Economic Report 6, 1962.

CHAPTER 27

Root Crops

Root crops include the beet, carrot, parsnip, turnip, rutabaga, and radish. These crops are grown for an enlarged fleshy structure called the root.

This enlarged root consists of both root and stem tissue. From the lower part arises the absorbing roots and from the upper part arises the stems and leaves. All root crops thrive best in relatively cool weather and have similar cultural requirements; and all are biennials except the radish, which is either annual or biennial. In a particular area, these crops should be planted so as to develop during a relatively cool part of the growing season.

BEET

Classification and History

The beet (*Beta vulgaris*) is a native of Europe, North Africa, and West Asia. Swiss chard, sugar beets, and stock beets or mangel-wurzels all belong to the same species as the garden beet. De Candolle states that though the ancients knew about the beet, they did not cultivate it until the third century A.D. The Germans and French became interested in beets about the year 1800. Since that time, many improved types have been developed.

Scope and Importance

Beets ranked 21st both in acreage and value among the 22 principal vegetables in 1965, and are relatively unimportant economically. They are grown commercially in limited sections of the country, but are produced for local market and home use in many areas.

The acreage for fresh market beets declined from 12,840 in 1939 to about 3,300 in 1965, but beets for canning rose from 8,240 to about 14,400 during this time. Farm value for the fresh market crop rose slightly from $1,114,000 in 1939 to an estimated $2,108,000 in 1965, while that for processing increased from $575,000 to an estimated $3,268,000 in 1965. Acre yields for both categories of beets increased substantially during this period.

The acreage, production, and value of beets for fresh market and canning are shown by states in Tables 27.1 and 27.2, respectively.

Table 27.1—Beets for Fresh Market: Shipping Season and Estimated Commercial Acreage, Yield, Production, and Value in Leading States, 1965.

State	Season	Harvested Acreage	Yield per Acre, Cwt.	Production, 1,000 Cwt.	Price per Cwt.	Value, $1,000
Texas	Winter	1,700	95	162	$6.40	1,037
New Jersey	Summer	700	160	112	4.20	470
Pennsylvania	Summer	500	190	95	4.20	399
South Carolina	Spring	250	70	18	6.70	121
North Carolina	Spring	140	130	18	4.50	81
All states		3,290	123	405	5.20	2,108

Table 27.2—Beets for Canning: Estimated Commercial Acreage, Yield, Production, and Value in Leading States, 1965.

State	Harvested Acreage	Yield per Acre, Tons	Production in Tons	Price per Ton	Value, $1,000
Wisconsin	4,900	12.1	59,300	$17.60	1,044
New York	4,800	13.3	63,800	18.00	1,148
Oregon	1,200	18.0	21,600	20.00	432
Michigan	360	9.6	3,500	22.40	78
Other states	3,120	9.1	28,360	20.00	566
All states	14,380	12.3	176,560	18.50	3,268

Trends in Production Efficiency

Efficiency in beet production has increased considerably in recent years. Between 1939 and 1959, labor required to grow and harvest the fresh market crop decreased from 201 to 94 man-hours per acre, while man-hour unit production increased 176 percent. Beets for processing experienced a more spectacular decrease from 146 to 58 man-hours per acre for the same period, while labor-unit output rose 381 percent. Average yields of fresh market beets increased from 93 to 119 hundredweight in the 1939-1959 period while those for processing rose from 108 to 207 hundredweight per acre (Table 1.4).

Plant Characteristics

The edible portion of the root consists of alternating circular bands of conducting and storage tissues. The bands of storage tissues are relatively broad and dark; those of conducting tissues, relatively narrow and light. The contrast in color between these alternating bands is known as zoning, which varies greatly between varieties and within a variety. High temperatures will usually result in poor color development of the root.

The beet has a relatively large absorbing system. Studies at the New York (Cornell) Agricultural Experiment Station have shown that the roots extend downward 2½ to 3 feet and that numerous branches arise in close proximity to the enlarged roots.

The stem is short and platelike; the leaves are simple and arranged in a closed spiral on a short stem called the crown. They vary from dark red to light green. Stomata occur on both the upper and lower surfaces. The so-called seed is really a fruit which contains from two to five or six seeds.

Selecting Varieties

In general, beet varieties are classified according to the shape and the time of maturity of the root. There are (1) flat or globular, early-maturing varieties, (2) globular, second-early-maturing varieties, and (3) long, late-maturing varieties. Representative varieties of the flat or globular, early-maturing sorts are Crosby's Egyptian, Green Top Bunching, Ruby Queen, and Early Wonder. Representative varieties of the globular, scond-early sorts are Detroit Dark Red and Perfected Detroit. A representative variety of long, late-maturing sorts is Long Dark Blood or Long Smooth Blood. The Crosby's Egyptian, Green Top Bunching, and Early Wonder are early market garden varieties. Detroit Dark Red is a second-early market garden beet and is used for canning and for general purposes in the home garden. Detroit Short Top, a strain of Detroit Dark Red, has small leaves and is well adapted for bunching. Perfected Detroit is a very good processing beet due to its superior interior color and globular shape at an early age. Figures 27.1 and 27.2 represent flat and globular types respectively.

Fig. 27.1—Acceptable range in type of Crosby Egyptian beet (flat type).

USDA Photograph

Preparing the Seedbed

Beets thrive best in well-drained, slightly acid soils including sandy loams, loams, silt loams, and high-lime mucks. Beets will do well over a fairly wide range of pH, but they are quite sensitive to soils of high acidity. The optimum pH range is from 6.0 to 7.0.

Soil preparation should be thorough. Deep plowing, immediately followed by disking, pulverizes the surface, promotes the formation of a fine seedbed, and conserves moisture.

For highest quality, beets must make rapid and uninterrupted growth. Well-rotted stable manure, where available, is recommended at the rate of 10 to 15 tons per acre. As with other crops, the kind and

Fig. 27.2—Acceptable range in type of Early Wonder beet (globular type).

USDA Photograph

amount of commercial fertilizer required varies with the soil type, soil fertility, previous fertilization, and the rotation. Commercial fertilizers containing 6 to 7 percent nitrogen, 5 to 6 percent phosphorus, and 5 to 6 percent potassium should be used at a rate of not less than 1,000 pounds per acre. Side dressing with a nitrate form of nitrogen fertilizer when the plants are 4 to 6 inches high is a recommended practice. On muck soils less nitrogen is needed and usually more potassium is applied. In certain areas of New York, Wisconsin, and Oregon, deficiencies of boron have to be corrected to prevent internal black spot. Applications of borax or boric acid in amounts varying from 10 to 40 pounds per acre will correct the deficiency. Too much boron is toxic, so care must be exercised in its application. Recommendations from local agricultural experiment stations and extension services should be closely followed.

Planting and Thinning

The seed balls are usually planted with a seed drill at rates varying from four to six pounds per acre, in rows 18 to 24 inches apart. Thinning is usually necessary for market crops, as each seed ball may produce from one to five or six plants. In market gardens and in home gardens thinning is frequently delayed until the plants are sufficiently large for use. In general, plants are thinned 3 to 4 inches apart. In fields of beets grown for processing, thinning is seldom practiced since labor costs are too high. Processors usually pay a premium for small-sized beets, so close spacing is desirable.

Cultivating

Cultivation is necessary to keep down weeds; investigations have shown that weeds markedly decrease the yields of beets. Continuous cultivation of a sandy loam in the absence of weeds slightly increased yields in some years, but decreased them in other years.

In general, the cultivation program will depend on the type of soil, the season at which the crop is grown, the character of the rainfall, and the prevalence of weeds. On light soils it is less necessary than on heavy soils. Seasons of heavy rainfall require more cultivation than seasons of light rainfall. Deep cultivation should not be practiced because many of the roots are found near the surface of the soil.

Controlling Pests

Principal pests are leaf spot and scab, both fungus diseases; and insects, especially the webworm and the leaf miner, which is a white maggot. Cutworms and wireworms sometimes cause damage. All of these pests are controlled largely by practicing sanitation and rotation. Leaf miners can be controlled with TEPP or malathion if applications are properly timed; webworms are best controlled with DDT.

Harvesting

Beets for market are harvested and bunched when they reach a diameter of from 1¼ to 1½ inches. Many beets are now mechanically harvested and topped. The washed beets are prepackaged in transparent film bags for sale in retail stores. Such a practice extends the shelf life over that of beets with tops. Nearly all of the beets for processing are mechanically harvested with a machine that lifts, tops, and conveys the topped beets into trucks. Beets can be stored under proper conditions for relatively long periods of time, as can most of the root crops. Beets are also satisfactorily dehydrated.

CARROT

Classification and History

The carrot (*Daucus carota* var. *sativa*) is a native of Europe and adjoining portions of Asia. The Vilmorins, notable seedsmen of France, are responsible for the early development of the carrot. In the short space of a few years, they developed roots similar in appearance to the well-known varieties of the present day from the thin wirelike roots of the wild carrot. In the sixteenth century, roots which varied in size, color, and shape were known in Europe. In the New World, the carrot soon became popular among the Indians. In fact, the Flathead Indians of Oregon were so fond of them that they could not forbear stealing them from the fields. Carrots are an excellent source of vitamin A and a good source of vitamins B_1, C, and G (B_2).

Scope and Importance

Carrots are grown throughout the country for home use and local markets and commercially in more than 20 states. Among the 22 principal vegetable crops, carrots ranked 15th in acreage and 11th in value in 1965. Acreage increased from 58,020 in 1939 to 97,300 in 1945 and declined to approximately 79,800 in 1965. Carrot yields rose gradually during this period and production increased from 8,969,000 to almost 17,500,000 hundredweight. Farm value rose from $11,831,000 in 1939 to an estimated $61,170,000 in 1965.

The leading states in production and value in 1965 were Texas, California, Michigan, and Wisconsin as shown in Table 27.3.

Trends in Production Efficiency

The carrot is a comparatively expensive crop to grow. Improved herbicides now eliminate expensive, repetitive hand weeding and hoeing and precision planters are especially helpful in reducing the labor requirements of thinning, a practice which has been eliminated on many farms. In 1939, 284 man-hours were required to grow and harvest an acre while

Table 27.3—Carrots for Fresh Market and Processing: Shipping Season and Estimated Commercial Acreage, Yield, Production, and Value in Leading States, 1965.

State	Season	Harvested Acreage	Yield per Acre, Cwt.	Production, 1,000 Cwt.	Price per Cwt.	Value, $1,000
Texas	Winter	30,000	140	4,200	$3.42	14,350
California	Winter	8,500	215	1,828	3.97	7,259
California	Early summer	7,300	275	2,008	4.79	9,626
California	Late fall	7,100	290	2,059	3.61	7,423
Texas	Early fall	5,300	190	1,007	3.95	3,978
Michigan	Early fall	4,600	240	1,104	3.76	4,151
Wisconsin	Early fall	3,200	395	1,264	2.12	2,676
Arizona	Spring	2,300	185	426	4.90	2,087
New York	Early fall	2,200	330	726	2.50	1,812
Washington	Early fall	1,700	380	646	1.81	1,172
Colorado	Late summer	1,500	190	285	6.10	1,738
Oregon	Early fall	1,400	410	574	1.30	748
All states		79,795	218	17,432	3.51	61,170

only 105 hours were used on the average in 1959. The acre yield of carrots increased from 154 to 190 hundredweight during the 1939-1959 period and production per man-hour rose 235 percent. Labor efficiency will undoubtedly continue to increase (Table 1.4).

Plant Characteristics

A cross section of the root shows two distinct regions, an outer core and an inner core. The outer core consists of (1) a thin periderm, a layer of cork cells; and (2) a relatively wide band of secondary phloem, the region where sugars are mainly stored. The inner core consists of (1) secondary xylem and (2) pith. High-quality carrots are those which have a relatively large outer core. Investigators have shown that the outer core contains more vitamin A than the inner core.

Carrots develop a deep, extensive, absorbing root system. During the seedling stage, the absorbing roots develop rather slowly, but as the edible portion enlarges, it gives rise to a large number of fine absorbing roots. Investigations at the New York (Cornell) Agricultural Experiment Station have shown that carrots growing in gravelly sandy loam fill the soil with roots to depths of 25 to 30 inches.

The stem consists of a small plate-like crown which develops from the plumule. During the second year the plate-like stem elongates and forms branches 2 to 4 feet high which bear the flowers and seed. The leaves arise in the form of a rosette and are long-petioled and decompound. The seed is a very small, dry, indehiscent, one-seeded fruit. It germinates very slowly and requires a fine, friable seedbed and a uniform supply of moisture.

Temperature Requirements

Investigations at the New York (Cornell) Agricultural Experiment Station have shown that temperature has a marked effect on the growth and shape of the root of the Red Cored Chantenay variety. Total growth was greater and type of growth more normal at 60° to 70° F. than at 70° to 80° F., or 50° to 60° F., or 40° to 50° F. As the temperature was increased, roots of the Red Cored Chantenay became shortened like those of Oxheart. When the temperature was decreased, the roots became long and pointed, more like those of Long Orange.

Low temperature has been found to be the main factor responsible for poor color development of the carrot root, which is a problem with winter-grown carrots in certain areas of the South. The orange color is chiefly due to the presence of beta carotene, a precursor of vitamin A.

Exposure of the developing plants to relatively low temperatures is an important factor in causing premature seeding, which is sometimes a problem.

Selecting Varieties

Carrots are generally classified according to shape and length of the root. There are (1) varieties which are blunt and (2) those which are pointed. Within the former class there are varieties which are short (length exceeding two but not four times the diameter) as well as long. Within the latter class there are varieties which are moderately short (length not exceeding four times the diameter) and those which are long (length exceeding four times the diameter).

Oxheart is a representative variety of the blunt-short type; Chantenay is representative of the blunt half-long type; Danvers Half Long is of the pointed half-long type; and Imperator is a representative variety of the pointed-long type. The varieties most popular with the fresh market trade are Imperator, Gold Pak, Gold Spike, and Empress, all of which have a long slender shape and good color. The processing varieties include Red Cored Chantenay and Royal Chantenay, which have excellent color development. Nantes and Danvers Half Long are used as home garden and market varieties. Varietal types are shown in Figure 27.3.

Fig. 27.3—Carrot varieties: (L to R) Imperator, Morse's Bunching, Chantenay Red Core, and Supreme Half Long.

Soil Preference

For best development the carrot requires deep, loose, well-drained sandy loams or loams with a slightly acid reaction. If carrots are grown on comparatively heavy soil, they are likely to produce abundant leaf growth and forked roots. Some carrots are grown on muck land, which is desirable because of its light texture, but the roots tend to be rougher than those grown on light mineral soils.

Since carrot seed is small, and since the seedling grows slowly, the seedbed should be in fine physical condition.

Planting

The seed is planted about one-half to three-quarters inch deep. The rate of planting ranges from two to four pounds of seed per acre in rows

18 to 24 inches apart. The time of planting varies, but seed may be planted as soon as hard freezes are over in the spring. Fall and winter plantings are usually made in the South and West. In the West, carrots are frequently planted on raised beds, two rows on each. In some areas of the West seed is scattered thinly in a row 3 to 4 inches wide to permit production without thinning. Seeds generally germinate rather slowly and irregularly, and seedling growth is quite weak. For this reason, soils that crust badly are poorly adapted for carrot production. Hand thinning of commercial plantings is seldom practiced as the cost is excessive. Therefore seeding rates should be controlled as accurately as possible.

Fertilizing

The kind and amount of fertilizer to apply varies with the locality and the time of year the crop is grown. The fertilizer practice, generally, is very similar to that for beets. Fresh manure should not be used as investigations have shown that the liquid portion of the manure apparently stimulates branching of the roots. If manure is to be used, it should be well rotted or applied to the preceding crop. On muck soils only small amounts of nitrogen are needed. Table 6.5 may be used as a guide to the application of phosphorus and potassium. On mineral soils in the West, nitrogen is applied at the rate of 60 to 100 pounds per acre, and about 50 pounds of P_2O_5 is applied as an average. Potassium is rarely used. A side dressing with nitrogen is a general practice, but care must be taken to avoid causing excessive top growth.

Cultivating and Chemical Weed Control

Since the seedlings grow slowly, weed control, particularly during the early portion of the growing season, is necessary. Weeds are difficult to control by machine cultivation while the carrots are small. Hand weeding is too expensive in commercial plantings. Since 1945, the use of herbicidal oils, which give excellent control, has been developed. Carrot fields are sprayed with Stoddard solvent after the first true leaves have formed and preferably not later than the four-leaf stage. Spraying should be done when the weather is warm but not over 80° F. as injury may result. Beds should be sprayed with 50 to 60 gallons per acre. On level plantings, 75 to 85 gallons per acre are required. The chemical treatment will keep most weeds under control until the foliage is large enough to shade weed seedlings within the rows. Conventional shallow cultivation will take care of those between the rows. At the last cultivation, a little soil should be moved to the rows to cover the tops of the roots and thus prevent greening.

Controlling Pests

A complete discussion of vegetable diseases and insects, some of which attack root crops, is given in Chapter 11.

CARROT YELLOWS. Carrot yellows is a virus disease that occasionally causes serious damage. It is transmitted by the six-spotted leaf hopper. A practical means of control is to spray or dust with DDT, malathion, methoxychlor, or carbaryl to control the leaf hopper.

Other diseases include bacterial blight, leaf spot, scab, and soft rot.

CARROT RUST FLY. The carrot rust fly (*Psila rosae*) causes serious damage in certain areas as the larvae burrow into the roots, often in large numbers. Satisfactory control has been achieved by soil applications of diazinon.

Other insects that may cause damage are the vegetable weevil, wireworms, and the carrot beetle.

Harvesting and Grading

Carrots are harvested either with or without the top. Those harvested with the top are called bunch carrots, while those harvested without the top are called bulk carrots. Most carrots for market are now topped, washed, graded, and packaged in transparent film bags. Topping greatly reduces weight loss of the roots and increases storage life. Washing and topping are usually done mechanically. Roots are sorted into various sizes for packaging. Processing carrots are harvested with beet harvesters in many areas.

Carrots store well under proper conditions. Cold storage at 32° to 34° F. with high humidity gives best results.

PARSNIP

Classification and History

The parsnip (*Pastinaca sativa*) is a native of Europe and Asia. It was brought to America by the early colonists. It is a member of the *Um-*

Fig. 27.4—Carrots being examined by federal-state inspector before packaging.

USDA Photograph

belliferae family, which also includes carrots, celery, and parsley. The parsnip is a long-season crop that will withstand freezing weather if left in the field. The crop is not grown extensively. Pennsylvania, Illinois, California, and New York lead in its production.

Selecting Varieties

Very few varieties are listed in seed catalogs. The most popular are Hollow Crown and All American. Parsnip seed does not retain its viability for very long, so freshly grown seed should always be obtained.

Preparing the Soil

A deep, fertile soil is essential for successful production of this crop. Smooth roots and good stands are difficult to obtain on heavy soils. In general, the methods of soil preparation are similar to those for carrots or beets.

Planting

Parsnip seed is usually planted in rows ranging from 15 to 18 inches apart for hand cultivation or from 24 to 30 inches apart for tractor cultivation. A half ounce of seed is usually sufficient for a 100-foot row and three to four pounds is sufficient to plant an acre with rows 15 inches apart. Seed is covered one-half to three-quarters inch deep. Plants are usually thinned to a stand of three to six per foot in the row. Parsnips grow during a long season and for this reason have a low fertilizer requirement.

Fertilizing

Commercial fertilizers should be applied at a rate slightly lower than is required for carrots under comparable conditions.

Cultivating

Cultivation for control of weeds should begin as early as possible. Parsnip plants develop slowly and are poor competitors with weeds. Weeding as well as cultivation is usually necessary. Much of the early cultivation is usually done with wheel hoes or small tractors. Shallow cultivation for control of weeds should continue until the leaves practically cover the ground.

Harvesting

The roots are usually left in the ground until late fall and sometimes throughout the winter. Where severe freezing occurs it is not practical to leave the roots in the ground because of the difficulty in digging them when needed.

The roots attain a length of 10 to 12 inches and care must be exercised in digging so as not to break them. At the time of harvest the roots are high in starch which changes to sugar upon storage at low temperatures. Storage of the roots is a common practice; methods similar to those for other root crops are used.

RADISH

History and Classification

The writings of ancient naturalists indicate that the radish (*Raphanus sativus*) has been cultivated for a long time. Pliny records that it was extensively cultivated in Egypt at the time of the Pharoahs. The Greeks were especially fond of radishes and always served them on dishes of gold in their sacrificial offerings to Apollo. The radish was introduced into England and France about the beginning of the sixteenth century. In 1806, eleven sorts were known in America.

Plant Characteristics

The edible portion consists of both root and stem tissue, which varies greatly in color, size, shape, and texture of the flesh. Color varies from white to black. Size and shape are the most distinguishing characteristics.

According to investigations at the Nebraska Agricultural Experiment station, the absorbing system is not very extensive. Though certain absorbing roots had a lateral spread of 12 to 16 inches, most of the roots were 2 to 8 inches long. Radishes can be cultivated 2 inches deep with little damage to the root system.

The stem is a short crown, and when the plant produces seed, the stem elongates and bears perfect, insect-pollinated flowers and podded fruits. Some varieties bear flowers and seed the first year, while others bear seed the second year; hence the radish is either an annual or a biennial. With the annual varieties, flowering is apparently controlled by the length of the day. The Scarlet Globe, an important commercial variety, was grown under a seven-hour day at Washington, D.C., in the spring; other lots were grown under a 12-hour day. The plants subjected to the seven-hour day produced a large, overgrown root, while those subjected to a 12-hour day produced flowers and seeds. The leaves, which arise in a rosette, are simple and lobed, and vary in size according to the variety.

Temperature Requirements

The radish is a hardy, cool-season crop which withstands subfreezing temperatures. Certain varieties, particularly the spring varieties, become pithy in hot weather.

Selecting Varieties

Varieties are classified according to the length of time needed for the roots to attain maturity, and the shape of the root. There are (1) the spring varieties, (2) the summer varieties, and (3) the winter varieties. Within each of the three maturity groups, long and globe-shaped varieties are to be had. The spring varieties grow quickly, mature in a relatively short time (20 to 30 days), and the root remains in an edible condition for a short time only. The summer varieties grow less quickly, mature in a relatively longer time (35 to 40 days), and the roots remain in an edible condition longer. The winter varieties grow slowly (50 to 60 days), attain a larger size, and can be stored readily.

The most popular spring varieties are globe shaped and bright red in color. Some of the best are Early Scarlet Globe, Cherry Belle, Comet Cavalier, Globe Master, and Red Prince. Long-rooted spring types include White Icicle, Cincinnati Market, and Long Scarlet Short Top. Typical summer varieties are White Strasburg and White Vienna, which are long types. Summer varieties are not grown to any extent in this country. The most popular winter varieties are Chinese White Winter (Celestial, California Mammoth White), Chinese Rose Winter (Scarlet China), Round Black Spanish, and Long Black Spanish. Commercial varietal types are shown in Fig. 27.5.

Selecting and Preparing Soils

In general, radishes produce satisfactory crops on well-drained, moderately to slightly acid sandy loams, loams, and clay loams, the type of loam depending on the type of radish grown. Muck soils are used in some areas. Sandy loams are preferred for spring market crops, while well-

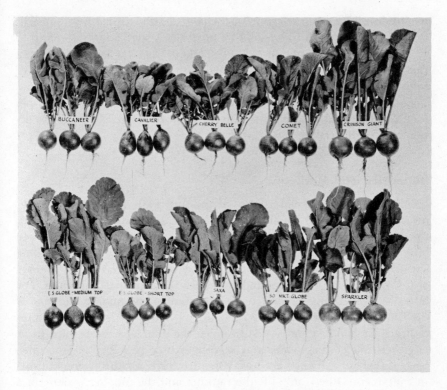

Fig. 27.5—Common varieties of radish.

Associated Seed Growers

drained silt and clay loams are preferred for the summer and winter sorts. The soil must be thoroughly prepared and the surface smooth in order to obtain uniform depth of planting.

Fertilizing

A rich fertile soil is necessary for rapid growth. Usually 1,000 pounds of 5-10-10 or a similar fertilizer is applied broadcast before seeding. Less fertilizer is needed if the crop follows one that has been heavily fertilized.

Planting

Plantings in the North are started very early in the spring. Winter plantings are common in the South. To obtain successive harvests, seed usually is planted at about 10-day intervals. Spacing of harvests can also be obtained by careful selection of varieties. Seed is drilled from one-half to three-quarters inch in rows 12 to 18 inches apart at the rate of 10 to 12 pounds per acre to obtain a stand of about 12 to 18 plants per foot. In the West two rows are planted per bed with seeding at the rate of three to four seeds per inch. Some seed is also sown broadcast. The larger-growing winter types are usually thinned to a stand of four to six plants per foot. Grading seed to a uniform size is a good commercial practice to obtain a uniform seeding rate.

Harvesting and Marketing

Harvesting operations consist of pulling, washing, grading, bunching, and packing. All small, diseased, and cracked roots are discarded. Bunching is frequently done in the field and the number of plants per bunch depends on the variety. Long-rooted varieties are bunched in fours and fives, while round and globular-rooted varieties are tied in bunches of 6 to 12. Baskets, hampers, and crates are the principal containers. For long-distance shipment, cracked ice is placed in the middle and top of the containers and the radishes are shipped under refrigeration. Winter radishes are handled and stored in much the same way as are turnips. A large portion of the commercial acreage is now harvested by machine. Several types of machines are used. One lifts, tops, and drops the radishes in containers. Others only lift the radishes and the topping is done in a packing shed. The topped radishes are washed and packaged in transparent film bags. Nearly all radishes are prepackaged for the retail trade.

RUTABAGA

The rutabaga (*Brassica campestris* var. *napobrassica*), sometimes called Swede turnip, closely resembles the turnip. Distinguishing characteristics between the two crops are given in Table 27.4.

The cultural requirements of the rutabaga are similar to those of

Table 27.4—Rutabaga and Turnip Characteristics.

Parts Compared	Turnip Characteristics	Rutabaga Characteristics
Leaves	Green and hairy	Grayish green and nonhairy
Crown	Indistinct	Distinct
Root	Small	Large

the turnip. The crop is widely grown in Canada and is grown commercially in Minnesota, Wisconsin, and Washington. It is generally planted in June and harvested in October and November. The roots are trimmed, washed, and waxed for market.

TURNIP

Classification and History

The turnip (*Brassica rapa*) is a native of Siberia. It was grown in olden times and introduced into England about 1550. It was brought to America by the early colonists. Turnips are grown both for greens and for the fleshy roots. The turnip is most extensively grown in the South.

Plant Characteristics

The turnip develops an extensive and finely branched root system. Studies at the Nebraska Agricultural Experiment Station have shown that plants three weeks old have deep roots 2 feet long. Plants 41 days old have roots which extend to the 3-foot level. The leaves, which arise in the form of a rosette, are simple, grass-green, and hairy. Seed is small, reddish black, and germinates quickly. The turnip is primarily a cool-season crop, hence it is grown in the fall, winter, and early spring in the South, and in the spring or fall in the North.

Selecting Varieties

Two groups exist, the white-fleshed group and the yellow-fleshed group. The white-fleshed group is more extensively grown. Within this group there are (1) varieties grown primarily for the top and (2) those grown primarily for the root. Japanese Shogoin is the most important variety grown for greens. Seven Top, an old variety, is still grown, but the roots are woody and of poor quality. The principal white varieties grown for the root are Purple Top White Globe, White Flat Dutch, White Milan, and White Egg. Some yellow-fleshed varieties are Yellow Globe, Golden Ball, and Yellow Aberdeen.

Preparing the Soil

Turnips thrive well on moist well-drained, moderately to slightly acid sandy loams and loams. Preparation of the soil in the manner recommended for beets will give satisfactory results with turnips. Actually, however, turnips are not as exacting as either beets or carrots. Both germination and seedling growth are rapid. Heavy fertilization to stimulate rapid development is essential for the spring crop, but not so important in the fall.

Planting

Seed is planted either by hand or by machine, at the rate of two or three pounds per acre. Rows are spaced from 12 to 15 inches apart for hand cultivation and about 24 inches apart for tractor cultivation. Seed is covered about one-half inch deep.

Cultivation

The cultivation program is similar to that of other root crops. The first or second cultivation may be relatively deep, but succeeding cultivations should be shallow.

Controlling Pests

The diseases and insects that attack turnips are usually the same as or very similar to those on cabbage, and these are discussed in Chapters 11 and 16.

Harvesting, Packing, and Marketing

Preparing turnip roots for market consists of (1) pulling, (2) grading, (3) bunching or topping, and (4) washing. Pulling is done by hand, and yellow, diseased, or injured leaves are removed. If bunched, four to six plants are tied together and washed to remove adhering soil. Most of the roots are now topped and packed for retail sale in transparent film bags. Beet harvesters are frequently used for the purpose of lifting and topping.

When the tops of turnips are harvested as greens, they are either picked or cut by hand or cut by improvised machines. Turnip greens may be graded and packed or sold in bulk.

MARKETING ROOT CROPS

The root crops are marketed much the same as other vegetables.

Quality and uniformity of variety, grade, color, and size are important in the market and consumers acceptance of these vegetables.

Volume buyers prefer to purchase from areas which can provide standard grades in sufficient quantities for economical transportation.

SELECTED REFERENCES

Anonymous, "Growing Table Beets," USDA Leaflet 360, 1966.

Anonymous, "Production of Turnips and Rutabagas," USDA Leaflet 142, 1966.

Barnes, W. C., "Effects of Some Environmental Factors on Growth and Color of Carrots," Cornell Univ. Agr. Exp. Sta. Memoir 186, 1936.

Beattie, J. H. and Beattie, W. R., "Production of Parsnips," USDA Leaflet 154. 1959.

Beattie, W. R., "Production and Preparation of Horseradish," USDA Leaflet 129. 1960.

Boswell, V. R., "Commercial Growing of Carrots," USDA Leaflet 353, 1966.

Franklin, D. F., "Growing Carrot Seed in Idaho," Idaho Agr. Exp. Sta. Bull. 294. 1953.

Seelig, R. A., "Carrots," United Fresh Fruit and Vegetable Association, Washington, D.C., 1963.

Seelig, R. A. and Roberts, E., "Radishes," United Fresh Fruit and Vegetable Association, Washington, D.C., 1959.

CHAPTER 28

Spinach

Classification, Origin, and History

Spinach (*Spinacia oleracea*) belongs to the *Chenopodiaceae* family which includes the beet and chard. Spinach was first introduced into Europe in the thirteenth or fourteenth century, coming from Asia, where it originated, by way of Africa. The date of its introduction to the United States is unknown, but records indicate it was commonly grown in the early nineteenth century.

Scope and Importance

Although cultivated for many generations, spinach attained commercial importance relatively late. It is highly recommended in the diet and has become the most important vegetable crop as greens. Spinach ranked 17th in acreage and 20th in value among the 22 principal vegetables in 1965.

Acreage of spinach for fresh market decreased from 65,830 in 1939 to about 20,400 in 1965. Production declined from 3,025,000 to 1,167,000 hundredweight during this period while farm value increased from $5,620,000 in 1939 to approximately $9,250,000 in 1965.

Spinach harvested for processing increased from 20,100 in 1939 to 51,720 acres in 1944 and declined thereafter to approximately 21,400 acres in 1965. Production rose from 54,200 to about 124,000 tons during this 26-year period, and farm value increased from $956,000 to approximately $5,000,000.

California, Texas, Oklahoma, Arkansas, and Colorado led in acreage, yield, production, and value of fresh market and processed spinach in 1965 as shown in Tables 28.1 and 28.2.

Table 28.1—Spinach for Fresh Market: Shipping Season and Estimated
Commercial Acreage, Yield, Production, and Value in
Leading States, 1965.

State	Season	Harvested Acreage	Yield per Acre, Cwt.	Production, 1,000 Cwt.	Price per Cwt.	Value, $1,000
Texas	Winter	6,900	38	262	$ 8.10	2,122
Colorado	Summer	1,800	50	90	11.00	990
California	Winter	1,700	130	221	8.70	1,923
New Jersey	Spring	1,600	70	112	5.20	582
New Jersey	Early fall	1,500	60	90	7.40	666
Maryland and Virginia	Spring	1,500	55	82*	6.74	539
Maryland and Virginia	Late fall	1,350	52	70	7.83	548
New York	Spring	500	95	48	6.00	288
New York	Early fall	500	70	35	7.90	276
Pennsylvania	Early fall	400	40	16	8.00	128
Missouri	Spring	400	45	18	5.30	95
Pennsylvania	Spring	400	30	12	7.40	89
Ohio	Early fall	350	65	23	12.30	283
Massachusetts	Spring	350	55	19	8.00	152
All states		20,430	57	1,167	7.94	9,250

*Includes some quantities not marketed and excluded in computing value.

Trends in Production Efficiency

Production and harvest costs per acre of spinach are low, primarily
because of highly mechanized practices. Spinach requires less labor than
any crop except green peas and sweet corn for processing. From 1939 to
1959, labor requirements decreased from 124 to 32 man-hours per acre
for the fresh market crop. During the same period, labor output per acre
dropped from 83 to 22 man-hours per acre for processed spinach, which
is harvested entirely by machines and hauled in bulk to processing plants.

Between 1939 and 1959, average acre yields of spinach for fresh
market increased moderately from 46 to 58 hundredweight while the unit
output per man-hour enjoyed a remarkable increase of 389 percent.
Correspondingly, spinach for processing increased from 54 to 91 hundredweight per acre, and the unit increase per man-hour exceeded that of any
other vegetable crop, a spectacular 559 percent increase (Table 1.4).

Climatic Requirements

Spinach is essentially a hardy, cool-season crop. When fairly well
hardened, it has survived temperatures of 20° F. or lower without suffer-

Table 28.2—Spinach for Processing: Harvest Season and Estimated Acreage, Yield, Production, and Value in Leading States, 1965.

State	Season	Harvested Acreage	Yield per Acre, Cwt.	Production in Tons	Price per Ton	Value, $1,000
California	Winter	6,100	8.6	52,500	$33.60	1,764
Florida	Winter	1,700	4.6	7,800	40.70	317
Oklahoma	Fall	1,400	4.7	6,600	49.00	323
Arkansas	Fall	1,000	5.0	5,000	49.00	245
Oklahoma	Spring	900	2.8	2,500	44.40	111
Arkansas	Spring	700	3.1	2,200	44.50	98
Washington	Fall	550	9.6	5,300	30.80	163
Other states		2,570	4.3	10,970	57.10	626
All states		21,380	5.8	124,310	40.20	5,002
For freezing		11,230	5.6	63,230	41.30	2,609
For canning		10,150	6.0	61,080	39.20	2,393

ing injury. High temperatures and especially long days cause spinach to bolt to seed, thus destroying its market value. In general, it is a short-season crop, maturing in 6 to 10 weeks, depending on climatic conditions.

JOB 1.   SELECTING VARIETIES AND SEED

Market demand, earliness, disease resistance, tendency to bolt to seed, and time of the year to be planted are factors which need to be considered in selecting a variety.

Varieties

Varieties have been classified into either prickly-seeded or smooth-seeded groups, and also into savoy-leaf (wrinkled) or flat-leaf groups. Most commercial varieties are now smooth-seeded, which are much easier to handle and to plant accurately. Varieties with savoyed leaves are usually preferred for market, while flat-leaved types are preferred for processing. Recently semi-savoyed types have been used for both processing and market.

Some varieties are more resistant to bolting to seed than others, and are called "long standing." High yielding F_1 hybrids are now in production. These hybrids and those soon to be released are expected to replace varieties now used in many areas of commercial production. The im-

Table 28.3.—Important characteristics of a Selected List of Important Varieties of Spinach.

Variety	Chief Use*	Season (Days)	Long-standing	Leaf Type	Heat	Resistance to		
						Cold	Mosaic	Mildew
America	H, M, S, C, F	48	Yes	Savoy	Exc.	Fair	No	No
Bloomsdale Dark Green	H, M, S, C, F	40	Med.	Savoy	No	Med.	No	No
Bloomsdale Long Standing	H, M, S, C, F	42	Yes	Heavy Savoy	Fair	Med.	No	No
Chesapeake Hybrid	F	40	No	Semi-Savoy	No	Good	Yes	No
Dixie Market	M, C, F	37	Med.	Savoy	–	Med.	Yes	Yes
Giant Nobel	M, S, C	45	Yes	Smooth	Fair	Med.	No	No
Hybrid 7	H, M, S, C, F	39	No	Semi-Savoy	No	Med.	Yes	Yes
Hybrid 424	H	38	Med.	Smooth	–	Med.	–	Yes
Hybrid 612	M	43	No	Savoy	–	Med.	Yes	Yes
Old Dominion	M, S, C, F	42	No	Savoy	No	Exc.	Yes	No
Viking	S, C, F	45	Yes	Smooth	Fair	Med.	No	Yes
Virginia Savoy	M, S, C, F	39	No	Savoy	No	Med.	Yes	Yes
Viroflay	C	45	No	Smooth	No	Med.	No	No

*H—Home; M—Market; S—Shipping; C—Canning; F—Freezing.

portant characteristics of a selected list of important varieties are found in Table 28.3.

Securing Seed

Most of the seed used by American growers comes from Europe (chiefly Holland). Relatively small amounts are also grown in California and in the Puget Sound district. Lower production costs favor the European grower. It pays to buy seed from a reliable seedsman who makes it a practice to supply high-quality seed.

JOB 2.   PREPARING THE SEEDBED

Soil Preferences

Spinach grows well on a wide range of soils, but it yields best on a heavy loam. In southwest Texas, much of the spinach is grown on well-drained alluvial soils, silt and clay loams, but sandy loams also are used fairly widely. In Virginia, there are large acreages of spinach on sandy and gravelly loams. Sandy soils are desired for winter and early spring crops. Muck soils are used in the North for main crop and processing spinach. A soil should have good drainage and if possible be well supplied with organic matter.

Breaking and Conditioning

Land to be planted to spinach should be put in a condition of good tilth, which requires that it be plowed at least 8 inches deep, and harrowed thoroughly. In irrigated section, it may be necessary to level the seedbed so that the water will flow evenly.

Fertilizing

General recommendations for fertilization are difficult to make because spinach is grown on widely varying types and fertility of soils. In the West profitable returns have been given by nitrogen applications alone. In eastern areas, relatively heavy applications of 1,200 to 1,500 pounds per acre of a mixture containing 7 to 10 percent nitrogen, 14 to 16 percent phosphorous, and 3 to 5 percent potassium have given good results. Higher proportions of potassium are recommended for the eastern peat and muck areas. Methods of applying fertilizer vary. Often fertilizers are broadcast and worked into the soil before planting. More frequently on lighter soils split applications are made.

On boron-deficient soils increased yields may be obtained by applying commercial borax at the rate of 10 pounds per acre. Broadcast applications should be worked into the soil before the seed is sown. Boron should not be used as a general practice, but only where a known need for the material has been demonstrated.

Liming

Experimental results indicate that spinach is very sensitive to acid conditions, and will not thrive on soils more acid than pH 5.5. Plants grown on soils with reactions below pH 5.0 usually show severe injury. Normally, for spinach to make optimum growth, a soil should range between pH 6.0 and pH 7.0. Unfavorable acid conditions can be corrected successfully by liming the soil. Aplications of one ton per acre of hydrated lime on two sandy loams, one with pH 4.6, the other with pH 4.7, greatly increased the yield of spinach. Where the soil was strongly acid, heavier applications increased yields still further. In spite of the response to liming, the practice can be overdone.

The spinach soils in Texas have a reaction of about pH 7.0 (neutral) with a tendency towards higher pH, rather than lower. Liming is unnecessary under average conditions in the Southwest.

Manuring

The relative scarcity and the high cost of barnyard manure make its use prohibitive to the average spinach grower, even though its addition is beneficial. Green manuring is becoming more common among Texas spinach growers. However, preliminary experiments at the Texas Agricultural Experiment Station indicate that such manures plowed under a short time ahead of spinach will not increase yields materially, if at all. A legume green-manure crop incorporated in the soil fully a year ahead of the spinach crops seems most feasible.

JOB 3.   PLANTING AND CULTIVATING

Planting

In the extreme South, and in areas of California and Arizona, spinach is planted at any time from September until early February. In more

northerly sections very early plantings are made for spring harvests, or
the crop may be wintered over after being planted in the fall. Spinach
planted in late summer is harvested in the fall. In certain areas of the
North as well as in some of the Pacific Coast, the crop is grown throughout the summer.

The rate of seeding varies greatly, depending somewhat on the spacing but to a greater extent on the section of the country and local experience. In the northerly sections of the South, seed is drilled at rates ranging from 15 to 30 pounds per acre, 20 pounds being an average rate. This
could perhaps be reduced by seed treatment. In Texas, when the seed is
broadcast, 8 to 10 pounds per acre is more normal, and even eight pounds
may give too thick a stand. When drilled in rows, four to six pounds
will suffice.

Row planting has long been an established practice in most sections.
Rows in Texas are usually either 14 or 16 inches apart, and may be flat
or raised on low ridges according to the method of irrigation. In Virginia,
spinach is planted on broad, slightly raised beds on which there are usually five to six rows 8 to 10 inches apart. Spinach is usually planted about
one-half to three-fourths inch deep, depending on the method of planting
and soil conditions. The furrow between the beds provides ideal drainage
conditions.

Thinning

In most areas, commercial crops are not usually thinned. A correct
stand is best obtained by using good, fresh, viable seed and accurate
seeding rates. The plants should be spaced 3 to 6 inches apart in the row.

Cultivating

Spinach does not compete well with weeds and the harvesting operations are complicated by them. Wherever spinach is planted in rows,
shallow cultivation is usually practiced. Frequent cultivation in the absence of weeds is unnecessary. Herbicides, such as Chloro IPC and vege-
dex, have been used successfully with spinach in certain areas. It may be
used alone or in combination with cultivation.

Irrigation

The spinach plant has a relatively shallow root system and thrives
best in a uniformly moist soil. In the irrigated sections of the Southwest,

Fig. 28.1—Irrigating spinach by the border method of surface irrigation.

irrigation is one of the major concerns of the spinach grower. The first irrigation immediately follows planting. This irrigation will frequently bring up the crop, but sometimes a second application is necessary within three or four days if the soil dries too quickly. Between emergence and harvesting, one to three irrigations are usually required, depending on soil and climatic conditions. Experiments at the Texas Experiment Station show that overirrigation of spinach will definitely reduce yields.

Fields are irrigated either by flooding (border method) or by the furrow method. In the former method the rows are flat, while in the latter they are on low, raised ridges (Fig. 28.1).

JOB 4. CONTROLLING DISEASES AND INSECTS

Diseases

Spinach is subject to a number of diseases, including damping off, mosaic, downy mildew, and fusarium wilt. It is seldom that all of these are injurious in any given region at the same time.

DAMPING OFF. Damping off and closely related rots of germinating seeds are largely responsible for poor stands and for the necessity in the past of high rates of seeding.

The disease can be controlled by seed treatment. To get rapid germination with a minimum of decay, the seed should be soaked for 24 hours, dried, and dusted with thiram (three-fourths percent), captan (1 percent), or dichlone (1 percent). Planting should then be done without delay.

MOSAIC. Mosaic, commonly known as blight, or yellows, is caused by the cucumber mosaic virus. It is widespread and sometimes causes serious losses. In the early stages of the disease, the young center leaves turn yellow and cease to grow. Later, all growth stops and the larger leaves become mottled, and even turn brown and die. It has been shown that insects, especially aphids, carry the disease from plant to plant. The most practical method of control is to grow resistant varieties (see Table 28.3).

DOWNY MILDEW. Downy mildew, caused by *Peronospora effusa* and known as blue mold, may cause serious losses in foggy or rainy weather. The disease first appears on the underside of the leaves, where irregular patches of grayish mycelia will be found. Later the upper surface of the leaves turns yellowish. Under favorable conditions, the disease spreads rapidly, and whole fields of spinach are quickly ruined. Resistant varieties and hybrids are now available that effectively control the disease (see Table 28.3). When the disease does appear it can be held down with zineb or maneb sprays.

FUSARIUM WILT. Fusarium wilt, caused by *Fusarium solani*, may be troublesome either in early fall or in late spring plantings. The fungus can live for several years in the soil. Young plants, if attacked, remain stunted, and old plants wilt and rarely recover. Air temperatures above 72° F. or soil temperatures above 70° F. at the depth of 2 inches favor spread of the disease. Growing spinach during cool weather and crop rotation are the only known means of practical control.

CURLY-TOP. Curly-top, a virus carried by the beet leaf hopper, causes the young leaves to become crinkled, deformed, and reduced in size.

The plants usually turn yellow and die. Control can only be effected by controlling the insect vector, since nothing can be done after the plant is infected.

HETEROSPORIUM LEAF SPOT. Heterosporium leaf spot, a widely distributed fungus disease, may injure the crop severely. The disease first appears as small brown spots that increase in size and number on both sides of the leaf. It is most severe on winter crops grown under cold, wet conditions. No definite control measures are recommended.

Insects

Any blemishes such as those of insect damage on spinach leaves would make the crop unsalable. Furthermore, aphids spread diseases. Consequently, insects should be controlled before any damage has been done.

APHIDS. Aphids (*Myzus persicae*) or plant lice sometimes cause serious damage to spinach by sucking the juice from the foilage, and by transmitting the mosaic disease from infected plants to healthy ones. Because the spinach plants grow close to the ground in a more or less compact rosette, control by dusting or spraying is not easy. Success in aphid control is dependent upon dusting or spraying when the infestation is small. Malathion is currently in use.

SPINACH LEAF MINERS. Spinach leaf miners (*Pegomyia hyoseyami*) damage spinach by feeding inside the leaves between the two leaf surfaces. The entire leaf may be destroyed or otherwise rendered unfit for marketing. Diazinon has been proved effective in certain areas if applied when the first miners' tunnels are seen. Crop rotation and destruction of crop residue will aid in their control.

OTHER INSECTS. Insects such as seed corn maggots, grasshoppers, and flea beetles may occasionally cause damage. Leaf hoppers may carry the curly-top virus and can be controlled with applications of DDT.

JOB 5. HARVESTING, GRADING, AND MARKETING

Harvesting

The time of harvesting depends on the market as well as the size of the plant. When the price is high, growers may harvest medium-sized plants having only five to seven fully matured leaves, but if the price is low, the plants will probably be allowed to continue growing. After a seed stalk begins to form, a spinach plant is no longer marketable; hence, high value is attached to long-standing varieties.

The harvesting period in the extreme South extends from early November to April of the following year; in more northerly sections, it occurs only during the fall, spring, and early summer. More than one cutting can be made in the same field, if only the large plants are taken.

Spinach plants are harvested for market by cutting the tap root at the soil surface, with various kinds of knives, hoes, or cutting implements. Unsightly and dead leaves should be removed. Trimming may be done in the field as the plants are cut, or in packing sheds. Spinach sometimes has to be washed, but before long-distance shipping such a practice should be avoided, if possible, as it hastens decay. Plants harvested for market are usually allowed to wilt slightly before hauling, in order to minimize the breakage of the leaves.

Spinach for processing should be cut about an inch above the surface of the soil. Mechanical harvesters have been developed for this operation. More than one harvest can be made from plants that have been cut above the growing point under short-day conditions. Spinach grown for manufacture is trimmed at the processing plant.

Grading

Spinach is commonly graded in accordance with the standards set up by the Federal-state inspection service. A certificate signed by an official inspector assures both the seller and the buyer that the product at the time of shipment was a certain grade. The grades applying to spinach change slightly from time to time, and it is well to obtain periodically the latest rulings direct from the U.S. Department of Agriculture. Because of the nature of a spinach plant, all grading has to be done by hand, and hence it is often done as the plants are harvested.

Packing

Spinach for market is packed in bushel baskets, hampers, and crates. For long-distance shipping, a shovelful of ice (approximately 10 pounds) is packed in the upper portion of each basket just before it is put in the car, and the car is also iced or refrigerated.

Marketing

Spinach is marketed in much the same manner as other vegetables. Volume buyers prefer to purchase from standard packing sheds or assembly points. That portion of the crop which is stored usually is not held in cold storage for more than 10 days. This commodity is moved to market under cool or refrigerated conditions, principally by trucks.

Consumers prefer clean, stem-trimmed spinach in standard size cellophane bags so they can inspect the product. The sealed transparent packages help to prevent the spinach from wilting and allow gaseous exchange for the maintenance of quality.

From 50,000 to 77,000 cases of canned spinach were exported annually from the United States to Canada, Kuwait, and a few other countries between 1957 and 1963. In 1963, only 43,536 cases valued at $139,361 were exported.

SELECTED REFERENCES

Bowers, J. L., Vose, H. H., and McFerran, J., "Turnip Greens and Spinach: Cultural and Fertilizer Studies," Ark. Agr. Exp. Sta. Bull. 654, 1962.

Drewes, H., "Spinach Varieties," Mich. Agr. Exp. Sta. Spec. Bull. 225, 1951.

Schwalen, H. C., et al., "Spinach Irrigation," Ariz. Agr. Exp. Sta. Bull. 250, 1953.

Seelig, R. A., "Spinach," United Fresh Fruit and Vegetable Association, Washington, D.C., 1958.

CHAPTER 29

Sweet Potatoes

Classification, Origin, and History

The sweet potato (*Ipomoea Batatas*) is a native of Central and South America and belongs to the morning-glory family, *Convolvulaceae*. Early explorers carried it to Spain and other subtropical and tropical countries, and the earliest writers mentioned different varieties and colors. The sweet potato has been grown in Virginia for nearly 300 years. The name "batatas" was used by the Indians in referring to this vegetable. The term "yam," as commonly used in the South, usually refers to the more moist-fleshed varieties, although there is a different group of plants known as yams.

Scope and Importance

The sweet potato is grown extensively in the South, and is the great carbohydrate food crop of the southern states, corresponding to the Irish or white potato in more northern sections. Unlike the Irish potato, it was not extensively shipped until the development of proper storage.

Although the sweet potato has declined in popularity over the years, it remains as one of the more important vegetable crops. It ranked eighth in acreage and seventh in value among the 22 principal vegetables in 1965. Sweet potato acreage declined from 728,000 in 1939 to approximately 202,000 in 1965. Production fell from 33,959,000 to about 18,000,000 hundredweight during this period while farm value increased from $45,340,000 in 1939 to an estimated $76,493,000 in 1965.

The approximate geographical distribution of sweet potatoes is shown in Figure 29.1. Louisiana, North Carolina, Virginia, and Texas led other states in acreage, yield, production, and value as presented in Table 29.1.

Table 29.1—Sweet Potatoes: Estimated Commercial Acreage, Yield, Production, and Value in Leading States, 1965.

State	Harvested Acreage	Yield per Acre, Cwt.	Production, 1,000 Cwt.	Price per Cwt.	Value, $1,000
Louisiana	58,000	73	4,234	$2.70	11,432
North Carolina	22,000	135	2,970	4.80	14,256
Virginia	20,000	100	2,000	3.40	6,800
Texas	16,000	80	1,280	5.00	6,400
Mississippi	15,000	80	1,200	5.40	6,480
Georgia	14,000	85	1,190	5.30	6,307
New Jersey	11,500	105	1,208	4.10	4,953
Alabama	9,000	65	585	4.60	2,691
South Carolina	8,500	75	638	4.80	3,062
California	8,400	95	798	8.00	6,384
Tennessee	4,200	100	420	4.40	1,848
Arkansas	4,000	77	308	4.80	1,478
Maryland	3,900	145	566	3.00	1,698
All states	202,200	89	17,957	4.23	76,493

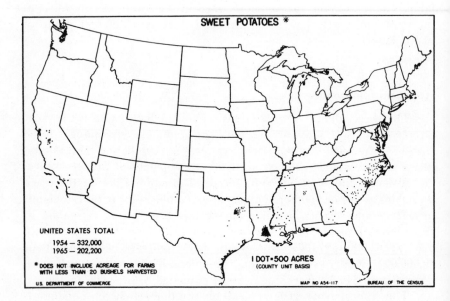

Fig. 29.1—Acreage and distribution of sweet potato production.

Trends in Production Efficiency

The sweet potato is comparatively expensive to produce. Cultural and harvesting requirements have been improved somewhat in recent years, but considerable labor is still necessary. Labor requirements were reduced from 118 to 96 man-hours per acre between 1939 and 1959. Yields of sweet potatoes increased from 47 to 74 hundredweight per acre in the 1939-1959 period while output per man-hour rose 95 percent (Table 1.4).

Climatic Requirements

The sweet potato thrives in the warmer portions of the United States from New Jersey to Texas. It can be grown under irrigation, although it is considered a drought-resistant plant. Irrigation water is best applied before the vines cover the ground, as late applications may result in excessive vine growth. The leaves, vines, and the entire plant are easily injured by frost.

Sweet potato production is best in areas with 175 frost-free days, although the more northern producing centers have as little as four months. Warm nights and plenty of sunshine increase growth, which continues to increase with temperatures up to 95° F.

JOB 1. SELECTING VARIETIES AND SEED

Varieties

Sweet potatoes that are used for human consumption have been referred to as "food types." These may be divided into soft-fleshed and firm-fleshed varieties. The former are sweeter and softer when cooked.

The Unit I Porto Rico is the leading soft-fleshed variety, but a number of recently introduced varieties are superior to it in characteristics such as quality, yield, and disease resistance. Among the more recent introductions are Cliett Bunch, Early Port, Allgold, Heartogold, Goldrush, Nemagold, All Gold, Red Gold, Nancy Gold, Red Nancy, Australian Canner, and Ranger.

The important firm-fleshed or Jersey-type varieties include Big Stem Jersey, Yellow Jersey, Orlis, Maryland Golden, and Rols. Hills of Porto Rico and Big Stem Jersey are shown in Figures 29.2 and 29.3 respectively.

· Non-food varieties produce high yield and have white flesh and a high starch content. Pelican Processor and Whitestar are leading varieties.

Fig. 29.2—A hill of Porto Rico sweet potatoes.

USDA Photograph

Securing Seed

If high yields of uniform, marketable potatoes are desired, only well-selected seed should be used, as unselected seed is often mixed in variety

Fig. 29.3—A hill of Big Stem Jersey sweet potatoes.

USDA Photograph

if not in type. Unless the local supply is known to be free from diseases and insects, certified seed should be purchased. Sporting or mutation is not very common, but may cause considerable variation. Hill selections can be used in maintaining type and to secure seed free from disease.

JOB 2.   PREPARING THE SOIL

Soil Preferences

It is generally agreed that a sandy-loam soil with a clay subsoil is best for sweet potatoes. Roots from such a soil tend to be smooth and not too large. Silt loams usually give good results, but heavy clay loams do not. Roots grown in such soils are usually rough and irregular in shape. Very light deep soils tend to produce long slender roots. Good drainage is essential for growing sweet potatoes. A soil more acid than pH 5.0 should be limed to bring the reaction within the desirable range of pH 5.2 to pH 6.7.

Preparing the Soil

A fair crop of sweet potatoes can be grown on carelessly prepared soil, but thorough preparation will usually give larger yields and reduce labor later. The soil should be plowed and worked down about the same as for corn and similar crops. Then the land is generally allowed to lie several days before being put into condition for planting. A large part of the crop is planted on ridges made up several days before planting. The tops of the ridges are rolled or dragged off at planting time. A low flat ridge is more desirable than a narrow high one, as the latter dries out badly. Level culture has some advantages on sandy, well-drained soils.

JOB 3.   FERTILIZING AND MANURING

Fertilizing

The New Jersey station found that potassium had a striking influence on shape of the Jersey type of sweet potato when grown on sandy soil. In similar experiments at the Tennessee station on clay loam soils, potassium had no appreciable effect on shape except where the soil was of very low fertility. In general, late planting and an excess of nitrogen tend to produce long slender roots that mature late. Early planting and an abundance of potassium tend to produce early-maturing chunky potatoes.

According to Table 6.4, the sweet potato can be expected to respond to 30 to 45 pounds of nitrogen (N) per acre, depending on soil type. In Table 6.5, the sweet potato is placed in Group II according to its requirements for phosphorus (P) and potassium (K). The table indicates that the sweet potato should be supplied about 18 pounds of P and 112 pounds of K per acre on a soil giving a medium test for these elements. They could be supplied by 500 pounds of a 6-4-20 fertilizer.

Heavy applications of mineral fertilizers in the drill often cause injury to newly transplanted plants. Several plans are followed to avoid this injury, such as: (1) broadcasting before making up the ridges, (2) mixing with the soil in the drill, and (3) applying as a side dressing after the plants have become established. The first may result in leaching on light soils. Side dressing costs somewhat more but on sandy soils should enable the plants to make good use of the fertilizer applied.

Manuring

Stable manure is usually scarce, expensive, and less profitable when used for potatoes than for other crops. It is a common practice for those who use manure to apply it in a furrow under the ridge and at the rate of two to five tons per acre. Fresh stable manure on fertile loams often results in oversize and irregularly shaped roots. Sandy soils often need a green-manure crop, such as crimson clover, soybeans, or cowpeas, to increase their water-holding capacity. These legumes should be disked and plowed under at least a month before the plants are set. The tops and vines of a peanut crop, after "hogging-off," often serve as a green-manure crop.

JOB 4. GROWING AND CARING FOR SLIPS

Size of Seed

It is standard practice to use small or medium-sized roots for seed. Roots from ¾ to 1½ inches in diameter (strings) will produce more plants per bushel of seed and per square yard of seedbed than will larger potatoes. Such seed should be free from disease, clean, vigorous, and true to the type desired for the variety.

Many experiments indicate that there is no significant difference between plants from large and small seed if other factors are equal. This is as one would expect in vegetative propagation.

Treating Seed

Even seed which is apparently healthy should be treated as a precaution against scurf, stem rot, black rot, and root rot before it is bedded.

U.S. Department of Agriculture Farmers' Bulletin 1059 presents the following treatment for seed disinfection: "Disinfect sweet potato roots just before they are bedded by dipping them for 8 to 10 minutes in a solution made by dissolving one ounce of corrosive sublimate (mercuric chloride) in eight gallons of water. Use only wooden vessels for the disinfecting solution.

"To control scurf, add 5½ pounds of wettable sulfur to 24 gallons of the corrosive sublimate solution. This treatment will not kill fungi within the sweet potato, but it will destroy spores on the surface. After about 10 bushels have been treated in 24 gallons of solution, add one-half ounce of corrosive sublimate dissolved in hot water and make up the solution to the original volume by adding water. Repeat this process after the treatment of each 10 bushels of seed until 30 bushels are treated. Then discard the solution and prepare a fresh one.

"If corrosive sublimate cannot be obtained, disinfect the seed sweet potatoes by immersing them for five minutes in a 2 to 2½ percent solution of borax. Prepare this solution by dissolving five pounds of borax in 30 gallons of water. Borax can usually be purchased at a grocery store. The disinfecting quality of the borax is not reduced by repeated use and it can be used in metal vessels. However, if the volume of the solution does not cover the sweet potatoes, add more solution.

"Bed the sweet potatoes immediately after they are treated and water them thoroughly. Otherwise chemical injury and reduced sprouting may result.

"Excessive amounts of boron are injurious to plants; therefore, do not pour the unused portion of the borax solution on land to be used for crop production. Corrosive sublimate is very poisonous. Sweet potatoes that have been treated with either corrosive sublimate or borax should never be fed to animals or used as food. The chemicals and the solutions remaining after treating should be carefully disposed of or kept out of reach of children and animals." In addition, all parts of the seedbed which were previously used for bedding sweet potatoes should be disinfected with a formaldehyde solution. Crates and storage rooms are occasionally treated in the same way.

Bedding

Clean, fresh sand on which sweet potatoes have not been grown for a number of years is preferred as a bedding medium. This is often hauled from woodlands to avoid all chance of contamination. Plant beds should be located on a sheltered slope where sweet potatoes have not been grown recently. About 25 square feet of bed are required for one bushel of so-called strings or 15 square feet for one bushel of No. 1's. About six to seven bushels of the small roots are allowed for each acre where one pulling is made and only the slips are planted. In long-season sections, growers bed enough roots for one-fifth to one-eighth of their planting and then take vine cuttings to plant the remainder of their crop.

In the warmer sections, unheated open beds or cold frames commonly are used (Fig. 29.4). The former are usually 5 to 6 feet wide and as long as necessary. A pit may be dug about 6 inches deep and the bedding medium filled in or the potatoes bedded in the soil without excavating. In either case, the roots are covered about 1 inch deep and additional sand is applied when the sprouts appear. A deep layer of soil delays sprouting of newly bedded potatoes. There should be 3 to 4 inches of soil over the mother potatoes at pulling time to insure long, stocky, well-rooted slips. Canvas and sash covers produce somewhat earlier plants.

In the more northern sections, plants are grown in heated beds to secure as long a growing season as possible. Such beds are started about six weeks before the plants are to be set in the field. The beds may be heated by manure, hot air, steam, hot water, or electricity, as described in Chapter 7.

Caring for the Beds

High temperatures increase the rate of growth, but produce soft, weak plants. An air temperature of 70° to 80° F. is considered best for most of the growing period. Covered beds will need ventilation on bright days to control the temperature. Beds with dry heat require more water than those heated by manure. Unheated beds often need covering on very cold nights, as the plants are easily injured by frost. It is well to harden off the plants by increasing the ventilation just before planting time.

JOB 5. PULLING AND SETTING SLIPS

Pulling Slips

In drawing the slips, the seed potato is held down with one hand while the plants are removed with the thumb and finger of the other. Only plants that have formed good roots are taken, and the others are

Fig. 29.4—Cold frames used for growing sweet potato slips.

USDA Photograph

left to grow (Fig. 29.5). Plants to be set with a transplanting machine must be arranged in the best possible way, which includes trimming the tops and placing all of the roots in one direction in such manner as to avoid sticking. Some growers puddle the roots in mud, while others only cover the plants with wet burlap. Water is usually applied with the transplanter but may be omitted if planting is done on cloudy days following a rain.

Setting Slips

Sweet potato slips are set in the northern section as soon as danger of frost is over. Where only a few hundred plants are to be set, hand planting with a dibble or a trowel is the common method. It is usually convenient to water such plants, if they are not puddled in a paste of clay and water before setting. For larger areas, the shovel and tongs method is fairly rapid and less tiresome than hand planting with a dibble. The shovel, a sharpened piece of lath, is used to open the soil and is managed in the right hand. Tongs made of wood are used to pick up the

Fig. 29.5—Sweet potato plants for transplanting. Plant on left is too short for easy handling.

USDA Photograph

slip by the roots and to thrust it into the ground. The soil may be firmed about the roots with the foot or by a second thrust of the shovel. The larger commercial areas use planting machines which can plant three to four acres a day under favorable conditions.

In Louisiana it was found that early-planted Porto Rico sweet potatoes produced more chunky roots than late-planted ones. However, the soil should be warm and all danger of late frosts over before the plants are set in the field.

Planting Rates

The distance between rows and spacing within the row depend on such factors as time of setting, variety, and soil type and fertility. Large-growing varieties such as Porto Rico and Southern Queen need more space than do those with shorter vines. Close spacing, 9 to 12 inches in the row, is desirable on rich fertile soils, as it reduces the number of jumbos, and experiments indicate it may increase the yield.

Setting Vines

A large part of the sweet potatoes in the lower South is grown from vine cuttings, the vines being secured from an early planting of slips. Such cuttings are usually about 15 inches long and should include two joints. The Georgia Agricultural Experiment Station found little difference between cuttings taken from various parts of the same vine. Such pieces of vines may be planted by pushing the middle portion into the soil with a notched stick or by inserting the butt end 6 to 8 inches into the soil. Vine cuttings are fairly resistant to adverse conditions. This method of propagation is relatively inexpensive and involves less danger of diseases than does growing the crop from slips. However, delayed plantings result in decreased yields.

JOB 6.   CULTIVATING AND WEEDING

Cultivating

Sweet potatoes are given the usual row cultivations practiced with other crops, mainly for the purpose of controlling weeds. Several cultivations, as well as two hoeings, are usually made before the vines seriously interfere with the cultivators. The sweet potato vine takes root at various places if left undisturbed. Moving the vines to permit late cultivations may slightly increase yields, but it is not likely to be profitable. Vine pruning to stimulate development of roots has, instead, retarded root development in several experiments and is of questionable value.

Weeding

Hand work is expensive, and some growers use level culture and cultivate in both directions. Dacthal applied at the rate of eight to ten pounds per acre at the time of setting is an effective herbicide for most annual weeds.

JOB 7.   CONTROLLING DISEASES AND INSECTS

Diseases

A number of serious diseases attack the sweet potato. The more important ones, including control measures, are discussed briefly.

BLACK ROT. Black rot, caused by the fungus *Ceratocystis fimbriata*, is generally considered to be the most destructive field disease of the sweet potato. It attacks all parts of the plant below the ground. This fungus lives from one year to another on the dead vines or other decayed vegetable matter in the soil and infects sweet potatoes by contact. Slips from diseased seed are usually infected.

Precautions necessary to avoid this disease include selecting disease-free seed, disinfecting as described under seed treatment, and avoiding all contaminated material in manure or about the plant beds. Crop rotation tends to prevent an accumulation of diseased material in the soil. Spring selection as well as fall selection helps to eliminate diseased roots.

STEM ROT. Stem rot, caused by *Fusarium oxysporium f. batatas*, is about second in destructiveness in most sections. This fungus, like the preceding one, can live for several years on decaying vegetation in the soil. They usually enter a plant through the roots, and the foilage of infected plants turns yellow. The vascular system is usually invaded by the fungus, and dark-colored lesions are found on the stem. The discoloration disclosed by splitting the stems is used to identify infected seed. Spores of the stem-rot fungi are developed on dead vines and are readily carried by wind and other agencies.

Varieties show a marked difference in susceptibility to this disease. Nancy Hall and Porto Rico are moderately susceptible, while Triumph is fairly resistant. The same sanitary measures described for black rot apply to this disease. Infected soil should not be planted to sweet potatoes for at least five years.

SCURF. Caused by *Monilochaetes infuscans*, scurf is one of the secondary sweet potato diseases, although it is widely disseminated. The fungus lives in the soil, can be carried on slips, and causes no apparent injury above ground. Diseased areas on the sweet potatoes are brown and are likely to continue to develop in storage. Discolored roots lose water and are likely to shrivel even in fairly humid storage houses. The use of disease-free seed and treatment with bichloride of mercury are important preventive measures. Infected soil should not be planted to sweet potatoes for at least three years.

FOOT ROT. This disease is caused by a soil fungus, *Plenodomus destruens*. Late-infected sweet potatoes develop a firm brown rot. Early-infected plants are attacked near the surface of the ground and are usually girdled. Control measures are the same as for black rot.

ROOT ROT. Root rot, caused by *Phymatotrichum omnivorum*, is often called Texas root rot and is induced by the same organism that causes root rot on cotton and alfalfa. Its distribution is limited to the southwestern United States. No satisfactory control is known; however, hard freezing is likely to kill the organism. Corn and cereals may be grown in an effort to starve out the fungus.

ROOT KNOT. Root knot, caused by the common garden nematode (*meloidogyne sp.*), may result in a superficial decay in sweet potatoes, which are likely to spread this pest. Nemagold is resistant and Porto Rico and Jersey varieties are claimed to be fairly resistant. Good crops of sweet potatoes have been grown on badly infested soil. No method of seed treatment is effective.

SOFT ROT. Soft rot, including ring rot, is usually caused by the common breadmold fungus, *Rhizopus stolonifer*. Ring rot develops in storage from a side infection and the diseased tissue forms a ring about the sweet potato. Soft rot under favorable conditions may start in the field. The middle cell wall is dissolved during the spread of this rot, which at first renders the potato soft and mushy. Loss of water later produces a dry, mummy-like condition often called a dry rot. Entrance starts at wounds, although a rotting sweet potato often infects surrounding ones. A relatively low humidity during the curing process decreases infections. As this fungus lives on a wide range of decaying vegetable matter, it cannot be excluded from storage houses. Proper curing and handling are the best preventive measures.

DRY ROT. Dry rot, caused by the fungus *Diaporthe batatatis*, like soft rot is widely distributed. It probably starts in the field and develops slowly from the stem end. Small domelike fruiting structures can often be seen with the naked eye. The tissue under the skin is coal-black in appearance.

STORAGE DISEASES. These include soft rot, dry rot, Java black rot, charcoal rot, black rot, internal cork, and field diseases that continue to develop in storage.

Their control starts with the development of a clean healthy crop in the field, and continues with careful handling during harvesting and storage. Injury resulting from careless handling favors the entrance of the rot-causing organisms. Proper curing and favorable storage conditions will keep the diseases from getting a start. Storage houses should be thoroughly cleaned and disinfected with formaldehyde or corrosive sublimate, as explained earlier in this chapter (under "Treating Seed"), before storing the crop.

Insects

The sweet potato is usually free from very serious insect attacks.

SWEET POTATO WEEVIL. The sweet potato weevil (*Cylas formicarius elegantulus*) is of Asiatic origin and is the most destructive insect pest of this crop, causing serious damage from Texas to Florida. Other host plants include members of the morning-glory family. The adult of this insect is a slender snout beetle about one-fourth inch long. The larvae tunnel through the vines to the roots and often riddle the sweet potatoes. The weevil overwinters in sweet potatoes in storage and in roots left in the ground. A 12 percent dieldrin dust heavily applied to the soil at the base of the plants gives good control with this contact insecticide.

Other suggested control measures include: (1) cleaning up sweet potato fields after harvest, (2) disposing of the crop as soon as possible after digging, (3) selecting only clean seed at bedding time, and (4) growing plants as far away from infested fields as possible. Another precaution is to disinfect storage with DDT.

OTHER INSECTS. Other insects which occasionally attack this crop include cutworms, sweet potato flea beetle, striped blisher beetle, and sweet potato whitefly. The injury resulting from these insects is usually slight.

JOB 8. HARVESTING, HANDLING, AND MARKETING

Harvesting

Mature sweet potatoes are characterized by high starch content, the cut surfaces drying on exposure to air. The crop may be dug at any time when the roots reach marketable size. Table 29.2 shows the influence of time of digging on total yield and grade of sweet potatoes. While these figures are for only one year, they indicate that very early digging must be accompanied by increased price to offset the reduction in grade and yield.

Producers in the northern part of the sweet potato-producing area usually allow the frost to injure the vines slightly before digging. Frosted vines should be cut from the sweet potatoes to prevent decay from starting in the dead vines and passing to the roots. Sweet potatoes are injured at temperatures below 50° F. So whether the plants are frosted or not, the roots should be harvested before the soil gets cold. Most growers try to dig sweet potatoes when the soil is dry, as the crop comes out clean and is easier to handle. A plow with a sharp rolling colter and an eight-inch shielded moldboard with rods attached is a popular implement for digging. The roots are usually permitted to dry slightly after they have been freed from the soil.

Table 29.2—Effect of Dates of Harvesting Sweet Potatoes on Grade and Yield.

Date Dug	Grades	Variety Yields				
		Triumph	Nancy Hall	Yellow Jersey*	Southern Queen	Porto Rico
August 15	Marketable	41.2	89.5	55.6	41.1	48.4
	Strings	26.6	72.6	91.9	44.8	46.0
	Total	67.8	162.1	147.5	85.9	94.4
September 1 ..	Marketable	111.3	179.1	96.8	85.3	111.3
	Strings	38.7	116.1	87.1	55.6	50.8
	Total	150.0	295.2	183.9	140.9	162.1
September 15 .	Marketable	248.3	280.7	137.9	179.1	227.9
	Strings	99.2	41.1	94.4	32.7	81.1
	Total	347.5	321.8	232.3	211.8	309.0
October 30 ...	Marketable	309.8	559.8	293.3	309.8	200.0
	Strings	96.8	77.4	116.1	71.0	100.0
	Total	406.6	637.2	409.4	380.8	300.0

*Yields and grades seriously affected by vines from larger varieties.
Data from Tennessee Agricultural Experiment Station.

Grading

Since sweet potatoes require care in harvesting and marketing, and field grading reduces the amount of handling, the marketable potatoes are picked up first, the culls and strings being gathered later. If the crop is to be stored, it is best to pack the sweet potatoes on padded tables in a shed. The U.S. Department of Agriculture will supply standard grades for this crop. This is a general standard and a minimum, but many growers prefer to put up a pack that is more than this minimum.

Fig. 29.6—Federal-state inspector examining sweet potatoes for shipping.

Packing

Hampers, bushel baskets, and boxes are popular commercial pack-ages, while baskets are in common use on local markets. Regardless of the container, it should be clean and neatly packed, and the product should be free from bruises when displayed for sale. The shape of the sweet potato makes it somewhat hard to handle in a jumble pack. Hand placing is justified on some markets. If the pack is only faced, it should be representative of the remaining contents.

Curing

Successful storage of sweet potatoes depends to a large extent on curing. When sweet potatoes are harvested in the lower South in early October, they may be cured by placing a large quantity in a fairly tight building. The heat of respiration together with fairly high outside temperatures are often sufficient for curing. In more northern districts, artificial heat is used to bring temperatures to 80° to 90° F. This treatment with a relative humidity of about 85 percent causes wounds to heal rapidly and brings about some drying of the roots. The U.S. Department of Agriculture Farmers' Bulletin 1442 gives plans for storage-house construction, as does Miscellaneous Publication 822 (1960).

Storing

The sweet potato should be stored in a warm building where the air is dry and the temperature uniform. Bins, crates, boxes, or baskets may be used as containers and these should be arranged to provide ventilation. Heat may be necessary to keep the air dry and warm. Injury occurs considerably above freezing.

Heat when the temperature drops to 48° F., ventilate at 60° F., and close ventilators at 55° F. Outdoor cellar houses often are used, but they should have provision for ventilation. Pits and banks lack provision for curing and ventilating, and storage in them often results in heavy loss.

Sweet potatoes should be disturbed as little as possible after they have been cured and stored, as rot is spread rapidly by handling. It is usually necessary to sort stored roots again before selling.

Marketing

Sweet potato production and consumption have been declining for many years. Competitive vegetables and other food items may continue to decrease the demand of this important crop. The volume being canned has increased, some are frozen, and an instant, mashed, dehydrated sweet potato is being tested for market. However, consumption will likely continue downward unless new ways are found to use this commodity for food or industrial purposes.

A large part of the sweet potato crop is consumed in the areas of production. Northern markets have long been supplied with dry-fleshed potatoes such as Yellow Jersey, establishing a demand for this type. Porto Rico and other soft-fleshed varieties are being shipped to these markets and the volume may be expected to increase.

Improvements in varieties, harvesting, curing, storing, packaging, transporting, and merchandizing will unquestionably increase demand and slow the downward trend in consumption.

SELECTED REFERENCES

Anonymous, "The Sweet Potato Weevil," USDA, (ARS) Leaflet No. 431, 1960.

Boswell, V. R., "Commercial Growing and Harvesting of Sweet Potatoes," USDA Farmers' Bull. 2020, 1950.

Bowers, H. A., Nettles, W. C., and Berly, J. A., "Sweet Potato Plant Production," S. C. Agr. Ext. Cir. 268, 1953.

Carter, W. C., "Growing and Marketing Georgia Sweet Potatoes," Ga. Agr. Ext. Bull. 482, 1953.

Covington, et al., "Grow Quality Sweet Potatoes," N. C. Agr. Ext. Cir. 353, 1959.

Harter, L. L., "Sweet Potato Diseases," USDA Farmers' Bull. 1059, 1959.

Lutz, J. M. and Simons, J. W., "Storage of Sweet Potatoes," USDA Farmers' Bull. 1442, 1958.

Minges, P. A. and Morris, L. L., "Sweet Potato Production and Handling in California," Calif. Agr. Ext. Cir. 431, 1953.

Park, J. K., Powers, M. R., and Garrison, D. B., "Machinery for Growing and Harvesting Sweet Potatoes," S. C. Agr. Exp. Sta. Bull. 404, 1953.

CHAPTER 30

Tomatoes

Classification, Origin, and History

The tomato (*Lycopersicon esculentum*) , a member of the nightshade family, is a native of tropical America.

The large-fruited forms of tomato are reported to have been taken from Peru to Italy, thence to Northern Europe, and finally to the United States by 1781. In 1812, tomatoes were commonly on the market at New Orleans. In 1817, tomato seed was first offered for sale in a seed catalogue in the United States, but it was not until about 1835 that the tomato became quite generally cultivated for culinary purposes in this country. Even at that time, there was considerable prejudice against its use. The first tomato fruits grown in the United States were large, oblate, and ribbed. Since 1895, the important developments include: (1) improvement of extra-early varieties, (2) development of disease-resistant strains, and (3) improvement of plant type and fruit quality.

Scope and Importance

The popularity of the tomato and its products continues to rise. Tomatoes ranked fourth in acreage and second in value, next to potatoes among the 22 principal vegetables in 1965. Although the acreage for fresh market tomatoes declined from 232,500 in 1939 to an estimated 158,530 in 1965, total production increased from 15,232,000 to almost 21,000,000 hundredweight. Acre yields practically doubled between 1939 and 1965 and farm value rose phenomenally from $38,983,000 to approximately $191,500,000.

The acreage of tomatoes for processing increased from 365,220 in

1939 to an average of 540,000 between 1942 and 1945, then declined to approximately 244,000 in 1965. During this 26-year period, yields almost tripled and the total production increased from 2,022,500 to about 4,400,000 tons. From 1939 to 1965 the value of the processed crop rose from $24,545,000 to almost $160,000,000.

The approximate geographical distribution of tomatoes is shown in Figure 30.1. California and Florida are the leading states in fresh market tomatoes while California, Ohio, Indiana, and New Jersey lead in tomatoes for processing as shown in Tables 30.1 and 30.2, respectively.

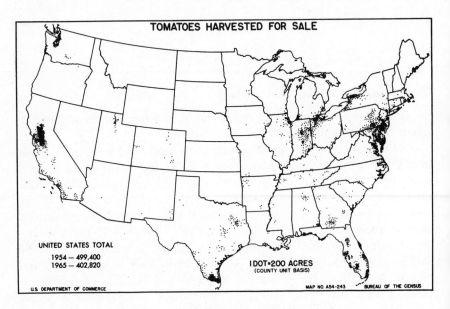

Fig. 30.1—Acreage and distribution of tomato production.

Trends in Production Efficiency

In general the labor required to grow and harvest tomatoes for fresh market approximates 186 man-hours per acre and has changed very little during the last two decades. Labor requirements for the processed tomato crop actually increased from 106 to 137 hours per acre between 1939 and 1959 while yields doubled. Average yields of fresh market tomatoes increased from 66 to 102 hundredweight per acre during the 1939-1959 period while labor output increased 57 percent. Tomatoes for processing increased from 111 to 238 hundredweight per acre for the corresponding period, and labor efficiency increased 67 percent (Table 1.4).

Table 30.1—Tomatoes for Fresh Market: Shipping Season and Estimated Commercial Acreage, Yield, Production, and Value in Leading States, 1965.

State	Season	Harvested Acreage	Yield per Acre, Cwt.	Production, 1,000 Cwt.	Price per Cwt.	Value, $1,000
Florida	Winter	19,100	165	3,152	$ 9.10	28,683
California	Early fall	17,600	200	3,520	10.60	37,312
Florida	Early spring	13,800	190	2,622	10.40	27,269
California	Early summer	10,700	185	1,980	10.30	20,394
Florida	Late fall	8,900	140	1,246	10.30	12,834
New Jersey	Early summer	8,200	115	943	7.80	7,355
South Carolina	Late spring	8,200	85	697	7.90	5,506
Michigan	Late summer	8,000	80	640	8.70	5,568
Texas	Early spring	6,700	55	368	7.30	2,686
Texas	Late spring	6,000	47	282	6.40	1,805
Alabama	Early summer	4,400	60	264	7.70	2,033
New York	Late summer	3,700	125	462	5.80	2,680
Arkansas	Early summer	3,600	105	378*	10,40	3,068
Virginia	Early summer	3,500	100	350*	8.80	3,036
Indiana	Late summer	3,500	90	315	9.10	2,866
California	Early spring	3,300	125	412	12.60	5,191
Pennsylvania	Late summer	3,300	100	330	6.60	2,178
All states		158,530	130	20,681	9.30	191,486

*Includes some quantities not marketed and excluded in computing value.

In 1965 the mechanical tomato harvester performed admirably in California. Some 262 machines harvested nearly one-third of the acreage for processing and did it considerably cheaper than by hand (an estimated $8 to $10 per ton less). By 1967, this crop should be harvested primarily by machine. The 1965 California employment of seasoned workers in tomatoes amounted to 29,600 workers as compared with 44,400 workers in 1964; a drop of one-third.[1]

Climatic Requirements

The tomato is a warm-season plant which requires three to four months from the time of seeding to produce the first ripe fruit. It thrives best when the weather is clear and rather dry and temperatures are uniformly moderate—65° to 85° F. Plants are usually frozen at temperatures below 32° F., and they do not increase in size at temperatures above 95° F. High temperatures accompanied by high humidity favor the development of foliage disease. If the night temperature stays above 85° F., the fruit does not become red enough for the U.S. No. 1 grade for canning.

[1]*Farm Labor Developments*, USDA, page 16, October, 1965.

Table 30.2—Tomatoes for Processing: Estimated Commercial Acreage, Yield, Production, and Value in Leading States, 1965.

State	Harvested Acreage	Yield per Acre, Tons	Production in Tons	Price per Ton	Value, $1,000
California	116,000	21.1	2,447,600	$41.30	101,086
Ohio	24,700	21.7	536,000*	30.20	15,366
Indiana	18,200	16.5	300,300*	29.80	7,647
New Jersey	17,600	18.5	325,600	34.50	11,233
Pennsylvania	8,400	14.2	119,300	32.30	3,853
Illinois	8,000	17.6	140,800*	35.00	4,235
New York	7,800	11.2	87,400	33.80	2,953
Virginia	7,800	8.5	66,300	31.70	2,102
Maryland	6,700	14.9	99,800	33.10	3,303
Florida	6,400	8.2	52,500	26.00	1,365
Texas	6,400	6.7	42,900	25.50	1,094
Michigan	5,700	14.2	80,900	30.40	2,459
Utah	2,300	7.0	16,100	24.50	394
Delaware	1,400	18.8	26,300	33.20	873
South Carolina	1,000	3.5	3,500	32.00	112
Colorado	1,000	6.0	6,000	42.70	256
New Mexico	300	11.0	3,300	32.90	109
Other states	4,590	8.9	40,760	30.50	1,242
All states	244,290	18.0	4,395,360	37.10	159,683

*Includes some quantities not marketed and excluded in computing value.

Hot, drying winds cause the flowers to drop. In the Southwest, where such winds prevail, the tomato field should be protected from the prevailing wind by a stream, woods, or hill. Varieties with pistils shorter than the staminal cone have less blossom drop than others. Irrigation will lower the temperature, raise the humidity, and prevent much of the blossom drop.

JOB 1.   SELECTING VARIETIES AND SEED

Varieties

The importance of good seed of the right variety or strain suitable for the locality cannot be overemphasized. Some tomato varieties produce exceptionally well under one set of conditions while under other conditions they are worthless. Many tomato varieties listed in the various seed catalogues are either synonyms or are varieties of little importance. Because of this and the fact that some seed houses continually exploit the public by advertising new unproved varieties, it is good judgment to use a proven variety for the main crop and try out the new varieties with discretion.

Where most of the tomatoes are grown for shipment, the fruits should be smooth, fleshy, medium-sized, highly colored, and solid enough to withstand transportation. A variety for processing should have well-colored, solid, good-sized fruits, and plants with enough foliage to shade the fruits.

A selected list of varieties is briefly described in Table 30.3 and the chief use of each is given.

Securing Seed

The quality, strain, and trueness of varietal type of seed have such an important bearing upon the yield, earliness, and uniformity of the crop that no pains should be spared in getting the best seed. Some seed firms specialize in producing tomato seed of the highest quality, and have their product certified for purity and freedom from disease. In view of the fact that only two ounces of seed will produce sufficient plants for an acre, seed cost should be of secondary importance, and only seed of the best quality should be used.

JOB 2.   PREPARING THE SOIL

Soil Preferences

The tomato will grow on nearly all types of soils. A light or warm, well-drained, and fertile soil is best suited to produce early fruit of high quality. The loams and clay loams have a greater water-holding capacity and are better suited to a longer season of production when large yield and not earliness is of prime importance.

If any soil is to give the best results, it should contain a good supply of organic matter and mineral nutrients. The degree of acidity which tomatoes will withstand is increased considerably by a plentiful supply of organic matter. Soils ranging from medium acid (pH 5.5) to neutral (pH 7.0) are best for tomato production.

Preparing the Soil

It is important to plow the soil for tomatoes some time in advance of planting so it will have time to settle. Fall plowing is preferable except on sandy soil. Any undecomposed organic matter should be well covered to prevent interference with transplanting.

Table 30.3—Brief Description of Selected Varieties of Tomatoes.

Variety	Chief Use	Season	Plant Type*	Resistant to**	Fruit		
					Color	Size	Shape
Big Boy†	Home	Med.	I		Red	Large	Globe
Bradley	Market	Med.	I	FW	Pink	Med. large	Flat globe
Campbell 146	Market, home	Med.	I	FW, cracking	Red	Med. large	Flat globe
Cardinal†	Market, home	Med. early	I	Cracking	Red	Large	Flat globe
Glamour	Market, home	Med. early	SI	Cracking	Red	Med.	Flat globe
Heintz 1350, 1370, 1439	Market, home	Early	D	Cracking, FW, VW	Red	Med.	Flat globe
Homestead	All-purpose	Med.	D	FW	Red	Med. large	Globe
Indian River	Market, home	Med.	I	FW, GLS, EB	Red	Small-med.	Long globe
Manalucie	Market, home	Med. late	I	FW	Red	Large	Long globe
Manapal	Market, home	Med.	I	FW	Red	Med. large	Globe
V.F. 145-22	Processing	Early	D	FW, VW	Red	Small	Long globe
Moreton Hybrid†	Market	Early	I		Red	Med.	Flat globe
Pearson Strains	All-purpose	Late	D		Red	Med. large	Flat globe
Red Cherry	Home	Early	I		Red	Small	Globe
Roma VF	Processing	Early	I	FW, VW	Red	Small	Pear
San Marzana, LF	Processing	Late	I		Red	Med.	Pear
Wonder Boy	Market	Late	I		Red	Large	Flat globe

*D—determinate; I—indeterminate; SI—semideterminate.
**EB—Early Blight; FW—Fusarium Wilt; GLS—Gray Leaf Spot; VW—Verticillium Wilt.
†Hybrid.

JOB 3. FERTILIZING AND MANURING

The amount and kinds of fertilizers and manure to apply economically for the tomato crop depend not only upon the available fertility of the soil but also upon the organic content, moisture supply, season, cropping system, variety, and the expected returns from the crop. However, in order to produce high yields of good-quality tomatoes a well-fertilized soil must be used. The tomato is listed with those vegetable crops giving highest response to fertility (Table 6.5).

With few exceptions, experiments have shown the following results: (1) applications of quickly available superphosphate result in earlier and increased yields, (2) rapid early growth is essential, (3) liming the soil is seldom beneficial, (4) the content of sulfur and its distribution in the tomato plant give evidence that this element is quite important, (5) soils high in humus are better for main-crop production, and (6) legume crops are desirable in the rotation.

As a rule, where it is necessary to add nitrogen, phosphorus, and potash, a complete fertilizer containing part of the nitrogen and all of the phosphorus and potash needed for the crop should be applied before planting. Where the plants are to be set close together or where large quantities of fertilizer are used, broadcasting is desirable, but where the rows are to be wide apart or where moderate amounts of fertilizer are used, the fertilizer is best distributed in the rows or in bands near the row. At the setting of the first fruit cluster, a side dressing of 100 pounds of sulfate of ammonia per acre may be desirable. Should the plant show signs of nitrogen deficiency later in the season, additional nitrogen side dressings should be applied, provided that climatic conditions are favorable.

JOB 4. GROWING AND SETTING PLANTS

Early tomato plants produce larger and more profitable yields than late ones. To secure the early and greater yields it is essential to have large, stocky, disease-free plants with a well-developed root system. For maximum production, the plants should be 6 to 10 inches tall in soil blocks, pots, or other containers at the time of the frost-free date when they can safely be set in the field. The least desirable plants are grown 200 to 300 plants per square foot in the hotbed and then pulled for setting.

Seeding and Growing Plants

Plants are either produced by the grower or bought from commercial plant producers as explained fully in Chapter 7.

Many growers produce their own plants, for either small or large plantings. In such cases, two ounces of seed will produce enough selected plants for planting one acre. Because of the prevalence of seed-borne diseases, which are at times quite serious, it is a good policy to treat the seed with a fungicide before it is sown. Two of the better treatments are Arasan and red copper oxide, thoroughly dusted on the seed at the rate of one level teaspoonful per pound of seed.

The seedbed soil should be friable, so that it will (1) drain well, (2) not crust, and (3) crumble easily from the seedling roots when plants are removed from the seedbed for transplanting. The addition of sand usually improves the texture. The soil should be free from tomato diseases. Soil not previously used for tomatoes is preferable, but, when it is necessary to use soil more than once, it should be sterilized with steam or treated with formaldehyde.

Early plants can be started in the greenhouse, hotbed, flat (Fig. 30.2), or cold frame, and then transplanted to the hotbed or cold frame, depending upon seasonal conditions. Six to eight weeks are required to produce large plants. Where the seedlings are to be transplanted to produce early plants, the seed is sown in flats or hotbeds at the rate of 8 to 12 seeds per inch in rows 1½ to 3 inches apart, and is covered one-quarter to one-half inch.

For later plants, which are to be transplanted directly from the seedbed to the field, the seed is sown in the hotbed or cold frame so that the thinned plants will stand ½ to 2 inches apart in rows 4 to 6 inches apart. Watering should be thorough and preferably limited to mornings of bright, clear days.

Transplanting

The potting or growing soil differs from the seedbed soil in that it must be fertile to supply nutrients to the growing plants and must be less friable, so that the soil will adhere to the roots in transplanting to the field. A good soil may be made by mixing four parts of loam, two parts of rotted manure, and one part of sand. It is usually well to add one-half pound of a complete fertilizer to each bushel of potting soil.

When the first pair of true leaves appear, 10 to 20 days after seeding, the seedlings are at the best stage for transplanting into beds or contain-

Fig. 30.2—Early tomato plants started in a flat. The plants are transplanted at this stage to other plant growing structures.

Okla. Exp. Sta.

ers (Fig. 30.2). Plants grown in pots or bands have the advantage of retaining most of their roots when set in the field, but are more expensive than those set 3 or 4 inches apart and grown in cold frame beds, being moved later to the field in soil cubes. Potted plants are plunged into the soil to prevent excessive drying. It is often necessary to shade the transplanted seedlings for a day or two until they are re-established, regardless of how and where they are transplanted.

To produce medium-sized plants in flats, the seedlings are set not to exceed 40 per square foot. For large early plants in the hotbed or cold frame, the plants are usually set 4 by 4 inches or 5 by 5 inches. The minimum spacing should be 3 by 3 inches.

Regardless of how the plants are grown, they should be hardened to the extent that they will withstand the transfer to outdoor conditions with as little shock as possible. The hardening may be accomplished by lowering the temperature, giving more ventilation, and lessening the water supply. The process may require from 3 to 10 days, depending upon the original condition of the plants. Over-hardening, causing the plants to yellow, produces later and lower yields.

Transplants are often grown in the field without protection from cold for shipment to regions farther north. They can be grown on a large scale and handled efficiently by machinery. This method is used almost exclusively when transplants are employed to produce tomatoes for processing. When the plants are large enough to be set in the field, the soil is loosened and the plants pulled and hauled to the packing shed. Here they are sorted and bunched in sizes convenient for transplanting machines. The roots of each bunch are dabbed with wet peat moss and wrapped with paper to prevent drying. The bunches are then packed in hampers or other containers for shipping. This is the least expensive method of growing plants and can be quite satisfactory when early yields are not important.

Setting Plants in the Field

A few days previous to setting the large plants in the field from the cold frames, they are blocked by cutting the soil in squares with a square spade. Blocking lessens the shock at transplanting. At setting time, each plant is lifted and set out with a 3- to 5-inch cube of soil on its roots.

Plants should be watered moderately a few hours before setting, so as to prevent wilting during transplanting. Watering also makes it easier to remove the plant from the pot and prevents crumbling of the soil from the roots of either potted or blocked plants.

After the field is thoroughly prepared, it is marked off in both directions, and a lister or small plow is used to open the furrows in which the plants are to be set. Small potted plants are often set with planting trowels. Transplanting machines may be used for setting plants without a ball of soil on the roots.

The planting distances vary with the locality and the methods of cultivation from $1\frac{1}{2}$ to 4 feet apart in rows that are from $3\frac{1}{2}$ to 6 feet apart. In setting the plants, it is essential to pack the soil around the roots or root ball. If the soil is not moist, water should be applied. After the water has soaked in, loose soil should be raked or cultivated in, to level the soil about the plants.

Occasionally the plants become leggy in the plant bed. When such plants have to be used for the spring crop, it is best to put the roots not more than 6 inches below the soil surface, then lay the long stem down in the furrow, allowing just enough of the top above ground to bear the first fruit cluster safely above the soil. At this season, the upper 6 inches of soil is warm and contains available nutrients. The buried long stem will take root, resulting in a vigorously growing, productive plant. For the fall crop, which, particularly in the Southwest, must make the early part of its growth during a relatively hot, dry season, a tall plant is often de-sirable. In setting this crop, the root ball is set as low as 8 to 10 inches in order to reach cooler soil and more abundant moisture. The plant grows slowly at first; then, as moisture becomes more plentiful it produces roots on the covered part of the stem and grows rapidly.

JOB 5.   CULTIVATING AND PRUNING

Cultivating

Unless there is a danger of frost, tomatoes should be cultivated soon after they are set, to stir the soil which has been packed in setting the plants. Early cultivation should be fairly close to the plant, but the suc-ceeding ones should be more shallow and farther away, the main object being to eliminate weeds. Cultivating equipment should be adjusted so that large plants will not be injured (Fig. 30.3).

If the plants are check rowed, most of the weed control can be done by cultivation, but where the plants are close together in the row, more hoeing will be necessary. Weeds permitted to grow not only rob the to-matoes of moisture and plant nutrients, but some of them also are hosts for diseases and insects that attack tomatoes.

Fig. 30.3—Plants pruned and trained to stakes on left, not pruned or trained on right.

Pruning and Training

The value of pruning and training tomatoes varies considerably with different localities, seasons, and varieties. Under humid conditions, training reduces losses from soft rot, but in the drier areas of the Southwest, the trained crop exposed to drying winds is less productive than the untrained plants.

The most common method of pruning and training tomatoes is to prune them to one-, two-, or three-stemmed plants by pinching out the lateral branches as they appear in the axis of each leaf, and then to tie the plant to a 5-foot stake driven a foot into the ground about 3 inches from the plant. The pruning should be done shortly after the branches appear. When more than one stem is desired, the larger lower branches are selected and all other branches are then removed. Strong, soft string is used to tie the plants. It is first tied tightly around the stake, and then a loose tie is made around the stem or stems of the plant. Three to four successive tyings about 1 foot apart are required to support the plant properly.

Plant Appearance as a Guide to Cultural Practices

In order to produce good yields of high-quality fruit, a high level of soil fertility must be maintained. Deficiency symptoms do not have to be apparent before yields are reduced. When they do appear, however, some correction can often be made.

An acute deficiency of some of the soil nutrients can be detected by certain plant characteristics. A white margin on the leaves of a vigorously growing young tomato plant may indicate potash deficiency. A purple under-color on the leaves of the young plant indicates insufficient available phosphorus. The more intense the purple under-color and the slower the plant growth, the greater the phosphorus deficiency. When there is ample phosphorus and potash and the plant is growing slowly with slender stems, the indications are that the nitrogen supply is low. Lack of nitrogen is characterized also by the lessening of the number of buds in the newly formed clusters and by the dropping of the unfertilized flowers. In the more severe stages, the terminal vegetative growth ceases and the plants become hardened and yellow-green in color. Lack of water may be the cause of lack of nitrogen in the plant.

It should be remembered that the growing green fruit consumes large quantities of nitrogen. Therefore, as the number and size of tomatoes increase, the nitrogen supply must be increased. To provide for this need, many growers start side dressing with nitrogen as soon as the first cluster of fruit is set. An oversupply of nitrogen is characterized by difficulty in setting the first cluster, rough, fasciated fruits, large succulent stems, and leaves of a light green color, especially at the top of the stem. This is usually a very temporary condition.

Tomato varieties differ in their manufacturing and utilization of the nitrogenous and carbohydrate foods. They also respond differently at different seasons. For maximum production, the growers should know the type of the variety he selects to grow, and then use cultural methods to attain this desired type (Fig. 30.4).

JOB 6. CONTROLLING DISEASES AND INSECTS

Diseases

Tomato diseases that are of importance are Fusarium wilt, bacterial wilt, early blight, nailhead spot, leaf spot, root knot, damping off, bacterial canker, anthracnose, blossom-end rot, sunscald, and viruses.

FUSARIUM WILT. Fusarium wilt, caused by the fungus *Fusarium oxysporium f. lycopersici*, is one of the most prevalent of the tomato diseases. The disease is characterized by a yellowing and dying of the tomato leaves progressively from the base upward, and by the discoloration of the vascular tissue.

The disease is controlled by use of disease-resistant varieties and disease-free seed, seed treatment, use of disease-free soil in seedbeds, disposal of diseased plants, and rotation. A number of varieties have a high degree of resistance to Fusarium wilt and one of these should be planted on soils known to be infested with the disease.

BACTERIAL WILT. Bacterial wilt is caused by *Pseudomonas solanacearum*, a soil parasite which enters the roots through wounds. Insects spread it from one plant to another. The diseased plants wilt during the day and partially recover at night. Freshly cut stems exude a gummy, yellow mass of bacteria.

Control is effected by planting disease-free plants, by removing the diseased plants, and by rotation.

EARLY BLIGHT. Early blight is produced by *Alternaria solani*, the same fungus that causes early blight of potatoes. The spores of the fungus may

Fig. 30.4—Tomato plant showing good set of fruit.

be in or on the seed or may live over in the soil, attacking the plants at any stage of their development.

To control, (1) sow only treated seed from disease-free plants; (2) practice sanitation by deep fall plowing, after burning all plant refuse;

(3) set stocky, well-hardened plants early in the season; and (4) spray plants with Maneb or Zineb.

NAILHEAD SPOT. Caused by *Alternaria tomato*, nailhead spot is a disease characterized by grayish-brown spots on the fruit, and is controlled by using resistant varieties, such as Marglobe, and by spraying with Maneb or Zineb.

SEPTORIA LEAF SPOT. Septoria leaf spot, associated with *Septoria lycopersici*, appears first as small water-soaked spots on the underside of the older leaves. The older spots have brownish borders with grayish centers. Small, elongated, brownish lesions occur on the stem.

Control methods are the same as for early blight.

ROOT KNOT. Root knot is an enlarged malformation of the roots caused by very tiny nematodes. The nematodes can be starved out by rotating for two or three years with such crops as Iron cowpeas, corn, oats, velvet beans, and peanuts. Care should be taken to use nematode-free soil in the plant bed.

GRAY LEAF SPOT. Gray leaf spot (*Stemphylium solani*) is a fungus disease receiving considerable attention recently. Small black specks appear on older leaves, causing them to drop after becoming glazed. Control is accomplished by using disease-free seedlings and spraying weekly with Maneb or Zineb.

DAMPING OFF. Caused by several organisms, *Pythium*, *Phytophthora*, and *Botrytis*, damping off attacks the small seedlings at the surface of the soil, causing the stems to shrivel and the plants to topple over.

The control consists of using fresh or sterilized sandy soil, treating the seeds with Arason or red copper oxide, and keeping the small plants and the surface of the soil dry.

BACTERIAL CANKER. Associated with the bacterium *Corynebacterium michiganense*, bacterial canker is one of the most serious diseases of tomatoes. It is carried on and in the seed.

The first signs are a curling downward of the lower leaves, which begin to wilt and die. Pale streaks appearing on the stems and veins of the leaves crack open and form cankers. A diseased stem lesion shows a mealy-looking layer of bacteria-filled tissue.

Diseased fruits are spotted first with small white specks, and later have brown spots encircled with a white ring.

The control is the same as that for early blight, except for application of fungicides.

BLOSSOM-END ROT. Blossom-end rot is a physiological disease of the fruit, caused by severe changes in moisture conditions, which bring about a physiological drought in the fruit, causing the breakdown. The disease appears as a dark brown, leathery rot on the blossom end of the fruit. Under some conditions the rot can be held in check by cultural practices which help to conserve the soil moisture, and by spraying plants with calcium chloride.

SUNSCALD. Sunscald is caused by sudden exposure of tender green fruits to the sun. Any measure which encourages foliar growth will tend to reduce this malady.

VIRUS DISEASES. There are several virus diseases of tomatoes including tobacco mosaic, cucumber mosaic, double virus streak, single virus streak, spotted wilt, and curly top. The virus diseases of tomatoes are important because of the large number of perennial weeds which are host plants. The diseases are highly infectious and readily spread by insects and cultural operations.

GROWTH CRACKS. Fruit cracking results in one of the most serious problems of tomato production, especially for processing. Decay organisms and fruit flies gain entrance through the cracked area. This part of the fruit must be cut away, adding to the waste and cost of trimming.

If conditions are favorable, cracking may begin from the mature-green through the turning stage. The ripe fruit are not susceptible, but cracks already started may grow during ripening.

Varieties with partial resistance are being developed, and these should be used where cracking is prevalent.

Insects

Several insects attack tomatoes and these are listed in Chapter 11. The two discussed below are particularly devastating in certain areas.

HORNWORM. Hornworms, of which two species (*Protoparce quinque, Maculata* and *P. sexta*) feed on tomatoes, are large, green larvae. They are ravenous feeders and quickly damage the plants if not controlled. Spraying or dusting with TDE is recommended.

TOMATO FRUITWORM. The tomato fruitworm (*Heliothis zea*) is also known as cotton boll worm and cornear worm. It eats into the fruit from the stem end, and thereafter feeds from the inside. Thorough, persistent spraying with TDE, DDT, carbaryl, or toxaphene reduces the losses. See Chapter 11.

JOB 7. HARVESTING, HANDLING, STORING, AND MARKETING

Harvesting

The picking basket should be rigid, smooth, not over one-half bushel in capacity, and preferably lined for protection against bruising.

The degree of ripeness at which the tomatoes are harvested depends upon the purpose for which they are grown and the time and method of shipping.

For canning and for manufacturing of tomato products, the fruit is fully ripened on the vine (Figs. 30.5 and 30.6). For local markets, it is harvested in the hard ripe and pink stages. For the bulk of the distant shipments to the northern markets, the fruit is picked in the mature-green stage. However, a considerable portion of the crop picked for shipment is in the turning and pink condition. The mature-green fruits are termed green stock and the turning and pink fruits called pink stock by the trade.

The green stock is shipped either without refrigeration on short hauls or with refrigeration on the last part of long hauls exceeding 8 to 10 days. Pink stock requiring over 24 hours to reach the market is shipped under refrigeration. Prolonged exposures to low temperatures interfere with coloring.

Distinguishing Mature Fruits

The future of the fresh-tomato industry depends largely upon supplying the trade with tomatoes of high quality. The longer the tomato can be left on the vine before picking for market, the higher will be the quality of the fruit when ripe. The grower should train and supervise his pickers to recognize and pick only the mature fruits. A practical test is to

Fig. 30.5—Tomatoes for processing harvested by hand.

Photograph by E. C. Wittmeyer

cut a few average tomatoes crosswise with a sharp knife. If the pulp sur-rounding the seeds is slightly jellylike, permitting the seeds to give way before the edge of the knife without being cut, the fruit is then mature.

Following are definitions of terms used in describing the degrees of tomato maturity:

Fig. 30.6—Tomatoes harvested by machine for processing.

Univ. of Ill. Photograph

IMMATURE. Before the seeds have fully developed and before the jellylike cells surrounding the seeds have developed.

MATURE-GREEN. The fruit is fully grown and shows a brownish ring at the stem scar after removal of the calyx; the light green color at the blossom end has changed to a yellow-green cast, and the seeds are surrounded with jellylike cells filling the seed cavity.

TURNING. About one-fourth of the surface, at the blossom end, shows pink.

PINK. About three-fourths of the surface is pink.

HARD RIPE. The fruit is nearly all red or pink, but the flesh is firm.

OVER RIPE. The fruit is fully colored and soft.

Ripening

Mature-green tomatoes require from 6 to 20 days to ripen in air at 68° to 70° F. and will not color faster at higher temperatures. When either storage or field temperatures remain continuously above 80° to 85° F., the fruit does not develop a red color.

Oxygen is essential for the coloring of tomatoes. Therefore, ventilation is beneficial, and wrapping in paper is detrimental to the development of the best quality when transporting and ripening tomatoes.

Grading and Packing

Different systems of grading are followed in different parts of the country. The U.S. Department of Agriculture has established U.S. grades, Numbers 1, 2, and 3, which have been adopted in many localities. The essentials of grading are to eliminate all injured fruits and to separate the sound fruits according to their grade, maturity, and size. When tomatoes are sold on grade, the careful grower is repaid for his production and careful handling of a high-quality product. Methods of packing vary in different parts of the country. Regardless of the pack, uniformity always makes it more attractive and commands a better price (Fig. 30.7).

Although the main requirement in packing for shipment is prevention of movement in the package during transportation, there has been too much tendency to overcrowd the containers, thus causing unnecessary cutting and bruising. Research work conducted by carriers shows that 20 to 35 percent loss in quantity of tomatoes occurs between producer and consumer. Five to 10 percent of this loss is caused by cuts and bruises in the containers, 5 to 10 percent never ripen because they are picked while too green, and 10 to 15 percent rot before ripening.

Storing

Tomatoes can be kept in storage for only a comparatively short time. The best storage temperature at which breakdown is not likely to occur and ripening will take place is between 54° and 59° F. Fruit picked when

Fig. 30.7—Fruits harvested at the "breaker" stage packed for market.

three-fourths ripe and placed in well-ventilated storage with low humidity and at 34° to 36° F. will keep for about three weeks.

For home use, picking green-mature fruit just before frost, storing it in the most desirable place about the premises, and sorting it every two or three days will give a gradual supply of ripening fruit for about a month.

Marketing

Most of the tomatoes for processing are grown under contract with prices based on grades determined by Federal-state graders at the time of delivery.

If tomatoes are to be sold directly to local retail stores, they may be harvested at the firm-ripe stage. When the channel from grower to retailer is not so direct, turning or pink fruit may be harvested. Although pink fruits are more susceptible to bruising than mature-green fruits, their quality is superior and less handling is necessary. The shipment of tomatoes harvested at the "breaker stage" is increasing.

Tomatoes shipped long distances to market are harvested at the mature-green stage. Some begin ripening in transit, while the remainder are held in ripening rooms at the terminal markets. As the fruits ripen, they are sorted and packed in retail containers. Despite the difficulties of obtaining really mature-green tomatoes, the average repacker prefers to handle them than the pinks. Practices now used in handling mature-green tomatoes would be too rough for turning fruits.

Tomatoes go to the packing house from the field partially culled or straight field run. They are usually handled in boxes that can be lifted and emptied readily. Packing house operations may include unloading, weighing, checking, cleaning, drying, waxing, sorting, grading, sizing, wrapping, packing, lidding, and loading into cars or trucks. The operations may depend on how and where the tomatoes are to be marketed.

The packing house may buy the tomatoes outright; pack them for a fee; handle them on consignment; or in the case of a co-operative, act for the grower-members as their sales agent.

Small growers may grade and pack their tomatoes on the farm. This type of operation is not likely to attract buyers for chain stores that demand a large volume of a uniform pack.

Exports of United States fresh tomatoes averaged 1,045,000 hundred-weight during the 1955-1959 period and declined to approximately 1,000,000 with a value of $8,975,000 in 1963. Canada was the principal recipient, followed by Mexico and the Caribbean areas.

Canned tomatoes to Canada and tomato juice and paste to most countries of western Europe and Latin America, as well as many other countries, have been popular export items. Canned tomato exports decreased considerably from the 1955-1959 annual average of 385,000 cases to 143,900 valued at $467,500 in 1963. Tomato juice also declined from an average of 1,448,500 cases for the 1955-1959 period to about 945,000 valued at $2,612,400 in 1963. Tomato paste and puree dropped from the 1955-1959 average of 711-700 cases to approximately 525,000 valued at $9,622,000 in 1963.

Imports of fresh tomatoes from Mexico and small quantities from islands in the Caribbean averaged 2,222,500 hundredweight between 1955 and 1963. These quantities exceeded exports from the United States during the same period. Likewise, considerably more canned tomatoes and tomato products were imported into the United States, primarily from Italy, than were exported during the last 10 years.

SELECTED REFERENCES

Austin, M. E. and Ries, S. K., "Predicting the Harvest Date of Harvesting Tomatoes Mechanically," *Proc. Amer. Soc. Hort. Sci.* 86, 1965, pp. 587-96.

Bird, J. J., "Commercial Tomato Production in Tennessee," Tenn. Agr. Ext. Ser. Pub. 403, 1965.

Corgan, J. N. and Bryant, M. D., "Producing Tomatoes for Processing," N. M. Agr. Ext. Ser. Cir. 369, 1964.

Cunningham, C. R. and Hemphill, D. D., "Pruning Tomato Plants," Mo. Agr. Ext. Cir. 624, 1952.

Doolittle, S. P., Taylor, A. L., and Davidson, L. L., "Tomato Diseases and Their Control," USDA Handbook No. 203, 1961.

Linn, M. B. and Luckmann, W. H., "Tomato Diseases and Insect Pests: Identification and Control," Ill. Agr. Ext. Cir. 809, 1965.

Manley, W. T. and Godwin, M. R., "Marketing Florida Vine-ripened Tomatoes," Fla. Agr. Sta. Cir. S-147, 1963.

McColloch, L. P., "Bruising Injury of Tomatoes," USDA Marketing Res. Rep. No. 513, 1962.

Morrison, W. W., "Preparing Fresh Tomatoes for Market," USDA Marketing Bull. 19, 1962.

Ogle, W. L., Black, K. B., and Cook, W. P., "Tomato Fertilization in South Carolina," S. C. Agr. Exp. Sta. Bull. 512, 1964.

Porte, W. S., "Commercial Production of Tomatoes," USDA Farmers' Bull. 2045, 1963.

Sims, W. L., Zobel, M. P., and King, R. C., "Growing Tomatoes for Mechanical Harvesting," Calif. Agr. Ext. Pub. AXT-150, 1966.

Spivey, C. D., "Growing Tomatoes under Plastic," Ga. Agr. Ext. Ser. Bull. 621, 1962.

Thompson, A. E., Hepler, R. W., Lower, R. L., and McCollum, J. P., "Characterization of Tomato Varieties and Strains for Constituents of Quality," Ill. Agr. Exp. Sta. Bull. 685, 1962.

Vincent, C. L., "Growing Tomatoes in Greenhouses," Wash. Agr. Exp. Sta. Cir. 276, 1961.

CHAPTER 31

Watermelons

Classification, Origin, and History

The watermelon (*Citrullus vulgaris*) is thought to be native to Africa, although evidence of possible American origin has been reported. Early French explorers found Indians growing melons in the Mississippi Valley. Melons are also reported as having been cultivated in New England in 1629, and in Florida prior to 1664. However, descriptions indicate that the early American melon was of the citron type and that the true watermelon came originally from Africa. Its culture was unknown in Europe until the sixteenth century.

Scope and Importance

Since the days of early American settlers, the watermelon has increased in importance as a commercial crop. It is grown primarily in the southeastern and southern parts of the country. Watermelons ranked 6th in acreage and 15th in value among the 22 principal vegetables in 1965. Acreage fluctuated considerably during the past 26 years but the general decline has been small, from 319,100 in 1939 to an estimated 317,470 in 1965. Total production increased 60 percent during this period, from 18,858,000 to 30,198,000 hundredweight. The value of watermelons rose from $9,056,000 in 1939 to an estimated $46,570,000 in 1965.

The approximate geographical distribution of watermelons is shown in Figure 31.1. Texas, Florida, Georgia, South Carolina, California, Alabama, and Missouri are the leading states in acreage, yield, production, and value as presented in Table 31.1.

Fig. 31.1—Acreage and distribution of watermelon production.

Trends in Production Efficiency

Watermelons are relatively inexpensive to produce, requiring less labor for cultivation and harvest than most vegetable crops, only 40 to 45 man-hours per acre. The average acreage production of watermelons increased from 59 to 82 hundredweight between 1939 and 1959, and rose to 95 hundredweight in 1965. During the 1939-1959 period, output per man-hour increased 90 percent and efficiency is continuing upward (Table 1.4).

Climatic Requirements

The watermelon requires a long, frost-free growing season with relatively high temperatures. It is not highly sensitive to extremes in humidity, and therefore, it can be grown over a wide range of varying climatic conditions extending from the humid regions of the Southeast to the arid sections of the Southwest. However, leaf diseases are more destructive in humid climates. Normally, the watermelon requires 80 to 120 days to mature fruit, the time varying with the date of planting and the locality in which melons are grown.

Table 31.1—Watermelons for Fresh Market: Shipping Season and
Estimated Commercial Acreage, Yield, Production, and
Value in Leading States, 1965.

State	Season	Harvested Acreage	Yield per Acre, Cwt.	Production, 1,000 Cwt.	Price per Cwt.	Value, $1,000
Texas	Early summer	82,000	60	4,900	$1.15	5,658
Florida	Late spring	73,000	125	9,125	1.90	17,338
Georgia	Early summer	41,000	80	3,280	1.40	4,592
South Carolina	Early summer	24,000	75	1,800	1.25	2,250
Alabama	Early summer	13,000	100	1,300	1.40	1,820
Missouri	Late summer	11,100	100	1,110	1.25	1,388
North Carolina	Early summer	9,000	65	585*	1.15	621
Oklahoma	Early summer	8,500	80	680	1.10	748
California	Early summer	8,200	175	1,435	1.85	2,655
Mississippi	Early summer	7,200	75	540	1.25	675
Arkansas	Early summer	6,400	85	544	1.25	680
Maryland	Late summer	4,600	165	759	1.10	835
California	Late spring	5,200	195	1,014	2.45	2,484
Indiana	Late summer	6,200	155	961	1.35	1,297
Arizona	Early summer	4,200	140	588	1.90	1,117
Virginia	Late summer	4,000	105	420	1.00	420
Louisiana	Early summer	3,800	80	304	1.05	319
All states		317,470	95	30,198	1.54	46,570

*Includes some quantities not marketed and excluded in computing value.

JOB 1. SELECTING VARIETIES AND SEED

Commercial varieties of watermelons may vary in color from gray to dark green; and in shape, from round to long and cylindrical. Varieties having deep red flesh and dark-colored seed are preferred because of popular association of those characters with proper maturity and desirable eating quality. The market demand in the past has been for medium to large melons. There are indications that the greater demand in the future will be for medium to small fruit. Toughness of rind and solidity of flesh, combined with excellent eating quality, are essential factors in a desirable shipping melon, while for home use, quality only is of prime consideration.

Varieties

There are many well-known market varieties; however, some of them are being replaced by disease-resistant types. A tabular description of some of these and other varieties is given in Table 31.2.

Table 31.2—Brief Description of Selected Varieties of Watermelons.

Variety	Chief Use	Season (Days)	Resistance	Size, Shape	Ext. Color	Flesh	Seed Color
						Fruit	
Black Diamond (Fla. Giant)	Shipping	90		40 pounds, round	Dark green	Red, sweet	Stippled black
Charleston Gray	Shipping	85	Anthracnose, wilt	30 pounds, oblong	Pale green	Red, sweet	Brown, dark veins
Chris-cross	Shipping	85	Wilt	large, oval	Striped	Red, solid	Black
Congo	Shipping	95	Anthracnose	25 pounds, oblong	Med. green, dark stripe	Red, firm, sweet	Light tan
Dixie Queen	All-purpose	85		25 pounds, oval	Light green, dark stripe	Red, crisp, very sweet	White, small
Fairfax	Shipping	85-90	Anthracnose wilt	30 to 35 pounds, oblong	Striped	Red	White, black rim
Garrisonian	Trucking	85	Anthracnose	35 pounds, oblong	Striped	Bright red, very sweet	Dark, marked, white
Hope Diamond	Shipping	90	Anthracnose, wilt	25 to 35 pounds, round	Pebbled green	Bright red, firm	Grayish black
Peacock Improved	Shipping	90		20 to 25 pounds, oblong	Striped	Blood red, crisp	Brown, small
Sugar Baby	"Ice Box"	75		8 pounds, round	Dark green	Red, good flavor	Dark tan, small
Tri-X 317	Market	90		Medium, oval	Striped	Red, sweet	Seedless
White Hope	Shipping	82	Wilt	40 pounds, oblong	Pale green	Bright pink, tender	Black, small

Securing Seed

Purchasing seed from reputable seedsmen should be a universal practice among melon growers. Knowledge of the origin of seed is preferable, so that repeated orders of desirable varieties or strains may be obtained from year to year. Good seed should be viable, true to name, and free from seed-borne diseases and insects. Commercial seed production is confined largely to the vicinities of Leesburg, Florida, and Rocky Ford, Colorado; however, it is not uncommon for melon growers in the various commercial sections to produce seed in limited quantities.

JOB 2. PREPARING THE SOIL

Soil Preferences

Watermelons thrive best on newly cleared, sandy-loam soils that are rich in humus, fertile, well-drained, and slightly acid. There should be enough litter to provide anchorage for the vines, thus preventing them from being rolled by high winds. It is a common practice in commercial sections to grow watermelons on almost any type of soil that is well drained, warm, fairly productive, and free from injurious insects and diseases. However, it has been observed that, when planted on heavy soils, the plants develop slowly and the size and quality of the fruit are usually inferior.

Preparing the Seedbed

Preparation of the watermelon seedbed should begin well in advance of the planting season. The land should be turned to a depth of 7 or 8 inches during the late fall or early winter to allow ample time for vegetable matter to decay. Just before planting, the land should be thoroughly harrowed. The field should then be marked off in checks varying from 8 to 12 feet apart, the distance being determined by the capacity of the land to produce light or rank vine growth. In the southeastern states, a 10- by 10-foot spacing is generally used. In Arkansas and some southwestern sections, spacing approximates or exceeds 12 by 12 feet. After fertilizer has been applied in the row that designates the direction in which the melons are to be cultivated, two furrows are thrown together with a turning plow, thus providing a slight ridge on which to plant. Seeding on this ridge elevates the plants and affords better drainage.

JOB 3.   FERTILIZING, MANURING, AND LIMING

Since watermelons normally are grown on the lighter soil types, fertilization is practically indispensable in the commercial production of this crop.

Fertilizing

All available data indicate that a complete fertilizer is essential for successful watermelon production. The most generally used analysis contains about 4 percent nitrogen, 4 percent phosphorus, and 4 percent potassium. The rate of application normally ranges from 400 to 800 pounds per acre. Fertilizer may be applied continuously along the row, or it may be placed in a more concentrated position around the plant by extending the application 2 or 3 feet on each side of the hill. If applied directly under the seed, it should be thoroughly mixed with the soil, although there is likely to be less injury to germination if it is placed in furrows 2 or 3 inches on either side of the seed. A supplemental side dressing of a nitrogen fertilizer may be applied at the time vine growth begins. This is considered an excellent practice among leading commercial growers in some sections.

Manuring

Because of the general practice of cutting hay from watermelon fields and feeding it to livestock on the farm, practically all barnyard and stable manure in commercial producing areas is contaminated with injurious disease organisms. Such manure, if used for watermelons, is likely to introduce diseases early in the growing season that will result in serious loss. However, if manure is known to be free of harmful diseases, it is an excellent source of nutrients and humus and may be used to advantage in supplementing commercial fertilizer. The usual rate of application is two to four tons per acre, applied in the drill in advance of the planting season. There are no data showing the value of green manure in watermelon production, although it is general knowledge that the lighter soils in the South are low in humus content and that increased yields almost invariably result from the use of cover crops. Green cover crops should be turned under about one month in advance of the planting season.

Liming

Since the watermelon is tolerant of the degree of acidity normally contained in the soils, liming has not been proved essential in the culture of this crop. Only when the pH is below 5 should liming be considered.

JOB 4. PLANTING

Starting Plants in Bands

Maturity may be hastened a few days and production slightly increased in the South by starting plants in bands or cups in greenhouses or hotbeds and then transplanting them to the field after the danger of frost has passed. It is doubtful, however, whether the narrow margin of profit justifies the practice, and most growers in the South have not adopted it. In areas with a relatively short growing season, transplanting may be profitable.

Seeding in the Field

Practically all watermelons grown in the South are seeded in the open field. The date of planting in the various sections should be such that the seedlings will appear above ground just after the danger of frost has passed. This may be brought about by planting the seed approximately 10 days to 2 weeks in advance of the average date of the last killing frost. To compensate for any frost injury that may occur to this planting, growers frequently make one or two additional seedings at seven-day intervals.

The watermelon hill usually is indicated by intersecting furrows marked off at 10-foot intervals in the field. After the fertilizer has been applied and a ridge has been established, eight to ten seeds are planted in each hill at a depth of ¾ to 1 inch. Planting normally is done by hand. Approximately one pound of seed is required to plant an acre. The date of planting varies from early February in Florida to the first part of June in the late-growing areas.

JOB 5. CULTIVATING AND WEEDING

Cultivating

The watermelon is a shallow-rooted plant; consequently, shallow tillage should be practiced. Cultivation should begin soon after the young plants emerge and should continue as long as vine length will permit. Usually not more than three or four thorough workings are necessary in producing a crop of melons. However, the crop should be cultivated often enough to prevent weed growth. In cultivating, care should be taken that the vines are not bruised as they are highly susceptible to mechanical injury. It is advisable to turn vines only at the tip as excessive turning is likely to roll the vines and thus cause shedding of the young fruit.

Where the hills have been carefully checked, watermelons may be cultivated in both directions with a harrow or weeder until vine growth interferes. These implements, supplmented with a cultivator for close work, will reduce the necessity for hand weeding. After the vines have grown to considerable length, they should be turned into a clearly defined row. This will leave an open space in the middle which will facilitate late cultivation. In the southern commercial fields, cowpeas are planted in this space and harvested for hay, thereby giving a supplemental crop from the same land.

Thinning and Weeding

Where there is no indication of disease or insect injury, thinning of the young plants should begin soon after they appear above the ground. It is advisable to reduce the plants gradually to the desired number. At the first thinning four or five of the most vigorous seedlings should be left. These plants should be well distributed in order that proper development may take place. The last thinning should be deferred until the plants are well established and several true leaves have developed. In the final stand, it is a general practice to leave two plants to each hill, but some growers leave only one.

Often it is necessary when the plants are small, to supplement cultivation with hand weeding and hoeing near the hills. This can be done while thinning. Cost of weeding can be reduced by applying Alanap-3 at the rate of three to six pounds per acre at the time of planting (Table 9.2).

Pruning

It is customary among producers of high-grade watermelons to prune or thin the fruit in order to obtain a larger, more uniformly shaped melon. Pruning does not mean cutting away the vine but rather reducing the number of melons on the vine. It is generally recommended that two melons be left to each plant or hill. However, in the light of data resulting from a pruning test at the Georgia Coastal Plain Experiment Station, it seems that better practice, in early-season pruning, would be to remove, only melons that are illshaped or that have no potential market value. After the early crop is set, subsequent pruning of the late-set fruit should increase the size of marketable melons. Four to six fruits may be left on small-fruited varieties.

The theory involved in pruning is that when the number of melons per vine is reduced, the plant's producing power will be concentrated in a smaller number of fruits, thereby increasing size and perhaps quality.

JOB 6. CONTROLLING DISEASES AND INSECTS

Diseases

The leaf, stem, and fruit of the watermelon are attacked by diseases, among the most destructive of which are wilt, anthracnose, root knot, and stem-end rot.

WILT. Wilt, caused by *Fusarium oxysporium niveum,* is widely distributed in commercial producing areas and is perhaps the greatest menace to watermelon production in the South. The organism lives in the soil and penetrates the roots, growing up through the water-conducting channels of the stems. The symptoms are a dark brown discoloration in the woody portion of the stem, and sudden wilting of the individual branches, which soon results in the death of the plant.

The disease can be controlled by using wilt-resistant varieties, some of which are grown commercially. Losses from the disease can be reduced by using long-time rotations with nonsusceptible crops, preventing drainage water from flowing in from infested fields, and avoiding the use of stable manure that is likely to carry infestation. After land has once become infested with the wilt organism, it is practically unfit for future use in production of susceptible watermelon varieties, as the disease has been known to survive from 10 to 15 years in the soil.

ANTHRACNOSE. (See Chapter 22.)

ROOT KNOT (NEMATODES) . (See Chapter 22.)

STEM-END ROT. Caused by a species of *Diplodia,* stem-end rot is primarily a transit disease and is common and destructive in all sections of the South. Uninjured fruits on the vine are entirely resistant to the disease. Any abrasion on the melon becomes a suitable entry place for the spores, thus causing infection of the fruit. However, the disease normally enters through the stem. It is effectively controlled by careful handling of the fruit to prevent bruises or scratches and by treating the stem with a fixed copper paste as the melons are loaded in the car.

Insects

The principal insects attacking watermelons are melon aphids, cucumber beetles, leaf hoppers, and pickleworms. Controls for these insects are given in Chapter 11.

JOB 7.   HARVESTING AND MARKETING

Harvesting

Watermelons should not be harvested until they are ripe, as melons do not develop the desired internal color or sugar content if taken from the vines while immature. There is no marked difference in the appearance of green and ripe melons; consequently, only experienced pickers should be used in harvesting. The sound method, which consists of thumping, is generally used. Other indications of maturity are (1) dying of the tendril accompanying the fruit, although this is not a true indication for all varieties and (2) change in color of the portion of the melon resting on the ground, from a pale white to a creamy yellow.

Melons should be cut from the vines rather than pulled or broken off, and the stems should be left as long as possible in order that they may be reclipped and treated for stem-end rot as they are loaded in the car.

Handling

In handling melons, care should be exercised to avoid bruising and scratching, as the stem-end rot fungus enters the fruit through abrasions. When being carried to heap rows in the field, melons should be placed carefully on the ground, and the trucks or wagons in which they are hauled should be well padded.

Grading

Uniformity is an essential factor in marketing watermelons. Consequently, grades have been established which group melons according to weight. Most wholesaling of watermelons is conducted on the basis of United States standards. Copies of these standards can be obtained from the Fruit and Vegetable Division of the Consumer and Marketing Service, U.S. Department of Agriculture, Washington, D.C. Most shipments by rail are inspected at shipping points and certified as to quality, condition, grade, and size by Federal-state inspectors. Truck shipments are seldom inspected.

Loading

Proper loading is highly important in the successful transportation of watermelons to distant markets. Only sound melons with fresh green stems should be loaded. Cars should be clean, ventilated on sides and ends, with walls amply covered with paper and the floor with dry bedding. It is preferable to haul to concentration points where several cars may be loaded during the same day, thereby making it possible to segregate grades. All stems should be recut and treated with bluestone paste as melons are placed in the car. In placing melons in the car, sizes should be selected that will give a smooth, tight pack (Fig. 31.2) as melons that are held firmly in place while in transit reach the consumer in better condition than those that are loosely packed. Watermelons that weigh over 20 pounds each should not be loaded more than four layers deep if long, or three deep if round. Lighter melons may be packed one layer higher. Over 80 percent of the shipped watermelons are moved by truck. Rail shipment is used primarily for long distances.

Marketing

Volume buyers prefer to purchase watermelons in production areas where dependable supply, quality, and prices are established. Growers in many sections have established cooperatives or selling agencies to supply this demand.

The principal crop of watermelons is still produced in the South, but substantial areas have developed in the middlewest and in California. Southern grown watermelons generally are shipped north, while those from other producing areas move in various directions to accommodate demand. Early melons bring higher prices, which generally decline as the peak of production is reached in hot weather.

Large quantities of watermelons are shipped from the areas of production in refrigerated or vent-cooled trucks or railroad cars. Considerable amounts are transported in open trucks to local markets, and a large volume is sold at roadside and drive-in markets and by hucksters.

Fig. 31.2—(Above) Doorway view of Congo watermelons loaded lengthwise in railway car. (Below) Melons loaded crosswise. This method results in less bruising in shipment.

Photograph by R. K. Showalter

United States watermelons have been exported to Canada for many years and small quantities go to the Netherlands Antilles, Mexico, and Bermuda. An average of 631,000 hundredweight were exported annually during the 1955-1959 period. This figure rose to 842,300 with a value of $1,952,000 in 1963.

SELECTED REFERENCES

Anonymous, "Watermelons for the Garden," USDA Leaflet 528, 1964.

Bowers, H. A., Nettles, W. C., and Smith, F. H., "Watermelon Production in South Carolina," S. C. Agr. Ext. Ser. Bull. 121, 1962.

Breakiron, P. L., Winston, J. R., and Kaufman, J., "Studies of Watermelon Loading for Rail Shipment," USDA Marketing Res. Rep. 62, 1954.

Breakiron, P. L., Winston, J. R., Kaufman, J., and Earle, C. B., "Crosswise Loading of Long-Type Watermelons," USDA Marketing Res. Rep. 133, 1956.

Doolittle, S. P., Taylor, A. L., Davidson, L. L., and Reed, L. B., "Commercial Watermelon Growing," USDA Agr. Information Bull. 259, 1962.

Singletary, C. C. and Moore, E. L., "Hybrid Watermelon Seed Production," Miss. Fm. Res. No. 6, 1965.

Woodward, R. S., Cox, J. A., and Montelaro, J., "Watermelon Production in Louisiana," La. Agr. Ext. Cir. 202, 1947.

CHAPTER 32

Other Vegetables

A number of vegetables which are either grown in restricted areas or which are of less general economic importance are discussed in this chapter. Special information on the most important phases of culture is included; but the more general practices are omitted, since they are treated in Section One. For example, Chapters 9 and 11 discuss cultivation and pest control, respectively, and Tables 8.1, 8.2, and 8.3 give information on planting dates, rates, depths, and methods. Since the vegetables are conveniently grouped according to botanical families or growing seasons in Chapter 2, complete information may be found on a related crop in one of the special crop chapters in Section Two. For example, Chapter 16 on cabbage contains considerable information which is applicable to collards, Brussels sprouts, and cauliflower.

For convenient reference, the vegetables in this chapter are arranged alphabetically by their common names.

BROCCOLI (SPROUTING)

Classification and Importance

Broccoli (*Brassica oleracea* var. *botrytis*) belongs to the Brassica group, and, in recent years, it has become an important addition to the seasonal supply of our cabbagelike vegetables. Broccoli is becoming increasingly important, ranking 18th in acreage and 19th in value among the 22 principal vegetables in 1965. From 9,000 acres in 1939, an estimated 37,670 hundredweight valued at about $18,500,000 was harvested in 1965. California produced about 75 percent of the commercial crop in 1965, followed by Oregon, Texas, New York, and Washington.

While the labor required to produce and harvest broccoli is relatively high, it has decreased more than 25 percent during the past 20 years due to improved practices and mechanization.

Broccoli does not form a solid head as does cauliflower, which in many respects it resembles. Broccoli is grown for its thickened flower shoots that arise from the crown and from the axils of the leaves, making a large, loose, short-stalked panicle in some varieties, and finer, taller, flower stalks in others. The shoots may and frequently do bear flowers that are not abortive; the stalks are harvested for eating before the flowers open (Fig. 32.1). In other sorts, the flower stalks are fasciated and terminate in club-shaped abortive flower receptacles. Such shoots are usually blue-green in color and covered with a heavy bloom.

Broccoli has gained rapidly in popularity. It is doubtful if any other vegetable as little known as was broccoli 30 years ago, has enjoyed, in such a short period, such universal acceptance by the buying public. It has attained considerable commercial importance in a comparatively short time. Fairly large quantities of broccoli are now being processed, chiefly by freezing.

Fig. 32.1—A good head of green sprouting broccoli.

Varieties

Varieties of broccoli may be classed as early, medium, or late according to their response to time of planting. When seeded or transplanted in the early spring, early varieties will mature rapidly enough to produce crops before the onset of hot weather. They may also be seeded in summer to be harvested in early fall. Early DeCicco and Early Spartan are included in this group. Varieties of medium maturity are seeded in late spring or summer and would include Calabrese, Waltham 29, Atlantic, Coastal, and Medium 90. Late varieties are adapted only to areas where broccoli can be grown throughout the winter. These are planted in fall for spring harvest. Medium Late and Neptune (F_1 hybrid) are late maturing varieties.

BRUSSELS SPROUTS

Classification, Habit, and Culture

Brussels sprouts (*Brassica oleracea* var. *gemmifera*) is one of the numerous cultivated forms derived from the wild cabbage. The plant is a nonheading cabbage which develops miniature heads (sprouts) in the axils of the leaves. It requires a somewhat longer growing season than late cabbage and must, therefore, be planted in the seedbed and in the field earlier than late cabbage. In other respects, its culture up to harvest is the same as that for autumn or late cabbage. The Brussels sprouts plant is as hardy as kale and can be planted in any area where this crop is grown during winter. Like all other cabbages, it is a gross feeder and does best on fertile soil.

Varieties

There are two general forms of Brussels sprouts, tall growing and dwarf. The dwarf varieties, Jade Cross and Long Island Improved, are grown in New York. A taller growing variety, Half Dwarf Improved, is commonly used in California.

Controlling Diseases and Insects

Brussels sprouts is susceptible to all insects and diseases which attack other cabbages. Among insects, the most troublesome during the warm weather are aphids, caterpillars, and the harleuin bug, all of which should be treated the same as when they attack cabbage. Among diseases, club root is the most troublesome. To control these pests, the seedbed should be on sterile soil, and the field for growing the crop should not have been in cabbage, turnips, or other cabbagelike crops for at least three years previous to the planting of Brussels sprouts.

Harvesting and Packing

The sprouts are produced earliest in the axils of the lower leaves of the plant (Fig. 32.2). When they have attained market size (1 to $1\frac{1}{4}$ inch in diameter), the lower leaves are broken away and the sprouts are cut off close to the stem with a sharp knife. They are carried in baskets or trays to a packing house and are conditioned for packing. Usually they are packed in quart berry boxes, which in turn are packed in 24- or 32-quart crates for shipment. In California, where 90 percent of the commercial crop is grown, plastic film bags are used for packing the sprouts. An increasing amount of the crop has been processed by freezing, and has been well accepted by the public.

From the manner of the growth of the plant, it is evident that there will be several successive harvests from the same plant during the season.

CAULIFLOWER AND HEADING BROCCOLI OR HARDY CAULIFLOWER

Classification and Importance

Cauliflower (*Brassica oleracea* var. *italica*) is the aristocrat of the cultivated cabbages. It is more exacting as to climatic and other environmental conditions than any of its relatives. For these reasons, cauliflower culture is carried on only in relatively few favored localities. California leads in its production, with New York second. It is also produced in Texas, Michigan, Oregon, Colorado, Washington, and Wisconsin. A portion of the crop, primarily on the West Coast, is processed by freezing. Most of the cauliflower in California is harvested from November to the first of April, while in New York, it is harvested from August to November. Cauliflower ranked 20th in acreage and 18th in value among the 22 principal vegetables in 1965 when the estimated 25,000 acres had a farm value of approximately $20,000,000.

Although cauliflower has decreased in yield per acre during the past 25 years, its labor requirement has been cut in half by improved cultural methods and harvesting machines.

Fig. 32.2—Brussels sprouts plants showing leaves removed and lower sprouts harvested.

Ferry Morse Seed Co.

Varieties

The number of actual varieties is rather small, but a large number of strains is available. These differ mainly in their season of maturity. Varieties can be grouped into two classes: early cauliflower, of which Snowball and its various strains are the most popular, and the late cauliflower. The late cauliflower is generally grown in the West, and varieties used are Snowball 421, Helios, and Mayflower.

Soil and Cultural Requirements

The culture of cauliflower should be undertaken only upon very fertile, moist, but well-drained soils. It is essentially a cool-weather crop and should not be planted at a time which will mature the crop in very hot weather.

The production of the plants, the transplanting to the field, and the subsequent handling of the crop up to the time of curd formation is the same as for cabbage. As soon as the heads or buttons appear, care should be exercised to protect them from full sunshine and injury from insects or dirt. Early-maturing varieties are protected from sun injury by tying the long outside leaves loosely over the forming heads. Late-maturing varieties are usually self-blanched by the incurving inner leaves.

Harvesting and Packing

The growing heads should be inspected frequently, so that they may be cut as soon as they have attained marketable size and before the curds become discolored, loose, or ricy. All off-type or soiled curds should be kept out of the commercial pack. Marketable heads should be cut with three or four whorls of leaves. These should be trimmed so as to leave a circle of leaf petioles about the head long enough to protect it (Fig. 32.3). The pack presents a better appearance if heads of uniform size are placed in the same receptacle. The style of package varies with the region and the distance to market, but most commercial growers use crates of some kind.

CHIVES

Classification and Habit

Chives (*Allium schoenoprasum*) belong to the onion family. In form and habits of growth they closely resemble the wild onion or garlic of the

Fig. 32.3—A cauliflower head ready for harvest.

southern states. The plant is supposed to be of European origin. It is a perennial, and propagated both by seed and by subdividing the clumps which it forms by natural multiplication (Fig. 32.4). This plant is not grown to any large extent in America, although it is listed in seed catalogs.

Cultural Requirements

Chives should be planted in rows where they may remain for several seasons. In practice, this plant is found to do best if reset every two or three years. In resetting, the compact clumps are lifted and broken into sections of about 25 bulbs each and these are placed in the new locations. The culture and fertilization is very similar to that of onions.

Harvesting and Use

The leaves are the part of the plant used, principally for flavoring soups, stews, omelets, cottage cheese, and cream cheese. Cutting off the leaves appears to stimulate multiplication of the plants. Small clumps may be placed in flower pots, forced to produce new growth, and marketed as potted plants.

Fig. 32.4—The leaves of the chives plant are used for flavoring.

USDA Photograph

COLLARDS

Classification and Habit

Collards (*Brassica oleracea* var. *virdis*) belong to the cabbage family, and are grown extensively for winter greens from Virginia southward throughout the Cotton Belt. In these regions the plants are winter hardy.

The collard is a nonheading type of cabbage (Fig. 32.5). The plant is a gross feeder and frequently attains the height of 3 or 4 feet. Collards, besides being winter hardy, will stand more heat than cabbages and provide a supply of cabbage greens long into the hot weather.

Varieties

The Georgia or Southern, Green Glaze, Morris Heading, and the Vates are the important varieties. Some seed companies list a cabbage collard, which is a cross between a Georgia collard and the Charleston Wakefield cabbage. Claims indicate that it has the hardiness of the collard and forms loose heads with the quality and flavor of the cabbage. It is also claimed that heads can be left on the plants all winter and used as needed.

Cultural Requirements

Seeds may be sown in the spring or in the fall where the plants are to stand, or they may be sown in seedbeds and transplanted to the field. They are spaced further apart than cabbage in rows 3 to 4 feet apart. The subsequent cultivation is the same as that for kale or cabbage. The leaves are gathered for food as they approach full size, but before they become tough or woody. This process produces a tall bare stalk with a tuft of succulent leaves at its top. Staking is frequently necessary to hold plants upright.

DASHEEN OR TARO

Classification and Importance

The dasheen (*Colocasia esculenta*) is a caladiumlike plant. The starchy corms are the edible portion of this widely grown tropical arum. It is closely related to and resembles the common, ornamental elephant's-ear.

The starch content of the dasheen is greater than that of either the potato or the sweet potato. Its protein content is about double and its sugar content about one-half that of the sweet potato. The sugar gives the cooked corm a sweet, nutty flavor, while the large percentage of highly digestible starch, in addition to the protein, renders it a more nutritious food than either the potato or the sweet potato.

This plant is capable, when forced, of providing succulent shoots that may be prepared in the same manner and used in the same way as asparagus, but with a flavor similar to that of the mushroom.

The dasheen is not a common vegetable in the United States, but is cultivated extensively in tropical America, South China, Japan, and the tropical islands of the world. The use and culture of the plant are probably more highly developed in the Hawaiian Islands than elsewhere.

Fig. 32.5—Georgia collards are non-heading but otherwise similar to cabbage.

Varieties

The Trinidad dasheen is considered the best of the large number of varieties collected and tested.

Soil and Cultural Requirements

The best environment for the dasheen is a rich, moist, but well-drained alluvial, silty soil of creek or river bottom. On hammock soils of North Florida a fertilizer carrying 4 percent nitrogen, 6 percent acid phosphate, and 10 percent potash (as sulfate) at the rate of 700 pounds per acre gave satisfactory results. The dasheen is a long-season crop and for that reason is best adapted to the South Atlantic and Gulf Coast states.

Planting should be done as early as conditions will permit, two to three weeks before the date of the last killing frost. Where the growing season does not exceed six months, it is best to start the tubers or cormels in a greenhouse, hotbed, or cold frame, at least a month in advance of the safe season for planting in the open.

Tubers weighing two to five ounces each are best for seed; they should be planted 2 to 3 inches deep, 2 to 2½ feet apart, with 3½ to 4 feet between rows. Such spacing will permit cultivation early in the season and complete shading of the ground later on. The dasheen is a shallow-rooted plant; therefore, deep cultivation should cease before the roots are injured by the practice.

Harvesting and Storing

A plow may be run under the hills in such a way as to turn the corms out of the ground after the tops have been removed. With small lots that must be harvested by hand, two men with long-handled, round-pointed shovels, one on each side of the plant to be lifted, can usually do the work satisfactorily. After the plants are lifted, the corms must be divided, cleaned, and the so-called tubers or cormels separated from the parent corm.

Dasheens keep satisfactorily at about the same temperature as sweet potatoes, as far as known; however, they do not require the high temperatures necessary for drying and curing sweet potatoes. As large corms do not keep so well as the cormels or tubers, the marketable or edible portion of the crop should be sold without holding too long.

ENDIVE OR ESCAROLE

Classification and Importance

Endive (*Cichorium endivia*) is probably of East Indian origin and belongs to the *Compositae* family. It was used as a food plant by the early Egyptians and later by the Greeks and Romans. It was eaten as a salad and potherb, but is now used mainly as a salad. Although endive has been grown by market gardeners on a small scale for many years, production did not show a marked increase until after 1940. In 1939 statistics were available only for Florida, where 1,000 acres were produced. The acreage there had increased to 6,800 by 1965 with 9,550 acres harvested in all states.

Varieties

There are two types of endive: the curled or fringed, and the broad-leaved, known on the market as *escarole*. Because of its attractiveness in tossed salads and for garnishing, the fringed-leaved type is more widely grown. Varieties of this type are: Green Curled, Green Curled Pancalier, and Salad King. The broad-leaved varieties include Full Heart Batavian and Florida Deep Heart.

Culture

Endive grows best in a mild climate. In the deep South, it may be grown as a winter crop. In most regions it can be grown as a spring or early summer crop. In the North, endive can be grown throughout the summer where irrigation is available. The plants flower in response to low temperatures (vernalization) and long photoperiods. The early spring crop should be grown from transplants produced at temperatures above 60° F. to avoid premature flowering.

Soil and fertility requirements for endive are   nilar to those for lettuce. Well fertilized soil and irrigation, where wa:er may be limiting, are important for rapid, continuous growth. This .s essential for good yields and high quality.

Plants may be spaced 12 inches apart in 18-inch rows or set in beds 12 inches apart. Crowding of the plants with the latter spacing will cause some blanching of the center leaves (Fig. 32.6). This may be desired to reduce bitterness associated with the green leaves. Blanching can be done by tying the leaves of a plant together loosely over the top, but this practice has been largely discontinued.

Harvesting and Marketing

Plants are harvested by cutting them off at the soil surface. Diseased, discolored, or blemished leaves are removed. Outer leaves are folded over the centers of plants before packing in crates or baskets. Refrigeration is used for distant shipments. Methods used for precooling and icing lettuce may be used for endive.

GARLIC

Classification and Importance

Garlic (*Allium sativum*) is a member of the onion group, but it differs from the onion in that it consists of a multiple bulb composed of small bulblets called cloves. Nature packs these cloves together in a rough bulblike mass and covers them with a parchmentlike membrane. This package of cloves makes up the garlic bulb of commerce.

Garlic is offered in every market catering to any considerable population of people from the south of Europe or their descendants. Since garlic is used chiefly for flavoring purposes, a small supply serves for many meals. The demand, while important and continuous, will never be large. On the other hand, the territory of the United States in which garlic can be grown most successfully is decidedly restricted. California produces most of the garlic grown in the United States. Some is also grown in Texas and Louisiana. As a special crop in the hands of a few growers, it should return a reasonable profit.

Fig. 32.6—Curled leaved endive.

USDA Photograph

Garlic acreage and production have fluctuated during the last 25 years. The commercial planting of 4,300 acres valued at $563,000 declined to around 2,500 acres during the 1951-1957 period, and then rose to approximately 4,600 acres valued at $4,295,000 in 1965.

Varieties

There are the early (White or Mexican) and the late (Pink or Italian) varieties. The early variety does not store well and has poorer quality. However, it will outyield the late type.

Seed Requirements

True seed is seldom used in the propagation of garlic. Cloves and top sets are used, but cloves are more common. Since the size of the cloves determines the number of planting units per pound, a sample of the stock to be used for seed should be taken and the average number of cloves per pound determined. From this, one can compute the number of pounds of seed required to plant a given area when the rows are set with plants at a given distance in the row. Usually 800 to 1,000 pounds of cloves are needed to plant an acre.

Soil and Cultural Requirements

Garlic thrives best on a friable sandy loam well supplied with organic matter. The culture and fertilization of garlic is essentially the same as for set onions. Seed is prepared by breaking the mother bulbs apart, so that the cloves of which they are composed become individual units (Fig. 32.7). These units are planted singly, 3 to 6 inches apart, according to variety, in rows 12 to 16 inches apart.

Fig. 32.7—Garlic bunched for market.

USDA Photograph

In California, plantings are usually made between October and January. Early planting is desirable because the plant remains vegetative during the short days and grows larger before bulbing. The larger plants produce larger bulbs.

Harvesting and Handling

If the soil is very rich, it may be necessary to break over the tops to prevent too much top growth, and to make the bulbs better, as is sometimes done with onions. As soon as the crop is mature, as indicated by the discoloring and wilting of the leaves, the plants should be pulled and placed in windrows, with the tops covering the bulbs to prevent sunscald. After curing for several days, the tops and roots are trimmed. The bulbs are then graded and bagged for market. Garlic will endure a wide range of temperatures, but must be kept dry to prevent sprouting.

No one kind of package is widely used for shipping garlic. A mesh bag or a well-ventilated slat crate may be used, but the volume in each crate should not be large because there is a tendency to heat when garlic is packaged in any considerable mass. Garlic is usually retailed in small film bags.

GLOBE ARTICHOKES

Classification and Importance

The globe artichoke (*Cynara scolymus*) is a robust, perennial, thistle-like plant, grown chiefly for the edible receptacles and scales of the blossom bud (Fig. 32.8). It is not hardy to cold, and so its culture is chiefly confined to the South Atlantic and Gulf Coast regions and to the Pacific Coast in California, south from San Francisco to Los Angeles. Only in California has the crop gained commercial rank, and most of the market supply comes from that state. Production in other areas is confined to local market and home gardens.

The production of artichokes has fluctuated slightly downward during the past 25 years. The commercial acreage of 10,400 valued at $1,762,000 in 1939 decreased to an estimated acreage of 9,200 valued at $5,761,000 in 1965. California produces most of this crop.

Soil and Cultural Requirements

Best conditions for the globe artichoke are obtained on rich friable

Fig. 32.8—Globe artichoke showing edible scales of the blossom bud.

USDA Photograph

lands under irrigation. Outside of the irrigated area rich, well-drained soil is best. The plant is a gross feeder and should have from 800 to 1,000 pounds per acre of a high-grade vegetable fertilizer in the form of a side dressing.

Globe artichokes grow readily from seed, but the seedlings are highly variable; hence, vegetative propagation by means of offshoots or suckers is recommended. These spring up from the base of the original plant after the blossom stalk has died down. Several sucker plants usually develop about the original crown. The most recent and preferred method of propagation is by division of the old crown so that each section includes a piece of stem from a sucker plant. The plants are usually spaced 6 feet apart in rows 8 feet apart, and set at a depth of 6 to 8 inches. The crop is usually planted in February and March, and renewed every four to seven years.

Controlling Insects

The insect enemies are chiefly two, the artichoke aphid, which may be controlled by dusting with nicotine or malathion, and the plume moth, the larvae of which bore into the blossom buds, causing considerable loss of the crop in California. Thistles are an alternate host of the plume moth, and they should be kept down in the vicinity of artichoke fields. Field sanitation and dusting with parathion or lindane have given control.

Harvesting and Handling

As soon as the blossom buds have attained maximum growth, but before signs of flower opening appear, the crop is ready to harvest. There is considerable variation in time of maturity among plants as well as among the buds on an individual plant; consequently, the harvest season is prolonged and is usually terminated by weather conditions rather than by the exhaustion of the crop.

The mature buds are cut with 1 to 1½ inches of the stem attached. They are graded for size and quality, and packed in large paperlined boxes carrying 48 to 125 buds. Lug boxes are usually used for local markets.

HORSERADISH

Classification and Importance

Horseradish (*Armoracia rusticana*) is a well-known garden perennial in many long-established vegetable gardens. It is a near relative of cabbage, turnips, and mustard, belonging to the *Cruciferae* family. Horseradish is highly prized as an appetizing condiment with oysters and cold meats.

As a commercial crop, horseradish is grown in but few places. An area about St. Louis, Missouri, has long enjoyed distinction as the chief horseradish-growing district of the United States.

Soil and Cultural Requirements

The plant will survive in most soils except deep sterile sands and shallow heavy clays with a hardpan subsoil. Best crops are grown on rich, moist, deeply-tilled, friable loams of river bottoms.

Although a crop of horseradish will remove large amounts of nutrients from the soil, it does not require highly fertile soil. The plant has a long growing season and an extensive root system for asorbing nutrients. It is important, however, to have a continuous supply of nutrients and moisture during the summer months. A plant that has survived the summer in good shape will produce large roots in the fall.

Horseradish is grown from root crowns and root cuttings. Most commercial crops are grown from sets or root cuttings. As the crop is prepared for market (Fig. 32.9) during the autumn and winter, all branch roots as large as or larger than a lead pencil are saved as cuttings. Good cuttings are 6 or more inches long and fairly straight. The bottoms of the roots are given a slanting cut and the top ends a square cut, which facilitates the work of planting.

Commercial practices have been highly developed. The land for horseradish is deeply tilled and plots of uniform length and width are laid off side by side. Furrows 4 or 5 inches deep and 30 inches apart are laid off the long way of the plots. The sets are usually spaced about 1½ to 2 feet apart in the furrows. Experience has demonstrated that the sets are best planted with the tops all sloping in the direction that cultivation is to proceed. By slanting the plants opposite ways in adjoining plots, cultivation can proceed in one direction in one plot and in the opposite direction in the neighboring plot. The idea is to keep the cultivator from dragging out the sets.

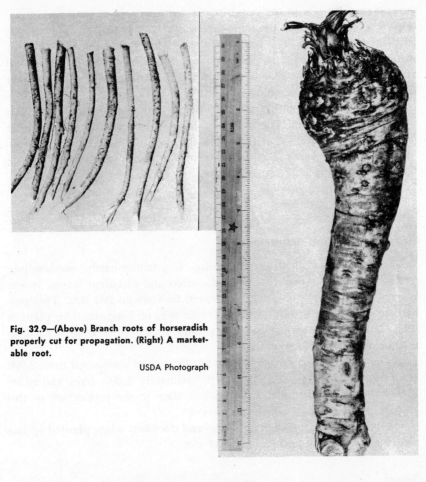

Fig. 32.9—(Above) Branch roots of horseradish properly cut for propagation. (Right) A marketable root.

USDA Photograph

In order to obtain straight merchantable roots, some growers remove the side roots early in the season. This is done by removing the soil and stripping off the side roots from the upper part of the main root. The soil is then replaced. This is usually done twice during the growing season.

Harvesting, Storing, and Marketing

Horseradish makes its best growth during the cool weather of autumn. Harvesting should not be started until such growth has taken place. Digging is accomplished with a heavy plow. A furrow is run along the outside row of roots in the opposite direction from that used in cultivation. A second furrow in the same direction as the first turns the roots out with the furrow slice. The roots are then gathered and placed in pits or storage cellars, to be prepared for market. Pits, cool cellars, or barns will answer for holding the crop over winter, but roots to be held for summer use should be placed in cold storage.

Preparation for market may be done at any time during the winter when weather permits. The merchantable roots are tied in bundles after all lateral and bottom roots have been removed. The lateral roots suitable for sets are prepared as described above. Yields range from 3,000 to 6,000 pounds of salable roots per acre.

KALE

Classification and Importance

Kale (*Brassica oleracea* var. *virdis*) is a winter-hardy, nonheading, cabbagelike plant grown for its much-curled and succulent leaves. It was known to the Greeks and was mentioned by Cato in 200 B.C. This potherb is extensively grown in the Norfolk area of Virginia. The plant is bulky and can be grown profitably only in localities enjoying cheap transportation over a short haul.

The commercial acreage of kale has fluctuated downward from 2,900 acres worth $268,000 in 1939 to approximately 1,200 acres valued at $580,000 in 1965. Virginia is the leading state in the production of this crop.

It is essentially a cool-season crop and does best when planted in late summer for autumn and early winter use.

Types

Two types of kale are grown in the United States. One, known as Scotch, has much-curled and crumpled foliage of a grayish-green color; the other, called Siberian, is less crinkled and is bluish-green. Both dwarf and tall forms are grown, with the dwarf forms being most popular. Kale and the closely related collards are favorite plants for the production of winter greens throughout the South.

Cultural Requirements

Quickly grown plants are less fibrous and more tender than slowly grown ones. The soil best suited for good production is friable loam well stocked with organic matter through the use of manure or cover crops. These should be supplemented by the application of a 5-10-5 fertilizer at the rate of about one ton per acre. For hand cultivation, kale is usually planted with a seed drill in rows 18 inches apart, but for tractor cultivation the rows are 24 to 30 inches apart. When the plants are well established, they should be thinned to stand about 6 inches apart in the row. Kale is subject to all the pests that affect cabbage and the same remedial measures should be employed.

Harvesting and Marketing

For home use, kale is best if harvested before the plants are large and tough; otherwise only the young leaves should be gathered. For market, quickly grown plants are cut at the surface of the ground and packed in tall hampers or bushel baskets. Some kale is now prepackaged in transparent film bags for retail trade. With an excess of more refined vegetables available at all seasons, kale has strong competition, but it is still extensively planted in the maritime section of Virginia.

KOHLRABI

Classification and Use

Kohlrabi (*Brassica oleracea* var. *gongylodes*) is grown for the turnip-like enlargement of the stem above ground (Fig. 32.10). It is little known and is not appreciated in the United States, although it is an excellent vegetable if used before it becomes tough and stringy. For good quality, growth must be rapid and unchecked. The plants may be started in the greenhouse or hotbed for an early crop, but the more common practice is to plant the seed where the crop is to mature.

Varieties

The most popular varieties are White Vienna, Green Vienna, Purple Vienna, and the Earliest Erfurt. The White Vienna is probably grown to a greater extent than all of the others combined.

Cultural Requirements

The seed is sown in rows 18 inches apart for hand cultivation, or 24 to 30 inches for tractor cultivation. The plants are thinned to stand 6 to

Fig. 32.10—Kohlrabi plants ready for harvest.

USDA Photograph

8 inches apart in the row. Planting at intervals of two to three weeks will secure the proper sequence and insure a continuous supply of tender kohlrabi.

A rich garden soil will produce excellent kohlrabi. If the soil is not already rich, a liberal dressing of manure is desirable. If manure is not available, green-manure crops and commercial fertilizer may be used as substitutes. A fertilizer similar to that suggested for cabbage would be satisfactory for this crop.

Cultivation similar to that given cabbage or cauliflower is satisfactory for kohlrabi, but when it is planted in rows less than 24 inches apart, garden tractors or hand cultivators are used.

Harvesting

Kohlrabi should be harvested when the swollen stem is 2 to 3 inches in diameter and before it becomes tough and woody. When prepared for market, the root is cut off and the plants are tied together in bunches like beets, or sold in bulk.

MUSTARD

Classification and Varieties

White mustard (*Brassica hirta*) is grown for salad and greens to some extent, but has been replaced largely by spinach and kale. This plant is a hardy annual of the *Cruciferae* family. The White London is one of the well-known varieties of this species. Black mustard (*Brassica nigra*) is grown largely for its seed, which is made into the mustard of commerce. This type is grown to a great extent on the adobe soils in Santa Barbara County, California.

Giant Curled and Tendergreen are varieties of *Brassica júncea* var. *crispifolia* grown to some extent in the South. Chinese Broad Leaf and Florida Broad Leaf are also extensively planted.

Soil and Cultural Requirements

Mustard is generally sown for greens very early in the spring for spring use, and in the fall for the winter crop. To provide a season's supply, successive plantings should be made at intervals of 10 days or two weeks. Seed is sown in drills 12 to 18 inches apart and the plants thinned as they become crowded in the row (Fig. 32.11).

On a good sandy-loam soil, 50 to 75 pounds of nitrogen, 100 to 150 pounds of acid phosphate, and 50 to 75 pounds of potash per acre should give good results, even without manure, provided the humus supply is maintained by turning under soil-improving crops. Where manure is used, an application of 25 to 30 pounds of nitrogen and 80 pounds of phosphoric acid should be sufficient.

NEW ZEALAND SPINACH

Classification and Habit

New Zealand spinach (*Tetragonia expansa*) differs from the true spinach in being a much-branched plant 4 to 5 feet across and 1 to 2 feet tall. It belongs to the family *Aizoaceae*. Its leaves resemble somewhat those of the true spinach, but the chief similarity between the two plants is in

Fig. 32.11—A plant of curled leaf mustard.

the flavor. New Zealand spinach lacks commercial importance as compared with true spinach, but it can be a valuable addition to the home garden. Unlike ordinary spinach, it does not withstand low temperatures, but thrives in warm weather, thus extending the spinach season. However, it will not survive the hot summers of the extreme South unless given protection.

Cultural Requirements

Seeds can be planted in warm, protected seedbeds in late winter to be later transplanted, or they may be planted directly in the field when the season permits. Whatever the procedure, plants need to be finally spaced 2 to 3 feet in rows 3 to 4 feet apart. Aside from the difference in time and method of planting, the general culture closely follows that for ordinary spinach.

Harvesting and Grading

As soon as the plants are large enough, the tender tips, 3 to 4 inches long, can be cut off. This stimulates the growth of more branches, and so harvesting continues until some unfavorable condition terminates the life of the plant.

OKRA

Classification and Importance

Okra, or gumbo (*Hibiscus esculentus*), is a popular home garden vegetable in the South. It is thought to be of Asiatic origin and is reported to have been used by the Egyptians in the twelfth century. Production has nearly doubled since 1939, with practically all of the commercial production for market and processing being in the southern states.

Varieties

Varieties of okra may be classified as dwarf, intermediate, or tall according to the height of the plant. Most commonly used varieties have spineless pods ranging in color from creamy white to dark green. Some of the popular varieties are Perkins Spineless, Dwarf Long Pod, Clemson Spineless, Louisiana Green Velvet, and Emerald.

Soil and Cultural Requirements

Any good garden soil will produce a satisfactory crop of okra if other conditions are favorable. Barnyard manure is desirable for poor soils and a supplementary application of 500 to 1,000 pounds of a 5-10-5 fertilizer per acre will pay under many conditions.

Okra is a tender plant and should not be planted until the danger of frost is over. Seed is drilled thickly on slightly bedded rows 2½ to 4 feet apart. When the plants are established, they are thinned so that the plants of dwarf varieties are 12 inches apart, and those of larger varieties 18 to 24 inches apart. The cultivation of okra should be about the same as for any other cultivated crop. Weeds should not be permitted to become established.

Fig. 32.12—Okra plant showing pods.

USDA Photograph

Harvesting and Use

Okra yields over a long period of time, usually from June to October. Only the young, tender pods are desired, and pods should be picked daily to secure a product of best quality (Fig. 32.12). All pods should be removed to keep the plants producing. Okra deteriorates rapidly, and consequently does not ship well.

Okra is used principally in soups and stews. The pods are sometimes stewed and eaten as a vegetable. A large portion of the crop is processed by canning, freezing, or preserving in brine for future use in canned soups.

PARSLEY

Classification and Importance

Parsley (*Petroselinum crispum*), a native of Europe, is a near relative of celery and parsnips. It is the universal favorite for garnishes and is used also for flavoring salads, soups, and stews. There are two types of parsley, one with fibrous roots and finely divided, much curled or crinkled leaves; the other with plain leaves and fleshy roots which are used for flavoring soups and stews. The leafy type is chiefly grown in the United States, while the fleshy-rooted sorts are largely grown in Europe.

Varieties

Parsley has been developed with three types of foliage: (1) the plain leaf, (2) the double-curled, and (3) the moss or triple-curled (Fig. 32.13). The fleshy-rooted parsley has plain celerylike leaves.

Soil and Cultural Requirements

The seed of parsley is small and slow to germinate. Soaking the seed overnight induces quicker germination. Young plants are small and quite delicate and require protection and frequent watering to prevent loss from drying. When established, the plants are more resistant to cold than to heat.

Because of their tender nature while young, the plants are frequently started in cold frames or hotbeds. Parsley, however, does well under favorable conditions in the open. Rich, fine, moisture-retentive soil is best. In the South, the crop is grown mostly in the autumn, winter, and spring, the summer heat being too severe.

In the North, parsley is grown in greenhouses, cold frames, and hotbeds during the winter months. The Norfolk, Virginia, area grows parsley in sash-and-muslin-covered frames as a winter crop. The plants can be set about 6 inches apart each way, kept free of weeds, and the entire top clipped off to thicken the crown of leaves on well-established plants.

SALSIFY

Classification and Importance

Salsify (*Tragapogon porrifolius*) is commonly known as the "oyster plant" or "vegetable oyster" because of its flavor when made into soups

Fig. 32.13—Parsley leaves bunched for market.

USDA Photograph

and cooked in other ways. The edible part is the long, fleshy white tap root. As a vegetable in this country, it is relatively unknown, but it is fully deserving of greater appreciation. It is a member of the *Compositae* family and is a native of the Mediterranean area. Only one variety, Mammoth Sandwich Island, is grown in this country. Salsify is distinct from black salsify (*Scorzonera hispanica*) and Spanish salsify (*Scolymus hispanicus*). The latter two are grown in Europe, but are practically unknown in the United States.

Cultural Requirements

The culture is practically the same as for parsnips. A long growing season is required for full development. Salsify is winter hardy in most regions and can be harvested throughout the winter. It can also be stored, using the same methods employed for other root crops.

SHALLOTS

Classification and Importance

The shallot (*Allium ascalonicum*) is an ancient, universally distributed, onionlike plant. It is believed to have come from western Asia. Nearly all of the commercial crop in the United States is produced in southern Louisiana.

Shallots have declined in importance from 5,400 acres valued at $317,000 in 1939 to about 900 acres with a farm value of about $305,000 in 1965.

Plant Habit

The plant is a perennial that seldom produces seeds and therefore must be increased by division of its compound bulbs, which are made up of several bulblets, or cloves, held together at the base. The bulbs are not encased by a sheath as is garlic. The bulblets are planted in the same manner and at the same season as are onion sets, each set developing into a compound bulb. The mature bulbs are harvested, cured, and stored in the same manner as onions. In suitable storage, the bulbs will keep from one season to the next.

Use

The flavor of shallots is somewhat milder than that of onions. The chief use is for flavoring, both leaves and cloves being used. Most of the crop is produced for sale in the green state, but some dry bulbs are also sold.

SOUTHERN PEA (COWPEA)

Classification and Importance

The southern pea (Cowpea) (*Vigna sinensis*) is an important forage and soil-improving crop, extensively grown in the South. It is a member of the great group of legumes of the bean type, and is used for human food both in the green-shelled and dry state. Its ease of culture and ability to grow on poor land makes it an important food crop in the South.

Varieties

There are a number of different kinds of southern peas, which may be distinguished mainly by the pod type and color and pattern of seed coat. Within each color group are what are known as the crowder types, in which the seeds are tightly crowded in the pod. Each group is represented by a large number of varieties and strains. Some of the different types are the purple-hull, the cream, and the blackeyed. The blackeyed group is extensively used as a culinary vegetable. Throughout the South and especially in parts of Texas and California, blackeyed peas are grown as a field crop to supply the marked demand for the dry shelled product. The Yardlong or Asparagus bean, one of the southern peas with seed pods of extraordinary length, is sometimes included in the southern vegetable garden for its edible pod, which is used as a substitute for snap beans. Commonly grown varieties include Brown Crowder, California Blackeye, Purple Hull Brown Crowder, and Purple Hull Bush Pinkeye.

Soil and Cultural Requirements

Although southern peas can be grown on poor soil under adverse conditions, an application of 200 to 300 pounds of 5-10-5 or some similar complete fertilizer will materially increase production.

As a field crop, southern peas are frequently sown broadcast, or they are sown in drills 6 to 8 inches apart. Approximately one to one and one-half bushels of seed are required to plant an acre. The pods are gathered when in condition for green or dry shelling. The vines are either cut for hay or turned under as a soil-improvement crop.

Southern peas are sometimes sown in rows $2\frac{1}{2}$ to 3 feet apart in the same manner as garden peas or beans, using about a peck of seed per acre. The rows are cultivated until the vines overlap. Weeding and thinning are seldom necessary.

SOYBEANS

Classification and Importance

The soybean (*Glycine max*) is a close relative of the southern pea. As a garden crop, it has not been generally cultivated in England or in the United States. In Japan and in Manchuria, it is a food crop of prime importance.

Varieties

The varieties of soybeans are exceedingly numerous, many of them having been developed by the Japanese. They vary from 75 to 170 days for maturity, and they also vary greatly in soil and climatic adaptation, color, quality, flavor, and ease of cooking. For garden purposes the Hahto, Zogun, Green Giant, and Favorite are commonly used. Kim and Kanrich are two promising varieties recently introduced.

Soil and Cultural Requirements

Soybeans do well under the conditions suitable for ordinary garden beans. They should be planted in rows 24 to 30 inches apart and the seed distributed so as to insure a stand of plants 3 to 4 inches apart.

The time of planting in the North is immediately after corn planting, and in the Gulf states the best time is from April 15 to June 1. Soybeans are not as sensitive to frost as are garden beans and may be planted somewhat earlier.

Harvesting and Use

Soybeans as a green vegetable should be harvested when the seeds are fully grown, but before they have hardened, as the pods are then rough, hairy, and hard to shell. The young beans resemble young lima beans, but have a richer, nutlike flavor. Tough pods, if boiled for about three minutes, may be shelled with comparative ease. Cooked immature soybeans are a rich source of protein, fat, calcium, phosphorus, and iron, and are also good sources of vitamins A and B, but are a poor source of vitamin C.

Soybeans are not a favorite food of the Mexican bean beetle, and can be grown in localities where this insect prevents the culture of bush beans. Japanese beetles and rabbits are fond of soybeans, however.

Soybean flour has long been used in making bread and cakes for diabetics, because of its low starch content. Soybean milk is extensively used as infant food and as a means of restoring normal flora in the digestive tract. As a food, it is non-acid forming.

SQUASHES AND PUMPKINS

Origin and Classification

For generations, the place of origin of pumpkins and squashes has been a matter of doubt. Archeological investigations conclusively prove that pumpkins, squashes, and gourds were widely distributed both in South America and North America, and were extensively used by the people of the Americas for receptacles, utensils, and food, long before these continents were discovered by Columbus. Overwhelming evidence is in favor of an American origin for all the species mentioned above.

The plants spoken of as squashes and pumpkins comprise no less than four species of the genus *Cucurbita*, namely *C. pepo*, *C. maxima*, *C. moschata*, and *C. mixta*. The nomenclature of this group of plants is greatly confused because of culinary terminology. The species characteristics have not been followed in distinguishing squashes and pumpkins.

SUMMER SQUASHES. Summer squashes, commonly *C. pepo*, are eaten in the immature stages when the rind is very soft. White Bush Scallop, Early Green Bush Scallop, Yellow Crookneck, Yellow Straightneck, Cazerta, Cocozelle, and Zucchini are popular varieties. All these are of the bush type.

WINTER SQUASHES. Winter squashes, utilized when the fruits are mature, have hard rinds and store well. The members of this group usually have flesh of mild flavor and fine texture, and are suitable for baking. Varieties of winter squash are included in all the species of *Cucurbita*. They include Table Queen, Butternut, Buttercup, Green Hubbard, Blue Hubbard, Golden Hubbard, Warted Hubbard, Boston Marrow, Delicious, Golden Delicious, and Banana.

PUMPKINS. Pumpkins are also used when the fruit is mature. The flesh is often coarse or strong and hence not generally served as a baked vegetable. The rind of most varieties of pumpkins is not hard even at full maturity and in this respect they may be distinguished from winter squashes. The name pumpkin is applied to varieties in all the species of cucurbita. Some of the important varieties are Connecticut Field, Small Sugar, Winter Luxury, Japanese Pie, Kentucky Field, Large Cheese, Dickinson, Mammoth Chili, and the cushaws.

Scope and Importance

The members of the genus *Cucurbita* are considered minor crops and consequently statistics of their production are meager. One or more varieties, though, are found in most home and market gardens; they are ever present in the markets; and pumpkins and squashes are extensively canned and used for stock feed. It is readily apparent that the group as a whole is very important in our agricultural economy.

The states most important in the production of pumpkins are Illinois, New Jersey, California, Indiana, New York, Ohio, Michigan, and Pennsylvania. Largest acreages of squashes are grown in Florida, California, Texas, New York, Georgia, New Jersey, Massachusetts, Michigan, North Carolina, and South Carolina. The relative positions of the states may vary from year to year because these crops can be grown most anywhere and with only a small investment of capital.

Soil and Climatic Requirements

Almost any good, well-drained soil will grow pumpkins and squashes. It should be well supplied with organic matter and provided with a uniform supply of moisture. Soil type is not critical if each is properly handled and fertilized. A light, fertile soil that warms up quickly is desired for summer varieties for the early market. Heavy soils are best for varieties grown during late summer and fall. Soils slightly acid to slightly alkaline (pH 5.5 to pH 7.5) are satisfactory. Extremely acid soils should be avoided or limed.

Squashes and pumpkins are warm-season plants and are easily injured by frost. Nevertheless, they will succeed in cooler climates than will melons or even cucumbers. Cloudless weather is especially important in the development of mature fruits.

Culture

Like other cucurbits, squashes and pumpkins are somewhat difficult to transplant, and the practice has proven profitable only with the summer squashes. When transplanting is to be practiced, the seeds are usually planted in individual containers and the seedlings are shifted to the field without disturbing the root systems.

Field plantings are made after the danger of frost is over. The bush and small-vine varieties are planted in hills as close as 4 by 5 feet apart, while varieties having long vines should be spaced 8 to 12 feet apart each way. Clean culture and protection from insects are essential to success (see Chapter 11). Hives of bees are often placed near fields to insure pollination, since the plants are monoecious and the flowers must be insect-pollinated (Fig. 32.14).

Fig. 32.14—Squash stem showing both male and female flowers.

Harvesting, Storage, and Shipment

The summer squashes are all harvested while immature and while the shell is soft and easily cut by the thumbnail (Fig. 32.15). If the fruits reach full size and the shell begins to harden, they are of no culinary value. The winter squashes, as well as the pie and stock pumpkins, should be well matured before harvest, but should not be exposed to frosts if they are to be stored for winter use.

Hard-shelled sorts, like Hubbard and Vegetable Marrow, keep best in storage. They should be well matured when harvested and cured at a temperature of 80° to 85° F., and with a relative humidity of about 80 to 85 percent for 10 days. After curing, the squash can be stored for several months on shelves in a dry, frost-free room at a temperature of 50° to 55° F. Fruit intended for storage should be handled with great care, so as to avoid bruises and wounds that break or scratch the skin and to avoid breaking off the stems of the fruit.

Summer squashes are often shipped in bushel baskets, lug boxes, or crates of various kinds. The fruit should be packed tightly to avoid jostling and bruising in transit. The hard-shelled winter sorts are usually

Fig. 32.15—Planting of Cocozelle squash showing harvested fruit.

S. C. Exp. Sta.

handled in bulk, but some of the smaller varieties, such as Butternut, Buttercup, and Table Queen are marketed in baskets, boxes, crates, and occasionally in bags.

SELECTED REFERENCES

Anonymous, "Growing Collards in South Carolina," S. C. Agr. Ext. Ser. Vegetable Leaflet 5, 1963.

Anonymous, "Growing Greens in South Carolina," S. C. Agr. Ext. Ser. Vegetable Leaflet 4, 1963.

Anonymous, "Growing Pumpkins and Squashes," USDA Farmers' Bull. 2086, 1963.

Anonymous, "Production and Preparation of Horseradish," USDA Leaflet 129, 1960.

Anonymous, "Production of Parsley," USDA Leaflet 136, 1966.

Anonymous, "Squash Production," Ga. Agr. Ext. Ser. Cir. 527, 1963.

Boswell, V. R., "Growing the Jerusalem Artichoke," USDA Leaflet 116. 1964.

Boswell, V. R., "Rhubarb Production—Outdoors and In," USDA Leaflet 354, 1954.

Boswell, V. R. and Reed, L. B., "Okra Culture," USDA Leaflet 449, 1962.

Holland, A. H. and MacGillivray, J. H., "Effect of Method of Harvest on Cauliflower Production," Univ. of Calif. Veg. Crops Ser. 129, 1963.

Sciaroni, R. H., et al., "Brussels Sprouts Production in California," Calif. Agr. Ext. Cir. 427, 1953.

Shear, G. M., "Growing Watercress," USDA Leaflet 448, 1959.

Tavernetti, A. A., "Artichokes, How to Grow Them in California," Calif. Agr. Ext. Leaflet 37, 1954.

Thompson, R. C. and Caffrey, D. J., "Cauliflower and Broccoli Varieties and Culture," USDA Farmers' Bull. 1957, 1961.

Wilson, W. F., Cox, J. A., and Montelaro, J., "Louisiana Okra," La. Agr. Ext. Pub. 1141, 1953.

CHAPTER 33

Home Vegetable Garden

Home gardens add materially to the well-being of farm and urban families by supplying foods that may not be available otherwise (Fig. 33.1). Vegetables are important in that they supply vitamins and salts which are invaluable for the human system. (See Table B, Appendix.)

Fresh home-grown vegetables are superior in quality to those generally sold on the market, and are readily available when needed. Home gardens can be managed to provide an ample supply of fresh vegetables throughout the growing season. As large numbers of gardeners now use lockers and home freezers, even more vegetables can be utilized than when canning and fall storage were the only means of preservation.

PLANNING AND ARRANGING

Choosing a Location

Very little can be said in regard to location of the garden, as the location of the house and various other permanent structures, to a degree determines the garden site. However, where possible, the garden should have a location that is convenient to the kitchen and that affords the maximum amount of sunlight. Also, frost is less likely to injure vegetables on high ground than on low ground or in valleys, and a southern exposure and sandy loam will produce earlier vegetables than a northern exposure and a heavy soil. It should be remembered, also, that a fairly level place, if properly drained, is desirable.

Selecting Soils

A good garden soil is one that carries an abundance of nutrients, is of open texture, is well supplied with humus, and is properly drained. It is necessary on most soils to add fertilizers, animal or green manures, and in some cases, lime and water. A large quantity of well-rotted vegetable matter adds nutrients to the soil, improves the texture, aids in the growth of beneficial bacteria, holds moisture, and helps to set free nutrients which are already in the soil but not available.

Determining Size

On the farm, it has long been the practice to grow melons, canning tomatoes, and other large and bulky vegetables in locations other than in the vegetable garden. In this case, the garden nearest the house is a kitchen garden and the field garden may be in some well-chosen fertile location on the farm where the necessary care may be given with the tractor and field-cultivating tools, while the farmer is in the field for the general crop work. As a convenience to the housewife, however, crops which need frequent harvesting, such as tomatoes for immediate use and beans, should be in the kitchen garden or nearby.

A garden 100 by 150 feet containing approximately one-third acre of land will furnish enough vegetables for a family of five. Since the discussion in previous chapters covers, in the main, the problems encountered in field production, this chapter deals with the kitchen or city garden located at or near the house (Fig. 33.1).

Planning and Arranging

A planting plan of the garden furnishes the grower with a record of the variety and amount he wishes to plant, the succession of crops, and other worth-while information necessary for proper management of the garden. In order to plan definitely, the length and breadth of the garden should be determined or measured and drawn to scale on a piece of white paper. A convenient scale is 1.8 inch to a foot. Accordingly, a garden measuring 100 by 150 feet would require a drawing 12½ by 18¾ inches. The kinds of vegetables and dates of planting can then be placed in the proper position on the plan. The plants should be grouped so that those needing the same cultural treatment may be together in the same section of the garden (Table 33.1).

The garden will have in general three main divisions, namely: (1) perennial section, (2) all-season section, and (3) part-season section. The last two divisions may be subdivided into cool- and warm-season crops. The perennial crops should, of course, be located at one side of the gar-

Fig. 33.1—Harvesting vegetables from home garden.

USDA Photograph

den where they will not interfere with other garden practices. The all-season crops, such as parsnips, cucumbers, and tomatoes, should be located so as not to interfere with the successive or succession planting as indicated in the plot. The part-season crops, such as beans, beets, peas, and lettuce, should be grouped together to allow a large section of the garden to be vacated as the crops mature. This permits the preparation of the land and the planting of succession crops. The plan (Table 33.1) includes only suggestions for a home garden. Many other plans might be drawn which would serve the individual taste and desire of the grower, especially as to quantities to plant.

Table 33.1—Suggested Plan of a 100- by 150-Foot Home Garden.

Distance Between Rows	Kind, Amount and Succession of Crops		Distance Between Rows
	Spring Planting	Summer or Fall Planting	
6 ft. cold ...	Asparagus	....	4 ft.
3 ft. frames .	Parsley, horseradish, rhubarb	(Adapted only to the mountain regions of the South)	4 ft.
3 ft.	Radishes, 50 ft.—early lettuce, 50 ft.—beets, 50 ft.	Followed by fall cabbage	3 ft.
3 ft.	Early peas	Followed by fall cabbage	3 ft.
3 ft.	Late peas	Followed by fall broccoli	3 ft.
3 ft.	Onion, sets	Followed by radishes and lettuce	3 ft.
3 ft.	Beets, 100 ft.—early turnips, 50 ft.	Followed by spinach	3 ft.
3 ft.	Early cabbage, 100 ft.—cauliflower, 50 ft.	Followed by bush beans	3 ft.
3 ft.	Early broccoli	Followed by bush beans	3 ft.
3 ft.	Early potatoes	Followed by radishes	3 ft.
3 ft.	Early potatoes	Followed by turnips	3 ft.
3 ft.	Early potatoes	Followed by turnips	3 ft.
3 ft.	Onion, seeded	....	3 ft.
3 ft.	Swiss chard, 50 ft.—salsify (oyster plant), 100 ft.	....	3 ft.
3 ft.	Parsnips	....	3 ft.
3 ft.	Carrots	....	3 ft.
3 ft.	Late beets for winter ...	....	3 ft.
3 ft.	Bush beans	....	3 ft.
3 ft.	Bush beans	....	3 ft.
3 ft.	Lima beans	....	3 ft.
4 ft.	Tomatoes	....	4 ft.
4 ft.	Tomatoes, peppers, eggplants	....	4 ft.
4 ft.	Potatoes or sweet corn .	....	4 ft.
4 ft.	Sweet potatoes or sweet corn	....	4 ft.
4 ft.	Sweet potatoes or sweet corn	....	4 ft.
4 ft.	Cucumbers	....	4 ft.
4 ft.	Squash (summer and winter)	....	4 ft.

CULTURAL PRACTICES

Since the preparation of seedbed, plant growing, fertilization, culti-vation, disease and insect control, and other necessary operations are dis-cussed fully in preceding chapters, they will not be reviewed here. The home garden, like a commercial crop, should receive every necessary at-tention to make it productive and profitable. Vigilance and careful plan-ning are necessary for success. Proper working facilities such as accessi-bility, protection, moisture regulation, adequate tools, and simple storage space are well worth providing.

Fig. 33.2—Canned and stored vegetables from the home garden.

Some vegetables mature in a short time, while others need the entire season to reach maturity. A good plan aids the gardner in grouping such plants for the convenience of planting, cultivating, and disposal. Table 2.1 lists the relative hardiness and may indicate approximate time to plant and harvest.

Valuable planting information is given in Chapter 8. Table 8.1 gives full information on the quantity of different seed needed and method and depth of planting. Figures 8.1 and 8.2 show average dates for the latest killing frost in the spring and the first killing frost in the fall, respectively; while corresponding Tables 8.2 and 8.3 provide spring and fall planting dates for different sections of the country.

CHOOSING THE KINDS AND VARIETY OF VEGETABLES TO GROW

The kind and variety of vegetables to grow will, of course, depend on the individual tastes of the family. Varieties should be chosen to meet special requirements, such as earliness, succession, adaptability, disease resistance, and productivity. The experiment stations of the state colleges of agriculture will supply lists of the varieties best suited to the states. Varieties are also discussed in the chapters on particular crops.

CHOOSING THE KIND OF HERBS TO GROW

Every home garden should contain some of the herbs used for their flavor and fragrance in cooking. Herbs are annual, biennial, or perennial. Most of them should be planted in the perennial section of the garden.

A few plants of the following herbs will supply the average family:

ANISE (*Pimpinella anisum*). Seed used in medicine, cooking, and for flavoring liquors (annual).

BALM (*Melissa officinalis*). Leaves used for their lemonlike flavor in liquors and medicine (perennial).

BASIL (*Ocimum basilicum*). Clove-flavored foliage used in flavoring meats, soups, and salads (annual).

BORAGE (*Borage officinalis*). Coarse leaves sometimes used as potherbs and for seasoning salads (annual).

CARAWAY (*Carum carvi*). Seeds used in making bread, also cheese, salads, sauces, soups, candy, and cakes (biennial).

CATNIP (*Nepeta cataria*). Leaves used in making sauces and teas; a mild condiment (perennial).

CHIVES (*Allium schoenoprasum*). Leaves used for flavoring; belongs to the onion family (perennial).

CORIANDER (*Coriandrum sativum*). Seed used in making confections and bread (annual).

DILL (*Anethum graveolens*). Stems and blossom heads used for making dill pickles and flavoring soups (biennial).

FENNEL (*Foeniculum vulgare*). Used in French or Italian cookery; stems sometimes used raw (biennial or perennial).

HOREHOUND (*Marribium vulgare*). Used in tea and for flavoring sugar candy; supposed to be good for colds (perennial).

LAVENDER (*Lavandula officinalis*). Used for pleasant fragrance; also used in medicine (perennial).

PEPPERMINT (*Mentha piperita*). Green or dried leaves used in soups, sauces, and for meats; also for flavoring puddings and gelatin desserts (perennial).

ROSEMARY (*Rosmarinus officinalis*). Aromatic leaves used for seasoning (perennial).

SAGE (*Salvia officinalis*). Used for seasoning dressings and strong meats (perennial).

SPEARMINT (*Mentha spicata*). Green or dried leaves used in soups, sauces, and for meats; also for flavoring puddings and gelatin desserts (perennial).

SUMMER SAVORY (*Satureia hortensis*). Green parts used in flavoring meats and dressings (annual).

SWEET MARJORAM (*Marjorana hortensis*). Leaves used in seasoning soups, meats, and dressings (annual or perennial).

THYME (*Thymus vulgaris*). Used for flavoring soups, gravies, stews, sauces, and meats (perennial).

SELECTED REFERENCES

Anonymous, "Drug and Condiment Plants," USDA *Agr. Handbook 172*, 1960.

Anonymous, "Growing Vegetables in the Appalachian Region," USDA Home and Garden Bulletin 116, 1966.

Butler, J. D. and Oebker, N. F., "Hydroponics as a Hobby," Ill. Ext. Ser. Cir. 844, 1962.

Dodge, John, "Home Gardens," Wash. Agr. Ext. Ser. Bull. 442, 1966.

Lawman, M. S. and Birdseye, M., "Savory Herbs: Culture and Use," USDA Farmers' Bull. 1977, 1946.

MacGillivray, J. H., "Home Vegetable Gardening," Calif. Agr. Ext. Ser. Cir. 449, 1961.

Partyka, R. E., "Plant Disease Control in the Garden," Ohio Agr. Ext. Ser. Bull. 434, 1963.

Vandemark, J. S., Shurtleff, M. C., and Luckmann, W. H., "Illinois Vegetable Garden Guide," Ill. Agr. Ext. Cir. 882, 1966.

Wester, R. E., "Suburban and Farm Vegetable Gardens," USDA Home and Garden Bull. 9, 1964.

Wittmyer, E. C., *et al.*, "Growing Tomatoes in the Home Garden," Ohio Agr. Ext. Ser. Bull., 1963.

APPENDIX

SOURCES OF INFORMATION

While this text covers a wide range of information on vegetable production, many problems are discussed only briefly and others not at all. Also, new developments in the industry, results of current investigations, and new varieties are continually being made available. The reader may, therefore, want to consult other texts and sources of information on particular subjects.

Additional information can be obtained on vegetables as well as other subjects in mimeograph, circular, or bulletin form. Requests for a list of available publications of the U.S. Department of Agriculture should be addressed to the Office of Information, U.S. Department of Agriculture, Washington, D.C. 20250.

The state experiment stations, which are listed in Table A, can supply many valuable publications on agricultural subjects, upon requests to directors or mailing rooms.

VITAMINS IN VEGETABLES

Vegetables have long been valued for their health-giving qualities. Certain vegetables are rich sources of minerals needed for body building and body regulating; some are good sources of fats, proteins, and carbohydrates; certain ones possess laxative qualities; and certain others are rich sources of vitamins. These are accessory substances occurring in foods and are essential for growth, for reproduction, and for the maintenance of health.

It was in the effort to find the cause of the disease beriberi that the vitamin B_1 was discovered. In 1912 Funk named this class of essential dietary factors vitamins. Today many vitamins are known, including A, B_1, B_2 (G), C, D, K, niacin, and other growth factors. Each vitamin is specific and cannot be replaced by another or a combination of others.

Vitamin A is essential for integrity of epithelial cells and is a stimulus for new cell growth. It aids in maintaining resistance to infections, increases longevity, and decreases senility.

Thiamine (vitamin B_1) is essential for maintenance of good appetite, normal digestion, and gastro-intestinal tonus. It is necessary for growth, fertility, and lactation and is needed for normal functioning of nervous tissue.

Table A—State Agricultural Experiment Stations.

State	Address	State	Address
Alabama	Auburn 36830	Missouri, Fruit	
Alaska	College 99730	Station	Mountain Grove 65711
Arizona	Tucson 85721	Montana	Bozeman 59715
Arkansas	Fayetteville 72701	Nebraska	Lincoln 68503
California	Berkeley 94720	Nevada	Reno 89507
Colorado	Fort Collins 80521	New Hampshire	Durham 03824
Connecticut, State		New Jersey	New Brunswick 08900
Station	New Haven 06504	New Mexico	University Park 88070
Connecticut, Ag.		New York,	
College and		State Station	Geneva 14456
Storrs Station	Storrs 06268	New York,	
Delaware	Newark 19711	Cornell Station	Ithaca 14850
Florida	Gainesville 32603	North Carolina	Raleigh 27607
Georgia, Main		North Dakota	Fargo 58103
Station	Experiment 30212	Ohio	Wooster 44691
Georgia, Coastal		Oklahoma	Stillwater 74075
Plains Station	Tifton 31794	Oregon	Corvallis 97331
Hawaii	Honolulu 96822	Pennsylvania	University Park 16802
Idaho	Moscow 83843	Rhode Island	Kingston 02881
Illinois	Urbana 61801	South Carolina	Clemson 29631
Indiana	Lafayette 47907	South Dakota	Brookings 57007
Iowa	Ames 50010	Tennessee	Knoxville 37901
Kansas	Manhattan 66504	Texas	College Station 77843
Kentucky	Lexington 40506	Utah	Logan 84321
Louisiana	Baton Rouge 70803	Vermont	Burlington 05401
Maine	Orono 04473	Virginia, Main	
Maryland	College Park 20740	Station	Blacksburg 24061
Massachusetts	Amherst 01003	Virginia, Truck	
Michigan	East Lansing 48823	Station	Norfolk 23501
Minnesota	Saint Paul 55101	Washington	Pullman 99163
Mississippi	State College 39762	West Virginia	Morgantown 26506
Missouri, Main		Wisconsin	Madison 53706
Station	Columbia 65202	Wyoming	Laramie 82701

Riboflavin (vitamin B_2 or G) has far-reaching biological significance. It functions in cellular metabolism and is believed to be especially important for respiration in poorly vascularized tissues such as the cornea. It is present in the retinal pigment of the eye, where it plays an important part in light adaptation.

Ascorbic acid (vitamin C) is essential for healthy gums and for the prevention of the disease scurvy.

Vitamin D is essential for the correct utilization of calcium salts and phosphates in the nutrition of the growing and adult skeleton, and for the prevention of rickets, osteomalacia, and dental diseases.

Vitamin E functions as an anti-oxidant, which preserves easily oxidizable vitamins and unsaturated fatty acids. It is necessary for normal reproduction in many animal species. It may act as a regulator of the metabolism of the cell nucleus, especially during maturation and differentiation.

Table B—Composition of Vegetables
(Constituents of 100 G. of Edible Portion).

Name	Calories	APPROXIMATE COMPOSITION					MINERALS		
		Protein (g.)	Fat (g.)	Ash (g.)	Total Carbohydrates (g.)	Crude Fibre (g.)	Calcium (mg.)	Phosphorus (mg.)	Iron (mg.)
Roots and Tubers:									
Beet, red, raw	42	1.6	.1	1.1	9.6	.9	27	43	1.0
Carrots, raw	42	1.2	.3	1.0	9.3	1.1	39	37	.8
Parsnip, raw	78	1.5	.5	1.2	18.2	2.2	57	80	.7
Potatoes, sweet, raw	123	1.8	.7	1.1	27.9	1.0	30	49	.7
Potatoes, white, raw	83	2.0	.1	1.0	19.1	.4	11	56	.7
Radishes, raw	20	1.2	.1	1.0	4.2	.7	37	31	1.0
Rutabagas, raw	38	1.1	.1	.8	8.9	1.3	55	41	.4
Turnips, raw	32	1.1	.2	.7	7.1	1.1	40	34	.5
Leaf and Stem Vegetables:									
Asparagus, raw	21	2.2	.2	.7	3.9	.7	21	62	.9
Beet greens, raw	27	2.0	.3	1.7	5.6	1.4	118	45	3.2
Brussels sprouts, raw	47	4.4	.5	1.3	8.9	1.3	34	78	1.3
Cabbage, raw	24	1.4	.2	.8	5.3	1.0	46	31	.5
Celery, raw	18	1.3	.2	1.1	3.7	.7	50	40	.5
Chard, leaves, raw	27	2.6	.4	1.2	4.8	.8	105	36	2.5
Chicory, French endive	21	1.6	.3	1.0	2.9	.8	18	21	.7
Chives	52	3.8	.6	1.8	7.8	2.0	48	57	8.4
Cress, water	18	1.7	.3	1.1	3.3	.5	195	46	2.0
Endive, raw	20	1.6	.2	.9	4.0	.8	79	56	1.7
Kale, raw	40	3.9	.6	1.7	7.2	1.2	225	62	2.2
Kohlrabi, raw	30	2.1	.1	1.0	6.7	1.1	46	50	.6
Lettuce, headed	15	1.2	.2	.9	2.9	.6	22	25	.5
Onions, mature, raw	45	1.4	.2	.6	10.3	.1	32	44	.5
Onions, young green	45	1.0	.2	.6	10.6	1.8	135	24	.9
Parsley	50	3.7	1.0	2.4	9.0	1.8	193	84	4.3
Spinach, raw	20	2.3	.3	1.5	3.2	.6	81	55	3.0
Turnip greens, raw	30	2.9	.4	1.8	5.4	1.2	259	50	2.4

(Continued)

Table B—Composition of Vegetables
(Constituents of 100 G. of Edible Portion)
(Continued).

Name	Calories	APPROXIMATE COMPOSITION					MINERALS		
		Protein (g.)	Fat (g.)	Ash (g.)	Total Carbohy-drates (g.)	Crude Fibre (g.)	Calcium (mg.)	Phos-phorus (mg.)	Iron (mg.)
Flower, Fruit and Seed Vegetables:									
Artichoke	63	2.9	.4	1.1	11.9	3.2	47	94	1.9
Beans									
Red kidney, raw	336	23.1	1.7	3.6	59.4	3.5	163	437	6.9
Lima, green, raw	128	7.5	.8	1.7	23.5	1.5	63	158	2.3
Lima, dry	333	20.7	1.3	3.8	61.6	4.3	68	381	7.5
Snap, green, raw	35	2.4	.2	.8	7.7	1.4	65	44	1.1
Broccoli, raw	29	3.3	.2	1.1	5.5	1.3	130	76	1.3
Cauliflower, raw	25	2.4	.2	.8	4.9	.9	22	72	1.1
Corn, sweet, raw	92	3.7	1.2	.7	20.5	.8	9	120	.5
Cucumbers, raw	12	.7	.1	.4	2.7	.5	10	21	.3
Eggplant, raw	24	1.1	.2	.5	5.5	.9	15	37	.4
Mushrooms, raw	16	2.4	.3	1.1	4.0	.9	9	115	1.0
Peas, green, raw	98	6.7	.4	.9	17.7	2.2	22	122	1.9
Peas, dry, split	344	34.5	1.0	2.8	61.7	1.2	33	268	5.1
Peppers, green, raw	25	1.2	.2	.5	5.7	1.4	11	25	.4
Pumpkin, raw	31	1.2	.2	.8	7.3	1.3	21	44	.8
Soybeans, dry	331	34.9	18.1	4.7	34.8	5.0	227	586	8.0
Soybean sprouts, raw	46	6.2	1.4	.8	5.3	.8	48	67	1.0
Squash, summer, raw	16	.6	.1	.4	3.9	.5	15	15	.4
Squash, winter, raw	38	1.5	.3	.8	8.8	1.4	19	28	.6
Tomatoes, raw	20	1.0	.3	.6	4.0	.6	11	27	.6

From **Nutritional Data** (second edition), H. J. Heinz Co., Pittsburgh, Pa.

Table C—Vitamin Content of Vegetables
(Constituents of 100 G. of Edible Portion).

Name	A (I.U.)	B₁ (mg.)	B₂ (mg.)	Niacin (mg.)	C (mg.)
Roots and Tubers:					
Beet, red, raw	20	.02	.05	.4	10
Carrots, raw	12,000	.06	.06	.5	4
Parsnip, raw	0	.08	.12	.2	18
Potatoes, sweet, raw	7,700	.09	.05	.6	22
Potatoes, white, raw	20	.11	.04	1.2	17
Radishes, raw	30	.03	.02	.3	24
Rutabagas, raw	330	.07	.08	.9	36
Turnips, raw	Tr.	.05	.07	.5	28
Leaf and Stem Vegetables:					
Asparagus, raw	1,000	.16	.19	1.4	33
Beet greens, raw	6,700	.08	.18	.4	34
Brussels sprouts, raw	400	.08	.16	.7	94
Cabbage, raw	80	.06	.05	.3	50
Celery, raw	0	.05	.04	.4	7
Chard, leaves, raw	8,720	.06	.18	.4	38
Chicory, French endive	10,000	.05	.20	—	15
Chives	500	.12	—	—	70
Cress, water	4,720	.08	.16	.8	77
Endive, raw	3,000	.07	.12	.4	11
Kale, raw	7,540	.10	.26	2.0	115
Kohlrabi, raw	Tr.	.06	.05	.2	61
Lettuce, headed	540	.04	.08	.2	8
Onions, mature, raw	50	.03	.04	.2	9
Onions, young green	50	.03	.04	.2	24
Parsley	8,230	.11	.28	1.4	193
Spinach, raw	9,420	.11	.20	.6	59
Turnip, greens, raw	9,540	.09	.46	.8	136
Flower, Fruit and Seed Vegetables:					
Artichoke	390	.15	.03	—	11
Beans					
Red kidney, raw	0	.57	.22	2.5	2
Lima, green raw	280	.21	.11	1.4	32
Lima, dry	0	.48	.18	2.0	2
Snap, green raw	630	.08	.11	.5	19
Broccoli, raw	3,500	.10	.21	1.1	118
Cauliflower, raw	90	.11	.10	.6	69
Corn, sweet, raw	390	.15	.12	1.7	12
Cucumbers, raw	0	.03	.04	.2	8
Eggplant, raw	30	.04	.05	.6	5
Mushrooms, raw	0	.10	.44	4.9	5
Peas, green, raw	680	.34	.16	2.7	26
Peas, dry, split	370	.77	.28	3.1	2
Peppers, green, raw	630	.04	.07	.4	120
Pumpkin, raw	3,400	.05	.08	.6	8
Soybeans, dry	110	1.07	.31	2.3	Tr.
Soybean sprouts, raw	180	.23	.20	.8	13
Squash, summer, raw	260	.05	.09	.8	17
Squash, winter, raw	4,950	.05	.12	.5	8
Tomatoes, raw	1,100	.06	.04	.5	23

From **Nutritional Data** (second edition), H. J. Heinz Co., Pittsburgh, Pa.

Vitamin K is essential for synthesis of prothrombin and normal blood clotting.

Niacin is the anti-pellagra and anti-black tongue factor.

GLOSSARY

Allelomorph. One of a pair of contrasting unit characters.

Alluvial. Stream-laid deposits.

Anaerobic. Pertaining to bacteria or other organisms which flourish without free oxygen.

Angiosperm. Any plant of the class having the seed in a closed ovary.

Anther. The pollen-bearing part of a stamen.

Anthesis. The time or process of expansion in a flower.

Axil. The angle formed by a leaf or branch with the stem.

Axis. The central line of any organ or support of a group of organs; a stem, etc.

Biennial. Living for two years under normal, outdoor conditions, usually producing seed the second year.

Buffer. Materials which prevent sudden changes in acidity.

Bulb. A subterranean leaf-bud with fleshy scales or coats.

Calyx. The outer perianth of the flower.

Cankers. Localized lesions on stems which generally result in the corrosion and sloughing away of tissues with the final production of an open wound, exposing or penetrating the wood.

Carbamates. Substituted organic nitrogen derivatives of carbamic acid, which may contain sulfur, used as insecticides, fungicides, and herbicides.

Carbohydrate. Any group of organic compounds composed of carbon, hydrogen, and oxygen.

Catalytic. Pertaining to chemical action in which the speed of the reaction is hastened or retarded by a substance which does not enter into the end products.

Cellulose. A shapeless white compound, insoluble in all ordinary solvents, forming the fundamental material of the structure of the plants.

Chlorinated organic insecticide. Also referred to as chlorinated hydrocarbons or chlorinateds, basically the DDT or chlordane group of insecticides which contain chlorine, carbon, and sometimes hydrogen and oxygen.

Chlorophyll. The green coloring matter of plants.

Chloroplast. A plastid containing chlorophyll, developed in cells exposed to light.

Chlorotic. Lack of chlorophyll, giving the plants a blanched appearance.

Chromosomes. A number of well-individualized units, in the nucleus, which transmit hereditary characteristics.

Clove. One of a group of small bulbs produced by the garlic plant.

Colloids. Uncrystalline materials, often gelatinous, which diffuse slowly or not at all.

Connate. Born or originated together; agreeing in nature.

Corm. The enlarged fleshy base of a stem, bulblike but solid.

Corolla. The inner perianth of distinct or connate petals.

Cotyledon. A seed leaf or first leaf of an embryo.

Cuticle. A continuous layer of structureless, waxy substance which covers the aerial parts of vascular plants except the growing points.

Cutin. A waxy substance which covers most of the aerial parts of vascular plants.

Cytoplasm. A more or less transparent, viscous fluid constituting all of the protoplasm except the nucleus.

Decompound. More than once compounded or divided.

Dextrin. A shapeless, brownish-white carbohydrate substance.

Dibble. Instrument for making holes in which to insert plants or bulbs.

Dicotyledonous. Having two cotyledons.

Diffusion. The passage of molecules or ions in solution from one part of the solution to another, especially through a membrane.

Dihybrid. A cross which involves two character differences.

Dioecious. Unisexual, with the male and female flowers on separate plants.

Dominant. A parental character which has the ability to express itself in the resulting hybrid offspring.

Emasculation. Removing the stamens.

Embryo. An organism in the early stages of development, as before hatching from an egg, or sprouting from a seed.

Emulsifiable concentrate. A liquid formation of pesticide which contains an emulsifier so that water may be added to form an emulsion.

Endodermis. A sheath composed of one or more layers of modified parenchymatous cells, which encloses certain fibrovascular bundles.

Endosperm. The stored food supply in a seed.

Exosmosis. The diffusion of solvent or solute outward from the cell vacuole.

Family. A division of an order. Usually a family comprises two or more genera, but one genus possessing sufficiently distinctive characters may form a family.

Fixed copper. Any one of several complex copper compounds, only slightly soluble in water, which do not burn plants as do the soluble copper materials.

Flora. The aggregate of plants growing without cultivation in a country or district, or indigenous to a particular geological formation; as, a desert flora.

Floret. A small flower, usually one of a dense cluster.

Foliar. Of, pertaining to, consisting of, or resembling leaves.

Formalin. An aqueous solution of formaldehyde; a trade name.

Formulation. The form or concentration of a pesticide usually as purchased.

Fungicides. Anything that kills fungi or destroys their germs.

Gene. That portion of the chromosome which serves to transmit a character from parents to progeny.

Genotype. The constitution of an organism with respect to factors of which it is made up; the sum of all genes.

Genus. A classificatory group of animals or plants embracing one or more species.

Granular pesticide. Small clay pellets which are evenly impregnated with the pesticide, conveniently applied from aircraft and fertilizer and seeding equipment.

Herb. A plant with no persistent woody stem above the ground.

Herbicide. A phytotoxic chemical used for killing or inhibiting the growth of plants.

Hermaphroditic. Being of both sexes.

Homologous. Alike, similar, or same.

Hybrid. The offspring of plants or animals of different genotypes, varieties, species, or genera.

Hybridization. The practice of crossing between genotypes.

Hydrocooling. The removal of field heat by cold water.

Indehiscent. Not opening by valves, etc.; remaining persistently closed.

Inert ingredient. A substance, specifically in a pesticide formulation, which is not active.

Inflorescence. General arrangement and disposition of flowers on an axis; flower cluster.

Inoculation. The process of improving soils by the introduction of special micro-organisms.

Inorganic pesticide. Compounds which do not contain carbon as a part of the molecule.

Insecticide. A substance used to destroy or to repel insects.

Internode. The portion of a stem between two nodes or joints.

Keel. The two anterior united petals of a butterflylike flower, such as a bean flower.

Lignin. A substance related to cellulose, which with it constitutes the essential part of woody tissue.

Longevity. Length or duration of life.

Miticide. Any substance used to kill mites.

Molecule. A unit of matter, the smallest portion of an element or compound which retains identity in character with the substance in mass.

Monocotyledon. Having only one cotyledon.

Monoecious. Having both sexes on the same plant.

Mosaic. Disease characterized by mottling of the plant due to spots of light green or yellow on dark green.

Mulch. Any substance, as straw, used to protect roots of plants from heat, cold, or drought, or to keep fruit clean.

Mutation. An hereditary change in the character of an organism.

Mycelium. The vegetative body of a fungus composed of threads.

Necrosis. A disease causing plant tissue to turn black and decay.

Nematocide. A material that kills nematodes.

Nematode. Eelworms, unsegmented round worms, not usually visible to the naked eye, inhabiting soil, water, and plants.

Nucleus. The more or less centrally situated organ of the cell containing the chromatin, known as the hereditary substance.

Organic pesticides. Pesticidal compounds containing carbon in addition to the other elements.

Organic phosphate insecticide or *Organophosphate.* Any of several derivatives of phosphoric acid which include the materials related to parathion, malathion, diazinon, TEPP, etc.

Osmosis. Passage of the solvent from one side of a membrane to another where the escaping tendency of the solvent on the two sides is unequal.

Ovary. In angiosperms, an enlarged portion of the pistil, containing ovules.

Ovicide. A chemical compound specifically toxic to the egg stage of arthropods. Truly effective ovicides prevent the full development of embryos.

Panicle. A loose, irregular compound inflorescence with pedicellate flowers.

Parenchyma. The fundamental tissue, usually composed of thin walled cells, making up the bulk of the substance of the leaves, the pulp of fruit, the pith of stems, etc.

Pectin. A neutral substance occurring in many vegetable tissues as part of the sap or cell wall.

Peduncle. A flower stalk.

Perianth. The floral envelope, consisting of the calyx and corolla (when present) whatever their form.

Pericycle. A thin cylinder of tissue sheathing the vascular tissues.

Periderm. The cortical tissue derived from the phellogen (cork cambium).

Pesticide. A material that kills pests such as insects, fungi, nematodes, weeds, rodents, etc.

Petiole. The stalk or stem of a leaf.

Phenotype. A type or strain of organisms distinguishable from others by some character, whether this character be due to heredity or environment.

Phloem. Part of the conducting tissue of plants, usually thought to be instrumental in the conduction of elaborated food.

Photosynthesis. Process of manufacturing food.

Pigment. A coloring matter, especially in the cell or tissue.

Pistil. The seed-bearing organ of a flower, consisting of the ovary, stigma, and style when present.

Pith. A roughly cylindrical body of undifferentiated tissue in the center of the axis, enclosed by the vascular tissues.

Plastid. A unit of protoplasm.

Plumule. The bud or growing point of the embryo.

Pollen. Dustlike male bodies capable of fertilization of ovules.

Pollinate. To transfer the pollen from the stamens to the pistils.

P.p.b. Parts per billion.

P.p.m. Parts per million.

Precooling. Lowering temperatures before shipping.

Progeny. The descendants of a single plant or pair of plants.

Propagate. To cause to multiply.

Protein. Any of several organic, nitrogenous compounds.

Protoplasm. The living substance within a cell.

Recessive. Pertaining to a character which is subordinate to or masked by an allelomorphic character.

Receptacle. The more or less expanded or produced portions of an axis which bears the organs of a flower or the collected flowers of a head.

Residue. That part of a pesticide which remains after application.

Rhizosphere. The immediate zone around the roots of plants.

Root crown. The region in a plant where root and stem join—usually the location of dormant buds.

Rouge (noun). An off-type plant or a diseased plant.

Rouge (verb). To remove off-type or diseased plants.

Sclerotium. A compact, waxy or horny mass of hyphal tissue found in certain higher fungi.

Seed. An embryonic plant with its surrounding integuments or coats.

Sepal. A leaf or division of the calyx.

Sheath. A tubular envelope, as in the lower part of the leaf in grasses.

Slurry. The mixture of a dry, usually wettable powder, form of a pesticide and enough water to make it adhere to the seed coat when tumbled together.

Species. A classificatory group of plants or animals, subordinate to a genus, and having members that differ only slightly among themselves.

Sperm. A motile ciliated male reproductive cell.

Spreader. Wetting agent that causes the spray to spread over the leaf surfaces.

Stamen. A pollen-bearing organ of a flower.

Sticker. A material added to a spray or dust to improve adherence to the plant surfaces.

Stigma. The part of the pistil which receives the pollen in pollination.

Stipule. An appendage at the base of the petiole of a leaf.

Style. The extended portion of a pistil connecting stigma and ovary.

Suberin. A fatty or waxy substance characteristic of cork tissue.

Sucrose. A non-reducing sugar, the most common commercial form of which is cane or beet sugar, having the empirical formula $C_{12}H_{22}O_{11}$.

Systemic insecticide. A substance which, when absorbed by plants, renders them toxic to insects feeding on them.

Tendril. A slender clasping outgrowth, such as found on cucurbit or grape plants.

Tolerance. The amount of pesticide residue that is permitted by federal regulation to remain on or in a crop.

Toxicity. The capacity of a substance to produce injury; the measure of damage resulting from exposure to a substance.

Translocation. The movement of food or other materials from one part of a plant to another.

Transpiration. The movement of water from the inside of plants out into the atmosphere by evaporation.

Tuber. A short thickened underground stem having numerous buds or eyes.

Umbel. A flower cluster in which the flower stalks spring from the same point, as in a wild carrot.

Unisexual. Of one sex; either male or female; not hermaphroditic.

Vacuum Precooling. Cooling by evaporation of water from plants under reduced pressure.

Viability. Alive or ability to remain alive.

Virus. A group of materials acting poisonously, produced and increased within the plant.

Vitamins. A group of food substances other than fats, proteins, carbohydrates, and salts which are essential to normal nutrition and serve to prevent various diseases.

Volatile. Capable of rapid evaporation in air at ordinary temperatures.

Weed. A plant growing where it is not desired.

Wettable powder. A powder form of an insoluble material so treated that it will readily become suspended in water.

Wetting agent. A compound which when added to a spray solution causes it to contact plant surfaces more thoroughly.

Whorl. A group of organs arranged about a stem; arising from the same node.

Xylem. A part of the vascular bundle or conducting tissue.

Zero tolerance. No amount of the pesticide chemical may remain on the raw agricultural commodity when it is offered for shipment.

INDEX